# Science and the Educated American: A Core Component of Liberal Education

Please direct inquiries to:
American Academy of Arts and Sciences
136 Irving Street
Cambridge, MA 02138-1996
Telephone: 617-576-5000
Fax: 617-576-5050
Email: aaas@amacad.org
Web: www.amacad.org

# Science and the Educated American: A Core Component of Liberal Education

Edited by Jerrold Meinwald and John G. Hildebrand

Cover image © iStockphoto.com/runeer

ISBN#: 0-87724-088-4

The American Academy of Arts and Sciences is grateful to the Simons Foundation
for supporting the publication and dissemination of this volume and the Academy's
ongoing work in science, technology, engineering, and mathematics education.
The statements made and views expressed in this publication are solely the responsibility of the authors and are not necessarily those of the Simons Foundation or
the Officers and Fellows of the American Academy of Arts and Sciences.

# Contents

## Part IV: How Can We Judge Success?

# Acknowledgments

The American Academy's project on *Science in the Liberal Arts Curriculum* pays special attention to the challenges of and opportunities for teaching science in a general education context, considering how best to engage those students not majoring in the physical or natural sciences. It also argues that scientific literacy developed during a student's undergraduate years plays a critical role in the quality of our national debate and, in turn, the health of our democracy.

In August 2007, the Academy convened academic leaders from thirty-four colleges and universities to discuss science curricula for non-science majors. The forum facilitated the exchange of ideas across institutions, focusing on innovative teaching methods and common barriers. The participants also completed a survey of their institutions' existing science requirements for non-scientists, the options available for fulfilling those requirements, and the assessments used to determine success in meeting science-education objectives. This volume grew out of the Academy conference and survey. (A list of participants and schools represented in the survey responses is included at the end of this volume.)

The essays contain descriptions of specific courses, concrete strategies for curricular reform, and spirited defenses of the value of science to the liberal arts curriculum. We hope that administrators and faculty members will find this publication useful in updating their institutions' curricula. We are confident that the many new ideas and thoughtful recommendations in this volume will have a positive influence on post-secondary science education in America.

The Academy thanks especially Jerrold Meinwald and John G. Hildebrand for their guidance of the project and for serving as editors of this publication. We are thankful to the Simons Foundation for supporting the publication and dissemination of this important volume and the Academy's ongoing work in science, technology, engineering, and mathematics education. We also acknowledge the partial support provided by the Podell Emeriti Awards for Research and Scholarship, awarded through the Cornell Association of Professors Emeriti. We are grateful to Katie Donnelly and Kim Durniak, the program officers who worked closely with Jerry and John on the conference and publication, respectively. Thank you also to the program assistants and publication staff for helping to produce this publication. Most of all, we express our gratitude to the contributors for bringing their knowledge and creative ideas together in an effort to inform curriculum debate at higher-education institutions.

Leslie Cohen Berlowitz
*President and William T. Golden Chair*
*American Academy of Arts and Sciences*

# Preface

An idea for a new approach to science teaching unexpectedly grew out of my experience at several small faculty dinner parties. More than once, I found myself responding to "and what do you do?" by explaining that my research, at the interface between chemistry and biology, was largely focused on exploring how various organisms (mostly insects and other arthropods) use chemistry to defend themselves and to communicate with the outside world.

A simple example I might cite was our discovery that a handsome local millipede (*Apheloria corrugata*) defends itself by secreting a mixture of deadly hydrogen cyanide and benzaldehyde when disturbed. In a short time, this topic might be followed by a somewhat lengthier explanation of how a female Florida Queen butterfly relies on a chemical signal provided by a courting male in selecting a mate. Her choice of a partner, it turns out, is based on the male's ability to provide chemical protection for her eggs (rendering them unpalatable to egg predators such as lady bugs). The male obtains this protective chemical from toxic plants (*Crotalaria spp.*) and incorporates it into a spermataphore, which is transferred to the female during mating. In courtship, the male "informs" the female of his defender status by applying a courtship pheromone, which he produces from the toxin itself, to her antennae. If a male lacks the toxin, he cannot synthesize the courtship pheromone, and the female will most likely evade his advances. Most listeners are intrigued by this example of chemical communication in nature.

What struck me about these interchanges was that I was actually explaining the first recognized example of Darwin's sexual selection based on a chemical signal to a thoroughly engaged audience whose primary interests were in subjects as diverse as music, economics, or ancient history. Without the benefit of a blackboard, slides, or props of any sort, my fellow diners became truly interested in this narration, and they came away with a new understanding of some previously unsuspected roles of chemistry in nature.

That a group of humanists and social scientists expressed interest in chemistry during casual conversation over a glass of wine provided a clue as to how we might teach chemistry and biology to a large body of undergraduate students whose own primary interests are not necessarily in science. These considerations led me to develop an unconventional chemistry course at Cornell University, with the support of the Andrew W. Mellon Foundation as well as the Henry and Camille Dreyfus Foundation and the National Science Foundation. I called the course "The Language of Chemistry," a phrase used by Arthur Kornberg in his 1989 autobiography, *For the Love of Enzymes*. Designed as a lecture course with a built-in writing requirement—with no prerequisites or laboratory component —it could nevertheless be used to fulfill part of the science requirement for students in the Cornell College of Arts and Sciences. "The Language of Chemistry" made no attempt to survey the entire field. Instead, it demonstrated, via carefully selected case studies, exactly how chemists have studied a variety of biological phenomena and have ultimately attained a deep understanding of these phenomena at the molecular level. Students came to appreciate why molecular structures are important and learned how those structures can be determined. As part of the course, they also studied an area of chemistry/biology on their own and wrote an essay explaining this body of science to a lay reader.[1]

During a subsequent sabbatical leave, which I spent as a Visiting Scholar at the American Academy of Arts and Sciences, I explored further the general question of what sort of scientific education our country's college undergraduates actually receive. In August 2007, a workshop was held at the House of the Academy in Cambridge, Massachusetts. A group of roughly forty participants, comprising physical and biological scientists as well as college and university administrators, met to discuss the importance to our society of incorporating a substantial science component in the "liberal arts" curriculum, and to learn about some highly original approaches to science teaching that several of our faculty participants, from a variety of institutions of higher learning, were pursuing. At an early stage in preparing for this exercise, I had asked my good friend John G. Hildebrand (Regents Professor of Neurobiology with joint appointments in Chemistry and Biochemistry, Entomology, and Molecular and Cellular Biology at the University of Arizona in Tucson) to join me in organizing the workshop. Following the workshop, we solicited and edited the essays collected in this volume, some of which describe and expand on material presented at the meeting, and some of which were written by nonparticipants whose expertise we sought to broaden the scope of the volume.

Our hope is that these essays will stimulate and perhaps even inspire colleagues involved in undergraduate education to devise courses and curricula that are particularly suited to developing science literacy in all their students. We look forward to a widespread reexamination and reevaluation of the contents as well as the methods of presentation employed in science courses designed to

---

1. For a detailed account of the course, which also incorporated a significant writing component, see Stacey Lowery Bretz and Jerrold Meinwald, "The Language of Chemistry: Using Case Studies to Teach on a 'Need-to-Know' Basis," *Journal of College Science Teaching* 31 (4) (2002): 220–224.

be of interest and value to all. Clearly, we need offerings that students will enjoy rather than dread. We need to provide undergraduates with insights and understanding of the scientific enterprise that will serve them well throughout their lives. Ideally, we would like to help our institutions of higher learning produce successive generations of students who see science for what it is: a creative, exciting, adventurous, and at the same time, profoundly useful human endeavor!

Jerrold Meinwald
*Goldwin Smith Professor of Chemistry Emeritus, Cornell University*
*Cochair, American Academy Project on Science in the Liberal Arts Curriculum*

# Introduction

## Jerrold Meinwald and John G. Hildebrand

In his inaugural address and subsequently, President Barack Obama has called attention to the importance of science for our nation's future. Our twenty-first-century democratic society depends on broadly distributed scientific understanding to guide its progress. Yet science hardly occupies center stage in American culture. Roughly one-third of recent graduates from America's colleges and universities majored in the sciences or engineering during their undergraduate years.[1] At the graduate level, about 40 percent of doctoral candidates in the sciences and engineering in the United States are from abroad, and many of these students will return to their countries of origin after receiving Ph.D.s.[2] While the declining preparation of professional research scientists in the United States is certainly a concern, we face an equally serious problem with respect to the scientific literacy of the entire undergraduate population.

Consider, for example, the findings documented in the revealing and award-winning 1988 film *A Private Universe*.[3] Asked what causes Earth's seasons and the phases of the moon, twenty-one of the twenty-three randomly selected students, faculty members, and alumni of Harvard University exhibited misconceptions. Ninth-grade students at a nearby inner-city school expressed similar misunderstanding. This film and other studies underscore the need for K-16 education in the United States to do a better job of demystifying and stimulating curiosity about the world around us.

How are we to secure a proper place in our society for science, as President Obama has called for us to do? Reaching this goal will require a massive, extended, multilevel educational effort; notably, it will include strengthening the contribution of science to undergraduate liberal arts curricula. This volume aims to examine some of the reasons why science education for all students is a significant educational objective; to present some views of what we mean by scientific literacy; to describe several imaginative approaches to teaching science for students majoring in any discipline; and to recommend steps that will help faculties and administrators devise undergraduate liberal arts curricula that will equip future generations of graduates to recognize and appreciate the beauty, value, and utility of scientific thought, investigation, and knowledge.

1. *Science and Engineering Indicators 2008* (Arlington, Va.: National Science Board, 2008).

2. This figure includes both temporary and permanent resident visas; see *Science and Engineering Indicators 2008*.

3. Matthew H. Schneps and Philip M. Sadler, *A Private Universe* (Pyramid Films, 1988).

We begin with two essays that make the case for strengthening science education for everyone. Don M. Randel (Andrew W. Mellon Foundation), whose personal scholarly training was in musicology, examines the place of science in the liberal arts curriculum from the point of view of a broadly experienced humanist. His discussion, which stresses the fact that science and the humanities have much more in common than is generally appreciated, sets the stage for the essays that follow and illuminates some of the deepest educational issues facing us today. The essay by Frank H.T. Rhodes (Cornell University) explores the reasons for pursuing scientific literacy from the viewpoint of a scientist (geologist) with exceptionally rich educational experience. He examines the evolution of the concept of "liberal arts" and reflects on the five broad areas of concern for undergraduate education: faculty commitment, content, methods, outcomes, and context. His essay underscores two important messages: that a meaningful education must include topics that are relevant to society; and that we should continuously seek ways to improve teaching and learning. These two essays make it abundantly clear that twenty-first-century citizens cannot be considered well educated if they have not acquired a sense that science is key to full participation in and enjoyment of contemporary life.

One objective of science teaching must be to give students examples (and, whenever possible, tangible experience) of how science progresses. In the early stages of any field of science, careful observation and description play a dominant role. Technological discoveries that expanded our ability to observe and describe the world around us have enabled enormous leaps of scientific progress. Dramatic examples include Galileo's use of the telescope to observe and even to measure the height of mountains on the moon and to observe the multiple moons associated with Jupiter. The invention of the microscope revolutionized our understanding of living things not only by enabling the observation of previously undetected microorganisms, but also by revealing the cellular nature of all organisms. Twentieth-century inventions, such as the radio-telescope and microwave technology, have led directly to the discovery of formerly unimagined astronomical objects, including pulsars and quasars, and provided strong support for the "Big Bang" cosmological theory of the birth of our universe. The development of advanced deep-sea exploration and collection modules allows us to bring forth new species whose life histories reveal entirely new modes of living. Much of this kind of science has the character of exploration rather than problem-solving. It is often forgotten that science frequently progresses on the basis of discoveries that were not, and could not have been, anticipated.

Driven by curiosity about how a natural phenomenon occurs, and what rules govern it, scientists often follow up on initial discoveries by making further observations of the phenomenon itself. They consider various possible explanations of puzzling observations, testing hypotheses with additional observations or experiments designed to discriminate among the possibilities. A hypothesis that is not contradicted by any of the known, relevant observations, and especially one that can successfully predict the outcome of thoughtfully designed new experiments, provides a satisfying feeling that the original natural phenomenon is "understood." In some cases, this knowledge can then be put to use in some valued area of human endeavor. Remember that the pursuit of "useful knowledge" was an important, explicit motivation for the founding of both the American Philosophical Society and the American Academy of Arts and Sciences in the eighteenth century.

The more we learn about the natural world, the more we realize that much of what we might like to understand remains unknown, waiting to be discovered. Of course, many areas of astronomy, physics, geology, chemistry, and biology are well understood. Nevertheless, questions such as why all known living organisms utilize only the same twenty "left-handed" amino acids to make proteins, or how the human brain records, stores, and accesses memories, or what is the nature of the "dark matter" and "dark energy" that constitute the bulk of our universe await elucidation by future investigators. How many undergraduates realize that contemporary scientists are not so much the keepers of vast stores of factual knowledge as they are seekers of a clearer and deeper understanding of how the world around us works? Many pressing questions of worldwide relevance involving applied science—how to control nuclear fusion for sustainable energy production, for example, or how to replenish the world's supply of fresh water—still need answers.

While there has been extensive discussion of the value of "scientific literacy," the term has different meanings for different scholars. Eugene H. Levy (Rice University) elaborates on the idea of general education and argues that appropriate core-curriculum science courses are as important for students in the sciences and engineering as they are for future humanists and social scientists. The two essays following Levy's present distinct approaches to teaching science: one supports a canon of fundamental scientific concepts essential to scientific literacy; the other underscores the importance of teaching goals that lack specificity regarding content. James Trefil (George Mason University) and Robert M. Hazen (Carnegie Institution for Science and George Mason University) make a strong case for imparting to our college population a specific body of knowledge that encompasses the chief intellectual content of the physical and biological sciences. They put forward a carefully assembled list of "twenty great ideas of science" with which they would like all students at institutions of higher learning to be familiar. Not surprisingly, other scientists with different backgrounds favor a somewhat different set of great ideas. Chris Impey (University of Arizona) reflects on some of the challenges and opportunities of teaching science to non-science majors. He emphasizes the importance of teaching the methods of science and the excitement of science through a "learner-centered" environment and inquiry-based teaching practices.

Next, several scientists describe imaginative courses they have designed for general education students. These courses have proved to be successful with their students, and we hope that they may serve as possible models for teachers seeking new approaches to general education instruction.

Richard A. Muller (University of California, Berkeley) offers a course intriguingly titled "Physics for Future Presidents." He describes a physics curriculum based on his own understanding of aspects of physics that are directly relevant to contemporary, everyday life. While he has also included material on relativity and quantum mechanics, he nevertheless has devised a syllabus that can be taught in a general education context. It is particularly encouraging that this course has turned out to be extremely popular with Berkeley undergraduates, even though it requires students to acquire and work with a large amount of specific, factual material.

Martha P. Haynes (Cornell University) has developed a class that provides its students with a sense of the scientific method and the process of discovery, as well as with a basic set of scientific facts. Through creative writing assignments, students explore, explain, and sometimes defend (in a memo to a senator, for example) how scientific discovery leads to scientific understanding while also learning about concrete astronomical concepts.

An entirely different, essentially orthogonal view of scientific literacy also has its strong supporters. After all, the case can be made that it may be overly optimistic to expect students majoring in subjects such as English, music, or economics to master even the most basic facts and principles of the physical and biological sciences. It would be fair to admit that even professional scientists are relatively naive about the details in areas of science distant from their particular expertise. Most physicists cannot read with comprehension the primary scientific literature in fields such as molecular biology, immunology, or organic chemistry, each of which utilizes its own highly specialized vocabulary and concepts. Unless science courses were to occupy a major portion of the entire liberal arts curriculum, a broad and deep science canon cannot be transmitted to all undergraduates.

Does this mean that we cannot teach science effectively within a liberal arts curriculum? Not at all! But rather than trying to fill students' minds with an encyclopedic body of knowledge that they cannot possibly long retain, we can give them a sense of how great (and small) scientific ideas have been, and continue to be, discovered. The National Public Radio classical music program *Composer's Datebook* reminds us, "All music was once new." In the same vein, all our knowledge of the world around us had to be discovered by someone or some group driven by curiosity to find answers to questions that interested them. How do we know, for example, the diameter of Earth, or that Earth revolves about the sun, or that its magnetic field reverses direction periodically, or that it is about 4.5 billion years old? How did we determine the three-dimensional molecular structure of disparlure, the remarkable pheromone that attracts a male gypsy moth to a "calling" virgin female gypsy moth from a distance of a kilometer? Or even more simply, how do we know that it is a chemical signal rather than sight, sound, or magnetism that is responsible for this behavioral interaction? Are there similar chemically attractive forces operating between men and women? (The answer to this question is that no one knows with certainty.) Scientific knowledge does not come to us as revealed truth, nor can it be acquired simply by thinking very hard about a problem. Rather, the process of solving scientific problems is often akin to the process by which Sir Arthur Conan Doyle's Sherlock Holmes approaches crime mysteries. Careful examination of seemingly disparate clues plays a key role, as does Holmes's imaginative speculation about the possible significance of these clues. Holmes then constructs and tests his hypotheses by making additional observations or performing carefully designed experiments. The process itself is exciting, intriguing, often frustrating, but ultimately enormously satisfying. In the case of the mystery story, every reader knows this to be the case. After all, we read mysteries or watch them on television or film for recreation! But how many undergraduates realize that this same spirit of curiosity and inquiry is what motivates the astrophysicist, the polymer chemist, or the tropical ecologist when he or she goes into the laboratory or the field each day?

Thus, perhaps we as educators should strive to illustrate how and why scientists may become curious about a particular problem and examine it in great detail, construct and test possible solutions to the problem, and make and then correct mistakes along the way, until finally arriving at a satisfactory answer to the original question. Part of the fun can be the realization that some "evidence" was actually irrelevant, incorrect, or misleading—or that one's predecessors or competitors arrived at a wrong answer! In any case, a student who has experienced the joy of solving a scientific problem will not soon forget the resulting profound satisfaction.

We could reasonably argue, then, that an understanding of how and why scientists pursue their studies is what we most want students to take away from science courses. That knowledge will help instill a lasting, positive attitude toward the entire endeavor. How might this goal be achieved? One traditional approach depends on an examination and analysis of some historically important discoveries. Many students, however, find this sort of course content to be unappealing, not to say deadly dull. What else might one do?

A highly imaginative general education course in biology, devised and described by Sally G. Hoskins (City College, City University of New York), provides an intriguing example of how students can be guided through the process of contemporary scientific discovery. Her course is based on close examination of both popular accounts of current research and, in select cases, careful reading of the primary scientific literature itself. While most of the contemporary scientific literature would be largely incomprehensible and off-putting to non-science majors, Hoskins has identified examples of research topics that college freshmen can read, understand, analyze, and enjoy. Although students do not emerge from the kind of course she describes with a comprehensive overview of biology, they do gain insight into the character of the scientific world and the actual activities of the men and women who populate it. Many science majors do not attain this depth of understanding of their field until late in their academic careers.

Organic chemistry, the dreaded "orgo" of generations of premedical students, would hardly seem a likely candidate for a general education course. Yet Brian N. Tse (U.S. Department of Health & Human Services), Jon Clardy (Harvard Medical School), and David R. Liu (Harvard University) have created such a course, "Molecules of Life," a hybrid of organic chemistry, biology, and medicine that aims to demystify the molecular basis of selected life processes. Most important, this team supplements lectures and reading material with genuine (and purposefully low-technology), hands-on laboratory experiences (described as "activities"). With only the simplest facilities, the Harvard students in this course are able to observe an insect sex pheromone (bombykol) in action and to isolate and hold in their hands the DNA from strawberries! Through such activities, words and concepts that may seem abstract and distant in readings or lectures take on a direct, concrete meaning. The students gain hands-on experience with materials used by real chemists. Of course, students in a course such as this would hardly be able to devise a synthesis of testosterone or insulin. However, they would know what is involved in isolating and characterizing biologically and medically important compounds from an organismal source, and they would recognize that this sort of chemistry is not learned solely by memorizing hundreds of structures and reactions.

Each of the classes described above typically focuses on a defined scientific subject area. A multidisciplinary introductory course is rare. However, as Darcy B. Kelley (Columbia University) explains, a group of faculty at Columbia has developed such a course that is now a requirement for all incoming freshmen. "Frontiers of Science" was created to develop the critical thinking skills arguably necessary to be scientifically literate, as well as to kindle interest in the latest discoveries in a variety of fields. Without a single theme, this course challenges faculty to teach across disciplines, while demonstrating to the students the analytical skills that are relevant to all fields.

Finally, we acknowledge the difficulty of assessing the success of any educational endeavor. All teachers want to know, "Am I doing this right?" Students certainly can demonstrate what they have learned, and what problems they can solve, in a final examination. Students can be asked to write a term paper that would reflect their ability to read, evaluate critically, and present in coherent, well-organized prose information on some scientific topic, either assigned by their teacher or of their own choosing. Institutions strive to teach scientific reasoning yet often do not assess whether graduates have acquired these skills. Diane Ebert-May (Michigan State University), Elena Bray Speth (Saint Louis University), and Jennifer L. Momsen (North Dakota State University) draw attention to the gap between teaching goals and assessments and what actually occurs in the classroom. Using the goals, outcomes, and assessment tools developed at Michigan State, they demonstrate through their own course how a variety of teaching techniques can be used to align what universities expect students to know with how teachers teach.

Several of our authors present encouraging evidence of what their students have learned as a consequence of taking their courses, and how the students' views of science have grown more positive. It will take time to ascertain objectively the long-range benefit of an educational endeavor. For example, Impey's essay examines a host of developing educational tools and points to techniques that should enhance educational success. It is true that many science faculty members, especially those at research universities, have not taken advantage of what can be learned from colleagues in the field of education who are experts in teaching techniques and learning skills. In designing courses for twenty-first-century curricula, faculty members would do well to familiarize themselves with current pedagogical research.

Another question that might be asked is how much scientific knowledge is retained five or ten years after graduation? Jon D. Miller (University of Michigan) presents some interesting facts (some sobering, some encouraging) about what he describes as civic scientific literacy. He emphasizes the importance of developing a set of measures that reflect the acquisition of basic scientific constructs that are likely to be useful to students and adults over the course of a lifetime. He then presents data on how science courses may have impacted civic scientific literacy and explores other factors as well. Miller's data point to some provocative results, including an apparent contradiction between the idea that "scientific literacy is about acquiring the tools to make sense of science and technology in the future" and the idea that "acquiring a core vocabulary of basic scientific constructs can confer a distinct advantage on adults who use emerging information technologies to become and remain informed about scientific matters." Miller argues that advancing scientific literacy is necessary to preserve our society.

## CLOSING REMARKS

In his *Perennial Philosophy*, Aldous Huxley describes three contrasting pathways to religious enlightenment and suggests that depending on one's body type (ectomorph, mesomorph, endomorph), one of these three pathways is more likely to function effectively. The various approaches explored in this volume make clear that there is also no single path to attaining an appreciation and understanding of science. Each approach has its particular strengths (and weaknesses), and individual students will respond best to different approaches. Furthermore, there is no one, unique "scientific method" by which we gain understanding of the universe. (In most fields, exploration, description, and discovery precede hypothesis-driven research.) Nor, for that matter, is there one, universally accepted definition of "scientific literacy." Different modes of teaching (emphasizing lectures, group discussions, problem-solving sessions, actual or virtual laboratory experimentation, reading the primary scientific literature, writing about science, and so on) may be preferred, depending on student interest, motivation, and ability, as well as on a school's educational philosophy, facilities, faculty time and motivation, and costs, among other factors.

What has become absolutely clear to us is that:

> (1) There is widespread interest in and beyond the academic community in strengthening science education at the college level; and

> (2) Many genuinely novel approaches to science teaching (some of which are described in this volume) have been devised by dedicated teachers and are being successfully pursued.

Consequently, we can be optimistic about making realistic recommendations that could contribute significantly to the science literacy of American citizens.

To start, we recommend two one-semester courses of the Trefil/Hazen persuasion to provide students with basic grounding in the fundamentals of physical and biological scientific knowledge. These courses need to be very carefully planned; they are not simply the introductory biology or chemistry courses designed to prepare students for further studies in these specific disciplines. Two additional one-semester courses emphasizing how scientific knowledge has been successfully gained in the past, and how much more remains to be discovered, should suffice to give students an appreciation of the opportunities as well as the intellectual and practical rewards that can be expected to follow from the ongoing pursuit of scientific research. Assuming that a typical four-year college curriculum consists of thirty-two one-semester courses, our recommendation would devote just less than 15 percent of a student's efforts (four courses), taken during the first two years of an undergraduate curriculum, to studying the sciences. We believe that expecting anything less of students attending a typical college of arts and sciences borders on educational irresponsibility. If properly planned and taught, a curriculum enriched by a set of science courses that have been designed for all liberal arts students, independent of their major interests, would go a long way toward producing the scientifically literate, well-educated population that is essential for America to retain the leadership position it has enjoyed in the past.

# CHAPTER 1

# Science in the Liberal Arts Curriculum

## Don M. Randel

No proper definition of the liberal arts omits science and mathematics. This has been true for as long as the concept has been around. Yet we have good reasons to worry that when we speak about the liberal arts curriculum, many people imagine a curriculum in which science and mathematics have only a modest presence. The term *liberal arts* seems to refer principally to the humanistic side of that curriculum, and, in practice, specialization within the liberal arts curriculum tends to undermine the very notion of an education that broadly prepares students and stands in opposition to vocational or professional education. Yet more than ever, our times call for students who are broadly prepared and who have genuine curiosity about and some fluency in the whole range of disciplines that the liberal arts curriculum, properly so called, should be thought to embrace.

Part of the problem derives from the public's increasing inclination to see all education as at least preprofessional or prevocational. Many students and their parents believe that every education, especially a very expensive one, should prepare for some way of earning a living. Thus, even proponents of a liberal arts education may be tempted to represent it as oriented toward something other than itself and the values that underlie it. The curriculum gives rise to two cultures that drift farther apart as each tries to make its own appeal to the desire for practical outcomes.

If we wish to put Humpty Dumpty back together again and assert the value of a citizenry that possesses the mental equipment to grapple with complex problems in both nature and society and to contemplate seriously what it means to be a human being and how one might want to live one's life, then we might start by examining the terms that have been used in the last half-century or so to describe the perceived separation between the sciences and the humanities as well as how the sciences and the humanities have been tempted to represent themselves in the debate. We cannot understand the place of the sciences in the liberal arts curriculum without giving some attention to both the sciences and the humanities and their proper relationship to one another in this context.

Fifty years have elapsed since C. P. Snow, in 1959, delivered the Rede Lecture at Cambridge University with the title "The Two Cultures and the Scientific Revolution."[1] The published title of the lecture, *The Two Cultures*, has become shorthand for the difference between the sciences and the humanities, and the phrase is often used by people who have long since forgotten, or perhaps never knew, exactly what Snow had to say. The idea of such a difference continues to have a powerful hold on our thinking, and much that is said about the sciences and the humanities at present not only assumes some sort of difference but acts to reinforce it. This often takes the form of a kind of rivalry, sometimes set about with jealousies small and large, in which one culture or the other feels underappreciated in relation to the other or simply underappreciated altogether. More often, both feel undervalued, even if for somewhat different reasons.

When we think about the importance of science in the liberal arts curriculum, we inevitably confront some of what has been at issue in discussions of the two cultures. If we take for granted the existence of two separate cultures, then the best that we can hope for is a kind of "two-state" solution in which the two cultures coexist peacefully, each secure within its own borders and engaging perhaps in some amount of trade. We should try instead, however, to loosen the grip this construct has on our thinking. By this I do not mean to suggest only that the terrain of the social sciences should be taken as a third culture, as Snow himself came to think possible and as Jerome Kagan (2009) argues in a recent book. Indeed, the colloquial distinction between the "hard" sciences and the "soft" social sciences provides further evidence of the power of the notion of two cultures. Snow's principal concern was the disparity between the world's rich and its poor. (He originally thought of calling the lecture "The Rich and the Poor" and later wished that he had not changed his mind.) This was not a matter of idle speculation. Snow was certain that the poor had observed the gulf that separated them from the rich and that they would not long tolerate that gulf before resorting to violence. Of the disparity between rich and poor he asserted, "Whatever else in the world we know survives to the year 2000, that won't." Further, he wrote:

> Since the gap between the rich countries and the poor can
> be removed, it will be. If we are shortsighted, inept, incapable
> either of good-will or enlightened self-interest, then it may
> be removed to the accompaniment of war and starvation: but
> removed it will be. The questions are, how, and by whom.

1. All quotations are from the 1998 edition published by Cambridge University Press. This edition includes a valuable introduction by Stefan Collini as well as Snow's *The Two Cultures: A Second Look*, from 1963.

The solution to this problem would require first a vast outlay of capital by the industrialized world.

> The second requirement, after capital, as important as capital, is men. That is, trained scientists and engineers adaptable enough to devote themselves to a foreign country's industrialization for at least ten years out of their lives.
>
> [ . . . ]
>
> These men, whom we don't yet possess, need to be trained not only in scientific but in human terms. They could not do their job if they did not shrug off every trace of paternalism [which characterized the work of "plenty of Europeans, from St. Francis Xavier to Schweitzer"]. . . . [Asians and Africans] want men who will muck in as colleagues, who will pass on what they know, do an honest technical job, and get out. Fortunately, this is an attitude which comes easily to scientists. They are freer than most people from racial feeling; their own culture is in its human relations a democratic one. In their own internal climate, the breeze of the equality of man hits you in the face, sometimes rather roughly, just as it does in Norway.

After expressing his doubts about how such a massive undertaking might be brought about, Snow begins his penultimate paragraph thus:

> Meanwhile, there are steps to be taken which aren't outside the powers of reflective people. Education isn't the total solution to this problem: but without education the West can't even begin to cope. All the arrows point the same way. Closing the gap between our cultures is a necessity in the most abstract intellectual sense, as well as in the most practical. When those two senses have grown apart, then no society is going to be able to think with wisdom. For the sake of the intellectual life, for the sake of this country's special danger, for the sake of the western society living precariously rich among the poor, for the sake of the poor who needn't be poor if there is intelligence in the world, it is obligatory for us and the Americans and the whole West to look at our education with fresh eyes.

A few years later, Snow characterized the relations between the two cultures: "Between these two groups—the scientists and the literary intellectuals—there is little communication and, instead of fellow-feeling, something like hostility."

To put the matter starkly, his was not only an assertion of the importance of the "scientific revolution" as the solution to all the world's problems, especially the problem of the disparity between the rich and poor; it was also an attack on "literary intellectuals" for standing in the way of what scientists and applied scientists could accomplish. That the two cultures did not communicate with one another was a terribly serious problem, but this outcome was principally because the literary culture and its "Luddites" (as exemplified in Britain's civil service) stood in the way of the ability of the scientific culture to cure the world's ills. In later comments Snow asserted, "[S]cientists in a divided culture provide a knowledge of some potentialities which is theirs alone."

One must admire the passion with which Snow viewed the need to improve substantially the condition of the world's poor, who still greatly outnumber the well-to-do of Western developed countries. But the disparity between rich and poor has now lasted well beyond the year 2000, and we cannot reasonably assert that this is because scientists and engineers have been held back from the effort by humanists.

The polemic that erupted was hardly surprising, except perhaps in the vitriol it elicited from "literary intellectuals." Nevertheless, Snow had made clear who the enemy was. Among many other things, to say that scientists are freer from "racial feeling" than are humanists can hardly have been much less outrageous then than it would be today. Hence, the enemy responded with all the literary gifts at its disposal. Snow's own rejoinder to this response was at moments even more pointed. After a critique of modernist literature, he wrote, "The question is this: how far is it possible to share the hopes of the scientific revolution, the modest difficult hopes for other human lives, and at the same time participate without qualification in the kind of literature which has just been defined?" He professed genuinely not to know the answer.

How are relations between the two cultures fifty years after Snow's Rede Lecture? Kagan writes:

> C. P. Snow would not have to alter the essential claims in his 1959 essay and would not have been surprised by the even broader gulf that exists between natural scientists and humanists. However, he might not have anticipated the strident rejection of evolutionary theory by advocates of creation ideology and a public less willing to regard the rationally based conclusions of natural scientists as the soundest bases for all decisions. (Kagan, 2009; 245)

I doubt that the gulf really is broader. But however broad, I believe it to be different in character from the one that Snow described; setting aside, at least for the moment, whether his description was entirely accurate even then. For a start, surely no one could reasonably claim that "literary intellectuals" could be responsible for holding back the progress of science in solving the world's problems. Regardless of what many scientists may believe about such people, at least in the United States, there have not been enough of them, or their students, in public office to do any harm or good.

Scientists have mostly been too busy and too well funded to worry much about humanists, except perhaps to make fun of one or another fad typically affecting only a small part of the humanities. For their part, humanists have mostly learned to live with the fact that scientists are busy pursuing their own work and require substantial resources to support that work. Some humanists fear that the disparity in resources, and the institutional energy devoted to pursuing them, distorts some of the basic values of universities and can even lead to their corruption by commercial or governmental interests. But except perhaps in times of university budget cuts, when all constituencies in the university are competing for the same dwindling resources, most humanists will be reasonably content knowing that they cannot do much about the matter.

Two questions then remain: (1) If not the humanists, what has prevented the "scientific revolution" from curing the world's problems? (2) What is science capable of accomplishing in the world, and why should we want to study it in any case?

The answer to the first question lies in Kagan's remark about what might indeed surprise Snow about "the rejection of evolutionary theory by advocates of creation ideology and a public less willing to regard the rationally based conclusions of natural scientists as the soundest bases for all decisions." I hope that not all scientists regard science as the soundest basis for *all* decisions. But apart from that, the people being referred to here are certainly not the humanists properly so called. Indeed, most scientists and humanists *properly so called* would be on precisely the same side with respect to this question. Two cultures *are* here arrayed against one another, but they are not the sciences and the humanities. The conflict is more accurately described as thoughtful people versus anti-intellectuals.

This suggests the answer to the second question. What has held back the application of science to the solution of many of the world's problems and has even used science to create a good many of those problems is the large population of outright anti-intellectuals. To these must be added the not insignificant group of people whom one might call either scientists or humanists but who are not able to think carefully enough about what science might be good for, about the responsibilities it entails, and about the most important reasons for studying it.

The real anti-scientists in our midst are every bit as much anti-humanist by any reasonable definition. In this sense, the real enemy in the struggle to improve the quality (both physical and intellectual) of the lives of the world's peoples is an enemy that scientists and humanists have in common. But the problem is still more complicated, because even if we could sweep away that common enemy we would not be likely to solve the world's problems. That is because the community of scientists and humanists itself includes people who are not sufficiently thoughtful. Some of them are even evil.

Unfortunately, science can be put to both good and evil purposes, as we all know. It can also produce terrible effects when it is used by even well-meaning scientists and engineers without a sufficient concern for possible longer-term consequences. For example, the destruction of the environment is made possible by science and engineering as deployed by scientists and engineers. Some humanists might be tempted to say that this all would be avoided if scientists and engineers studied more humanities. Clearly this is no truer than Snow's claim that all would be better if humanists simply got out of scientists' way. Some people with deep knowledge of the humanities and indeed some of the world's greatest artists and writers have been despicable people. Alas, training more scientists and engineers and training more humanists and obliging them all to study with one another will not by itself deliver the results that Snow imagined. Realizing that the problem is more complicated than it has sometimes been said to be, however, might just be the beginning of working toward at least partial solutions. In the present context, this entails realizing that both the sciences and the humanities as formal courses of study have often been oversold as cures for our ills.

If we wish to enhance the place of the sciences in the liberal arts curriculum, we will need to take a harder look at what we can honestly claim to have as goals. We might even ask some very good scientists why they study science and care about it so deeply. This is likely to lead us away from the instrumental arguments that are so often advanced. The curriculum might then begin to take on a different look and feel. Then we might begin to see what the sciences and the humanities hold in common and how important it is that they work closely together.

The instrumental arguments for teaching science follow from the instrumental arguments for science itself, and the latter are closely related to Snow's arguments. Science solves the world's problems; it raises the standard of living by creating economic prosperity and curing disease. In national contexts, its darker virtue, which is cited almost as often as any other, is its contribution to national defense or, all too often, its contribution to the ability to make war. In the present American context, given the national practical turn of mind, these are the arguments most likely to work. Indeed, some in the scientific community have been willing to make cynical use of the national defense argument to justify the allocation of resources to science that ought to be justified in other terms, only they have less appeal to the general public and its elected representatives.

These instrumental arguments are not wrong or unimportant. Science and engineering are at the heart of what has made the United States the most prosperous country the world has ever known, and the somewhat frail public commitment to continued and enhanced investment in science and engineering puts the nation's future prosperity at grave risk. Unfortunately, this frailty is not merely the function of a general public that is ignorant of science and technology. The private sector, including some corporations led by scientists and engineers, has as steadily disinvested in research as has the government. One has only to recall the disappearance of corporate research laboratories that were among the most distinguished scientific enterprises in the modern world.

Despite the level of prosperity in the United States, not all its people have benefited from the fruits of science and engineering. The nation could afford to feed, clothe, house, and keep much healthier all its people with the science and technology now available. That we choose not to suggests that science and technology, though necessary for the solution of the nation's and the world's problems, are not sufficient.

The national defense argument has its proper role as well. The world is a dangerous place, and human beings have throughout history been quite willing to use whatever technology was available to slaughter one another. We cannot prudently neglect the kind of strong national defense that science and technology make possible. We might reasonably ask, however, whether the fraction of the nation's resources devoted to military uses of science and technology is not now and has not long been much greater than strictly necessary. And we might ask whether the active and vigorous sale of these technologies to other countries, including quite poor countries, constitutes a responsible use of our scientific and engineering prowess. Yet many scientists and engineers are among the advocates of using the products of science and engineering for these purposes. This suggests yet again that the training of scientists and engineers does not alone solve the world's problems.

Nevertheless, the United States does need more scientists and engineers. In order to have more, the country will need to start by wanting more. That desire will need to come from both the public and private sectors. Rebuilding great corporate laboratories would be a clear sign of improved priorities. If we are to have more scientists and engineers, we will need to get them both at home and abroad. This will entail an attempt to understand why more American young people do not want to become scientists and engineers. Such lack of interest is as great a problem as the failure of much of the general public to understand and appreciate science and engineering. Too many young people who have the ability and who are not in any real sense opposed to science and engineering simply decide that they would rather do something else. In the absence of more American scientists and engineers, we will need to welcome people from other countries who want to be educated here and to become part of America's workforce. Recent years have seen the creation of altogether too many barriers to this effort.

Beyond these instrumental arguments for the training of more science and engineering professionals lie the arguments for greater education of the general public in these disciplines. These arguments, too, have their instrumental character. More education in science would enable more people to make the right decisions about scientific issues, the argument goes. Depending on the issue, this overstates the case. Even several pretty good courses in science and mathematics in college will not be likely to give the English major enough real knowledge to make real decisions about the uses of science in society. Furthermore, the particulars of that knowledge are not likely to be retained all that long if not put to use in the daily life of the non-scientist.

Some scientific issues are the subject of substantial disagreement and debate within the scientific community, and the layperson may find it difficult to form a reasoned assessment of these issues even if he or she is capable of describing, say, nuclear energy in lay terms. Other issues that might be less controversial in purely scientific terms, such as whether the nation should have devoted substantial resources and persevered in building the superconducting super collider, are perhaps even less likely to be decidable on the basis of a general education in science. The best we can hope for from the general public who might study science in a liberal arts curriculum is some sense of how scientists go about their work, some enthusiasm for that work, and some respect for the people who do that work and in whom the general public will ultimately need to put its trust. This approach offers an important clue to how science should be taught in a liberal arts curriculum.

Other arguments often made for teaching more science to non-scientists move away from the narrowly instrumental and toward what might be a more appropriate goal. Advocates claim that teaching science to non-scientists helps them better understand the world we live in. Teaching them how scientists think also teaches them about the importance of evidence and fact as the basis for drawing conclusions and making decisions. This model will in turn enable them to make better decisions in their own lives about a wide range of matters outside the realm of science. Courses in the sciences also teach the importance of free inquiry and the freedom of expression, especially the right to question received opinion. Non-scientists thus learn not only the underlying principles of scientific progress but the underlying principles of democracy, making them better citizens in a democratic society.

All of this is true up to a point. Locating that point is important for the sake of designing our pedagogy and also for the sake of honesty. Science helps us understand only certain aspects of the world we live in—namely, the natural world—and there is much that we will not soon understand even about that. Indeed, the way in which science proceeds is by demonstrating that some previously agreed-upon understanding was simply wrong. At a minimum, this practice calls for a certain modesty with respect to acting on what science claims to understand at any given moment. Furthermore, the scientific method embodies only one—though powerful—method of knowing, and many of the things that we might like to know and that might aid us in going about the world are simply not amenable to the scientific method. John Maynard Keynes, in his *General Theory* (1936), gives a nice illustration: "the statement that Queen Victoria was a better queen but not a happier woman than Queen Elizabeth [is] a proposition not without meaning and not without interest, but unsuitable as material for the differential calculus" (40).

Finally, not even scientists decide everything, even in their work, on the basis of the facts in evidence. Important decisions in science can be taken on the basis of passion, instinct, and what are essentially aesthetic principles. And what is allowed to count as a fact may depend on how well it fits a particular theory. In going about the world, we make life's most significant decisions in ways that have absolutely nothing to do with the way scientists think as scientists. For a start, whether and how science is applied in society is not a decision arising from the scientific method. Otherwise, science would need to take credit for war and a good many other evils. This is to say nothing of decisions such as whether to get married or have a child or, I would wager, whether to do science.

The teaching of science, then, to both scientists and non-scientists, needs to be clear about the limits of science, about the dangers of misapplying it, and about why the best scientists do it in the first place. To be sure, many scientists will be glad if their discoveries cure disease or create jobs or lead to some kind of improvement in the lives of others. But underneath it all, they do science because they cannot help it. They do it for the love of it and for the beauty they find and make there. They do it for the same reasons that artists make art. And just as this impulse is the starting point in the life of the scientist, it must be the starting point in the teaching of science in the liberal arts or any other curriculum.

Because I am a humanist, some may suppose that I am now about to launch into an assertion of the importance of the humanities in a liberal arts curriculum that should be imposed on scientists. Such an assertion, of which there have been many, likely would rely, however, on a justification of the humanities that is as incomplete as the typical instrumental arguments so often advanced to promote the sciences. It would merely throw us back into the clutches of the current uneasy peace, with its occasional border skirmishes between the alleged two cultures. In order to avoid this outcome, we must consider some aspects of the humanities and their place in society.

Humanists long believed that the study of the humanities required essentially no justification. The importance of the humanities was self-evident in this view, and school curricula embodied it. To study the humanities was to acquire culture, and, in Matthew Arnold's words, "Culture is to know the best that has been said and thought in the world." In the English-speaking world, the definition of "the best" remained rather narrow for quite a long time. A number of things conspired to undermine this view, however.

In the United States this view was perhaps always somewhat at odds with a practical spirit oriented toward discovery and creation of the new. Then, in the latter part of the twentieth century, a great diversity of cultural voices demanded admission to "the best," which encouraged the view in some quarters that all was relative in the humanities. In the worst of cases, this alleged relativism meant that the humanities had lost their claim to the national attention at anything like the level of the sciences, which had experienced since at least

World War II an enormous rise in prestige and resources. All of this continued the line of C. P. Snow.

This development engendered a kind of envy within the humanities as well as the arts, with resulting calls for increased resources and, perhaps more than anything, for signs of attention and respect. Envy was most apparent on university and college campuses, but to a limited degree it made itself felt in the public sphere as well. Universities created centers for the humanities, and government created a National Endowment for the Humanities and numerous state councils for the humanities. By comparison with the sciences, however, the resources allocated to these activities were still trivial.

In pursuing these objectives, humanists were increasingly drawn to advancing the kinds of arguments that seemed to work so well for the sciences. These were instrumental arguments. Although demonstrating the contributions of the humanities to the gross domestic product or the national defense was not so easy, these were the kinds of arguments that seemed to be required. Thus, even while wistfully recalling an earlier era in which it had been sufficient to advocate the humanities for the humanities' sake and while objecting to society's seeming insistence on justifying everything only in material terms, many in the humanities gave in to the need to justify their enterprise in precisely such terms.

For example, Stan Katz (2009), writing in *The Chronicle of Higher Education*, remarked, "The more important point is that the humanities community has not developed a plausible case for enhanced public support. If we are to make our case to the nation, the community has to articulate its goals and capacities much more clearly than it has done thus far." Andrew Delbanco (2009), also writing in *The Chronicle of Higher Education*, referred to the traditional view but went on to say, "There is a certain prideful purity in such a view, but if educators hope for renewed public trust in the value of liberal as opposed to practical or vocational education, we have to come to terms with the utility question one way or another." Soon after, the topic even made it onto the front page of the Arts section of *The New York Times*, where an article largely stimulated by Delbanco's piece was headlined, "In Tough Times, the Humanities Must Justify Their Worth" (Cohen, 2009).

As in the case of the sciences, the instrumental arguments are in large degree quite sound and should be taken seriously. The danger is that in the attempt to gain public trust for liberal as opposed to practical or vocational education, we resort to making liberal education seem more practical or vocational. Sometimes the claims are for the generalized intellectual skills that will be useful in any profession: the ability to write and communicate effectively or the ability to think critically (though just what this means is not always clear). At other times the humanities are seen as a preparation for life under globalization, in which knowledge of foreign languages and cultures can prove valuable. One might even say, under the heading of contributions to the national defense, that knowledge of history could spare one the need to repeat it. The humanities are also said to develop morals and values.

The trouble is that none of this can be guaranteed. Many high-ranking Nazis were highly "cultured" and had a deep knowledge of the literature, philosophy, and art of the Western tradition. Closer to home, many American undergraduates fulfill their distribution requirements at distinguished institutions without seeming to have developed the intellectual equipment that the humanities claim in these terms to develop. Some of these students even go on to hold the highest political offices in spite of that, as if to prove the point. Of course, many students do have thrilling experiences in their study of the humanities, as do many in the sciences—both will have sat in classes alongside those that did not.

We can now begin to see the many things that the sciences and humanities have in common. Thoughtful scientists and humanists are equally dismayed at the quality of the nation's intellectual life, and for the same reasons. Science, in which much more money has been invested and where the economic outcomes are expected to be much greater, has pressed the matter harder. But what scientists and humanists both lament is the scarcity in society of a certain quality of mind. The issue is not how many people can recite the second law of thermodynamics or describe what happened in 1789. To be sure, scientists and humanists have different tools that are suitable for studying different kinds of things. But both are driven by curiosity and a passion to know and understand more. They cannot imagine being bored, and they do not know the difference between work and fun.

Truly thoughtful scientists and humanists may know different things and employ different methods in the effort to learn still more. But neither would (or should) claim that theirs are the only things worth knowing and theirs the only tools worth applying. Their common aim is to develop ways to think about whatever needs thinking about, taking care not to allow their own tools to blind them to the utility of others. Above all they revel in the life of the mind, and this habit is what they seek to develop in others. This inclination suggests that their most fundamental goals in educating students and the general public really are the same. And this in turn calls for a much deeper collaboration between them.

The question then becomes when and how do we develop that quality of mind irrespective of the particular field of study. For a good many students, college may already be too late. The same would need to be said of many in the general public. Once an openness to new ideas has been sealed off, once the imagination has atrophied, and once curiosity has shriveled, little hope remains for reversing course toward the quality of mind that we would like to cultivate. This can happen at different times in the lives of different people. Unfortunately, it can happen very early. And this possibility requires a massive assault by all who care across all the stages of life, beginning in the cradle. College and university professors cannot assume the responsibility for the whole of life, though they may participate at times in the education of the very young. But they are utterly reliant on others to deliver to them minds that are at least favorably disposed and can be further stimulated.

As for how to develop that quality of mind, we ought to begin by recognizing it as the goal. With the goal clearly in mind, we will be better able to create the curriculum in both the sciences and the humanities that might reach it. The goal of teaching the sciences in the liberal arts curriculum should be to enable students to appreciate more deeply the beauty of, and think more intelligently about, the natural world rather than to enable them to do problem sets, however useful doing problem sets might be for some purposes. Indeed, if we are honest about our goal, we are bound to admit that we cannot reasonably expect the non-scientists in the general public to remember for all of their lives how to do the problem sets that they might have completed as undergraduates. But we can expect them to retain the sense of wonder at science's ability to formulate problems that describe the natural world in exquisite and beautiful detail.

As a humanist by profession, I offer up a modest bit of autobiography. I clearly remember simultaneously studying physics and calculus as an undergraduate. My physics teacher was a young assistant professor who subsequently became a Nobel laureate. I revere him to this day because, among other reasons, in his class I learned to solve problems embodying Coulomb's Law. It was as if the scales had fallen from my eyes. That experience and others remain with me and doubtless have much to do with how I think about how science is done and how thrilling it is to be able to describe and understand the natural world with such precision. Yet I could not begin to solve such equations today. The quality of my experience in college with James Cronin was undoubtedly prepared for much earlier in my life by my father, a man without higher education but who was a ham radio operator when I was a child and who seemed to me to know a lot about airplanes and cars and clouds and minerals and who could, while requiring my assistance even then, fix lots of things around the house.

Science belongs in the liberal arts curriculum for the good of both scientists and non-scientists. The primary goal of teaching science to anyone and everyone is to enrich their lives and their experience of going about the world; it is not to teach them to become scientists, though we hope many will choose to do that in consequence. Similarly, we do not teach literature principally in hopes of producing more professors of literature. This primary goal calls for substantial changes in the way that science is often taught both to those who will major in science and those who will not.

The first-year course for the prospective major in some branch of science should not be the same as the first and perhaps only course for the student who will not major in science. But for both types of student, that first course must convey something of the excitement of doing science for its own sake, and it needs to convey something of what scientists actually do today. A whole semester of Newtonian mechanics will not likely satisfy that condition, however interesting and important the subject may be. The danger that science will come to seem like an endless grind requiring the memorization of very many things must be avoided for the sake of both prospective scientists and non-scientists.

On the other hand, nothing about this should encourage a belief that science for the non-scientist should be made easy so as not to scare them off. This, too, distorts the nature of science. To leave out the serious application of mathematics, for example, is to leave out something important about the very nature of science. Students should also be given some sense that mathematics, too, is beautiful in its own right. Calculus should be taught as a useful tool but also as one of the most beautiful and powerful ideas the mind of humankind ever conceived. The latter is what must stick with students for the rest of their lives, long after they have ceased to be able to do the problem sets.

Part of what afflicts the place of science in education (and afflicts a great deal else in our society) is the culture of professional athletics, with its small number of big winners and many losers and its insistence on being able to rank the top ten in every activity. Because ranking students from best to worst in science and mathematics is relatively easier in early education, we too often create a great many losers who will conclude much too soon that they do not have the ability to pursue science and mathematics and will therefore cease to allow it any space in their thinking. In the worst of cases, we let a facility with science and mathematics serve as the measure of who is smart and who is not. This tendency is not good for anyone. It may be part of what lends science a certain kind of prestige among the general public, but it is the enemy of educating a general public to have a deeper understanding and appreciation of science. To be sure, doing good science takes talent and hard work. But this is as true in philosophy and history as it is in physics and chemistry.

We might hope, then, that scientists and humanists would get together in thinking about the liberal arts curriculum and look for the common ground that they might cultivate together rather than simply assembling in the name of general education the list of prerequisites for the majors in their own disciplines. The study of history might be one place to look for common ground, because science is too often felt to be detached from any historical circumstance—as if, because the laws of nature are eternally true, it makes no difference when and under what circumstances any one of them was discovered. Similarly, some sense of the state of science could contribute a great deal to the understanding of a given period of history and its literature or philosophy.

Ultimately, an effort to raise the quality of intellectual life incorporating both science and the humanities will require a recognition that curricula do not change people. People change people. Those who teach either the sciences or the humanities, whether earlier or later in the lives of their students, must aspire to be that transforming individual in the life of a student. It will not be sufficient simply to transmit a vast and complicated body of knowledge and leave it to the student to figure out that it might be interesting and even exciting to accumulate that knowledge. Students will learn best if they believe someone cares that they learn, and putting this principle into practice may require all of us, whatever part of the liberal arts curriculum we principally cultivate, to adjust our priorities in our own daily lives.

REFERENCES

Cohen, P. 2009. In tough times, the humanities must justify their worth. *The New York Times*, February 24.

Delbanco, A. 2009. A new day for intellectuals. *The Chronicle of Higher Education*, February 13.

Kagan, J. 2009. *The Three Cultures: Natural Sciences, Social Sciences, and the Humanities in the 21st Century: Revisiting C. P. Snow*. Cambridge: Cambridge University Press.

Katz, S. 2009. The bottom line for the NEH. *The Chronicle of Higher Education*, February 18. http://chronicle.com/blogPost/The-Bottom-Line-for-the -NEH/6672/.

Keynes, J. M. 1936. *The General Theory of Employment, Interest and Money*. London: Palgrave Macmillan.

Snow, C. P. 1998. *The Two Cultures*. New York: Cambridge University Press.

# CHAPTER 2

# Science as a Liberal Art

Frank H.T. Rhodes

## THE TASKS OF THE UNIVERSITY

To our forebears, the goals of a university education were simple and succinct. Its purpose was, in the words of John Henry Newman in the mid-nineteenth century, to prepare a man (inevitably so in those days) "to fill any post with credit, and to master any subject with facility." Newman concluded:

> Such an education should include the great outlines of knowledge, the principles on which it rests, the scale of its parts, its lights and its shades, its great points and its little, so that it produces an inward endowment, a habit of mind of which the attributes are freedom, equitableness, calmness, moderation and wisdom. (Newman, 1996; 126)

The task of the nineteenth-century faculty member was equally clear: to produce "not a book, but a man" (Pattison, 1892; 435). To Newman, the task was "training good members for society. Its art is the art of social life, and its end is fitness for the world" (Newman, 1996; 125).

Newman's university offered no place, no provision, and scant respect for the professions. Science, though it existed, survived on sufferance and was present on, but peripheral to, the campus. The arts—liberal, traditional, scholarly—were not only a part of the university, they *were* the university. The arts formed and shaped the gentleman, and the gentleman—informed, humane, reflective, enlightened—defined, shaped, and embodied the professions.

## THE UNIVERSITY IN 2009

The university has become far more complex since Newman's day, far more inclusive in its membership, far more comprehensive in its component programs, and far more engaged in contemporary society. The university now has not only many more students, departments, sponsors, and patrons but also many more goals and many more demands on its services. It also has many more critics.

We live today at a time of less conviction and less clarity than did Newman in the mid-nineteenth century, and nowhere is that lack of clarity and conviction more apparent than in the contemporary university. Drew Gilpin Faust, president of Harvard, recently reflected on the university's struggle "to meet almost irreconcilable demands: to be practical as well as transcendent; to assist immediate material needs and to pursue knowledge for its own sake; to both add value and question values." Noting the steep decline in the percentage of students majoring in the liberal arts and the corresponding increase in preprofessional majors—especially business, which accounts for twice as many bachelor's degrees as any other field—Faust urged universities to respond to the need of individuals and societies for "meaning, understanding and perspective as well as jobs" (Faust, 2009; 1–2).

Faust is not alone in her criticism. Derek Bok, a previous Harvard president, has been equally forceful. The title of one of his recent books is *Our Underachieving Colleges: A Candid Look at How Much Students Learn and Why They Should Be Learning More* (Bok, 2006). Bok concludes that undergraduate education is less good than it could be, especially in such areas as writing, critical thinking, quantitative skills, and moral reasoning. Some of the very areas in which many colleges tend to celebrate their success—cultural appreciation and preparation for effective citizenship, for example—are areas where a substantial majority of graduating seniors feel that they have made little progress during their college years. And all this at a time when more and more courses are piled onto the curriculum and less and less attention is devoted to effective learning.

Nor are these two distinguished educational leaders alone in their concerns. A spate of books published over the last two decades reflects a wide range of concerns. (See the following for a sampling from varying viewpoints: Anderson, 1992; Barba, 1995; Bowen, Chingos & McPherson, 2009; Bowen & Shapiro, 1998; D'Souza, 1991; Ehrenberg, 1997, 2006; Hersh & Merrow, 2005; Pascarella & Terenzini, 1991, 2005; Rhodes, 2001, 2010; Smith, 1990; Sykes, 1988.) The tone of most of these reviews is critical, most constructively so. The danger of such studies, however, is that criticism of undergraduate teaching and learning is liable to be so preoccupied with imperfection and the need for improvement that it overlooks or undervalues much that is already good. In countless institutions across the country—community colleges, technical institutes, liberal arts colleges, universities of all sizes and kinds, both public and private —one can find much that is good and some that is admirable. Devoted instructors—from graduate teaching assistants and part-time lecturers to the most senior chaired professors—provide not only conscientious teaching but also inspired learning for vast numbers of the nation's students. To raise concerns is not to criticize what is: it is rather to ask if what is already good could be better.

Though most discussions within the academy tend to focus largely on courses and their content, the criticisms of the more knowledgeable writers about the undergraduate learning experience tend to reflect wider public concerns that involve five broad areas of undergraduate education:

- The commitment of faculty members to teaching and learning;
- The content of teaching and learning, especially the overall curriculum;
- The methods of teaching and learning;
- The context of teaching and learning; and
- The outcome of teaching and learning.

Some of these concerns arise chiefly in the case of student experience at so-called research universities, but most exist also in other institutions.

### Faculty Commitment to Teaching and Learning

The concern that faculty are less than fully committed to active participation in effective undergraduate education is widespread and is expressed in several forms. All such critiques, however, deplore the neglect of personal engagement and the dwindling participation by significant numbers of faculty members, many of whom are viewed as regarding research and graduate teaching as more significant and more rewarding than undergraduate teaching. This dwindling commitment is reflected in several ways:

- Large and impersonal introductory courses, especially in such "gateway" preprofessional areas as chemistry;
- The widespread use of "unskilled" graduate student teaching assistants or part-time lecturers for much formal instruction;
- The quality of both lecture presentations and lab exercises;
- The "impersonality" of the classroom, together with the absence of meaningful opportunity for student-faculty interaction;
- The lack of adequate office hours for student advising, guidance, and career counseling; and
- The sharp line of separation between "the classroom experience" and every other aspect of student campus life.

Some of these concerns are related to campus size—many liberal arts colleges provide better integration of living and learning than do larger institutions—but, in one form or another, the concerns listed are widespread.

### The Content of Teaching and Learning: The Character of the Curriculum

Although the form and content of the curriculum differ from institution to institution, few seem satisfied with the curriculum as it now stands. Perhaps few ever were, but present concerns are deeply felt and range widely. Overall, critics are frustrated by a lack of cohesion and articulation and by what is seen as a failure to consider and explore meaningful relationships and implications between the disciplines or even, sometimes, between courses within a single discipline. Graduation requirements, the critics assert, have come to represent the passive accumulation of 120 credit hours of almost randomly selected or required courses, each existing in silo-like isolation from all the rest. Nor is this fragmented pattern of learning confined to so-called general education, because even within a chosen major discipline students complain of a narrow disciplinary territorialism among some faculty members, leading them to promote and defend their own particular scholarly niche with little regard for its context and relationships.

A gap is growing, some critics argue, between the lofty rhetoric of the college catalog and the dreary reality of the student experience. Far from being a bold map for the joint exploration of unknown terrain, the curriculum has become, so some critics assert, a battleground for subdisciplinary imperialism. Nowhere do these concerns run deeper than in the humanities and social sciences, where criticism of "political correctness" is widespread. Rightly or wrongly, the university's sternest critics see the university as having become a place of narrow indoctrination, required cultural relativism, and fashionable inconclusiveness.

Perhaps one of the most startling findings of some criticism is how little is known of the relative merits of different concepts of the curriculum and its content. For faculties devoted to inquiry and discovery, this is a remarkable but discouraging gap. Conclusions on the outcome of curriculum selection remain largely speculative.

*Methods of Teaching and Learning*

If what is taught has become a matter of concern, the question of how learning takes place has become an even more widespread and urgent concern. Though more is known about effective pedagogy than about the results of curriculum choice, numbers of writers conclude that the existing faculty emphasis on undergraduate teaching, such as it is, is misplaced and that more attention should be devoted to student learning rather than teaching. The goal and outcome of a successful undergraduate experience, the critics argue, should be learning, to which teaching makes a major contribution. But teaching is the means, not the end, of education. Learning is the product of education and teaching is but one means—though a significant one. To devote faculty time to tinkering with course requirements, to the neglect, some argue, of the learning outcomes associated with them, may be as inappropriate as the preoccupation and reimbursement of hospitals for length of patient stay rather than the beneficial results of patient care. The emphasis on teaching as an end in itself, rather than a means of learning, reflects a wider neglect of interest in pedagogy. The heavy reliance on the conventional lecture format—representing, some critics argue, almost everything that is the antithesis of what we know about the best methods of effective learning—is an unhappy example.

The work of my colleague Stephen L. Sass, professor emeritus of materials science and engineering at Cornell, provides a striking example of the relationship between method, content, and outcome. Sass relates the following anecdote:

Spring had come to Ithaca—for the second or third time that year—with mild temperatures melting the mounds of grimy snow, snowdrops peeping through here and there, and V's of Canada geese honking exuberantly overhead on their journey northward. I was giving a lecture to my sophomore-level materials science class at Cornell. A glance at the students told me I was losing them in the haze of an April morning. I wondered what I could do to prop open their spring-heavy eyelids. I had been talking about the heat treatment of steel. In an act of desperation and hope, I abandoned my course notes.

"Isn't it remarkable," I asked, "that just a sprinkle of charcoal, which we use in our backyard barbeques, changes iron into steel, and transforms a weak metal into a strong one? And isn't it lucky that both iron and charcoal are so cheap? What form would our world take without iron and steel?"

The change in my voice caused a few eyes to open. One student replied. "Well it's hard to imagine a Corvette without iron and steel."

"And of course sports cars are the highest expression of civilization," I teased the student. "In addition to your car," I continued, "our great cities would not exist today." (Sass, 1998; 1)

Sass's approach to teaching, and also, I would suppose, his student's experience in learning, was transformed on that April morning. He decided later, he told me, to "tell stories" in his class to illustrate the linkage of the material he was describing. One result of that transformation was the publication of a remarkable book, *The Substance of Civilization*, in which Sass explores the relationships between materials and the progress of nations. "History," he concludes, "is an alloy of the materials we have invented or discovered, manipulated, used and abused, and each has its tale to tell" (Sass, 1998; 6).

Inevitably, some concerns about method reflect differences of opinion unsupported by meaningful data. Others, however, do not. Thus, Bowen, Chingos, and McPherson (2009), in reporting the results of a comprehensive study of two hundred thousand student records from sixty-eight public colleges and universities, conclude that only about half of those who enroll for a baccalaureate degree graduate within six years. Among the most counterintuitive aspects of the study, the authors discovered that students with comparable qualifications, such as similar high school grade point average (GPA) and SAT scores, are significantly less likely to graduate from the less selective public institutions than from the more selective. Thus, the University of Michigan, Ann Arbor, has a graduation rate of 88 percent; Michigan State, 74 percent;

Western Michigan, 54 percent; and Eastern Michigan, 39 percent for students in the same high school GPA and SAT achievement cohort (Bowen, Chingos & McPherson, 2009, as reported in Leonhardt, 2009). Nor is this concern only of "purely academic" interest. Leonhardt, in reviewing this study, suggests that public universities should be included, together with Wall Street firms, regulatory agencies, and the Big Three automakers in "the list of organizations whose failures have done the most damage to the American economy in recent years." Leonhardt quotes Mark Schneider's description of such universities with low graduation rates as "failure factories" (Leonhardt, 2009).

### The Outcome of Teaching and Learning

Two other concerns about the outcome of undergraduate learning seem to extend across the spectrum of institutional varieties. Assessment of student performance is seen as less professional, less meaningful, and less useful than it could or should be. Grade inflation—though pervasive—is but one aspect of this. Studies show that over the last half-century the percentage of As and Bs awarded at universities and colleges has steadily increased. Thus, in 1950 about 15 percent of Harvard students received a grade of B+ or better. Today, the figure is nearly 70 percent. Merrow (2004) reported that 50 percent of grades at Harvard were either A or A-, up from 22 percent in 1966; 91 percent of Harvard's seniors graduated with honors. Nor is Harvard alone in this. Eighty percent of grades at the University of Illinois are As and Bs. All this when over the last thirty years SAT scores of entering students have declined. Grade inflation has become so pervasive that some graduate and professional school admissions officers and corporate employers now require criteria other than (or in addition to) GPA in assessing student performance.

But beyond the grades and grade point averages is a larger concern with current student assessment practices: no clear agreement exists among, or even within, the universities as to what assessment means, what it measures, on what it is based, how it is to be judged, or how it should be used or even understood. Perhaps in no other professional area is the evaluation of both outcome and performance a matter of such ambiguity.

Another concern about outcome of undergraduate learning is also widespread: increasing numbers of recent graduates appear to lack the basic skills involved in oral and written communication and in simple analytical comparisons. In a recent survey of employers, only about one-quarter of four-year college graduates were perceived to be excellent in many of the most important skills, and more than one-quarter of four-year college graduates were perceived to be deficiently prepared in written communications (Barrington & Casner-Lotto, 2006).

A comparable dissatisfaction exists among a majority of graduating seniors. Lack of student skill in such broad areas reflects a lack of faculty attention to the responsibility for the cultivation of these basic skills, which extend across departmental and disciplinary boundaries.

Alongside this particular concern for the development of student competence in these important areas is a concern for the virtual absence of any serious longitudinal study of comprehensive and cumulative learning outcomes at the undergraduate level. Even the criteria and tools of such measurement, evaluation, and comparison have yet to be agreed on and developed.

There are serious potential consequences of this institutional inattention to these aspects of professional assessment. If institutions decline to accept responsibility for such studies, other external bodies may well be tempted to do so.

One other aspect of assessment is institutions' neglect of any published self-analyses of their own performance and results and their level of success in relation to that of their peers. Institutional "rankings" developed by external groups, though now widespread, remain generally unpopular with the institutions themselves, for reasons that vary from one institution to another. So unpopular have these rankings become with one group of institutions that they have agreed to deny external access to the institutional data on which the published rankings are based. Serious interest and analysis, such as it is, is left to *U.S. News and World Report*, *The Times*, and Shanghai Jiao Tong University, all of which publish university rankings. Yet, though universities stoutly complain about the basis and value of such rankings, they equally stoutly resist any suggestion that they themselves should prepare studies that would allow some public assessment of their performance and provide some measure of public comparison and accountability.

### The Context of Teaching and Learning

Universities came into existence so that scholars could enjoy the benefits of community learning, rather than study in shuttered isolation. From the first, these learning communities were international in their membership, cooperative in their learning, and heavily influenced by the leadership and choices of their students. In some of the earliest twelfth- and thirteenth-century learning communities, students jointly selected and individually compensated their instructors. Learning was a group experience, and the responsibility for the content and style of learning rested largely with the students. This history gives added poignancy to the complaint that group learning has become rare, or even absent, in the experience of many undergraduates. Group study sections, lab project teams, class community service partnerships, and undergraduate cooperative research projects tend, in some institutions, to be the exception rather than the rule. However, group learning can be used successfully in most, possibly all, courses and disciplines.

The recapture of a more active student role in learning today requires faculty leadership and support. A large gateway course in physics, for example, can be revitalized by the introduction of inquiry-based cooperative projects, but these will succeed only with faculty initiative and active engagement.

This nurture of cooperation and widening of interest can be encouraged still further by its linkage—direct or indirect—to every other aspect of campus life: by linkage to plays, movies, speakers, events, clubs, and community projects of all kinds. What is required is imaginative leadership and creative discussions between faculty and students, as well as between faculty members. Not only students will benefit from such discussions. Faculty members themselves sometimes complain about the lack of departmental support or encouragement for such "added" engagement, and they are probably correct in this. That is why, both within individual departments and between schools and colleges, someone must be given the responsibility and the resources to encourage and reward this more active community learning. Reciprocity and cooperation among students, as Chickering and Gamson (1987) noted, are among the best means of effective learning.

These educational complaints are added to the longer, more general list of "demands" that come from social critics of the university. Broadly categorized, the demands include calls for greater inclusiveness, more effective teaching, more creative learning environments, research that is more useful, more social benefits to the local community, more relevance to the job market, more public accountability, more responsiveness to social needs, and even, sometimes, more-competitive athletic teams: in fact, more of everything, except cost and price, which, all critics agree, should be reduced.

Few are satisfied with the contemporary university. Perhaps in our age that is inevitable, as the university is now suspended between Newman's nineteenth-century ideal of reflective scholarly detachment and our twenty-first-century society's reluctant search for sustainability and urgent pleas for social engagement.

Any discussion of the place of science in the undergraduate curriculum must be a part of the larger discussion of the concerns about and the goals of the undergraduate experience. To neglect what even the most informed and sympathetic spokespersons for universities and colleges have to say about the larger situation in undergraduate education would be to ignore the context in which science can play a role. It would ignore, too, the possibility that science can make a useful contribution to addressing at least some of the discontents these concerns represent.

Consider, for example, the concern that too much emphasis is given to teaching rather than learning, to imparting information rather than encouraging discovery. Nothing in science is "given"; each so-called fact is the fruit of a hard-won discovery that is itself the product of a personal inquiry, an individual experiment, a persistent interrogation of nature. What better medium could we have, what better context, for the spirit and style of learning we seek to cultivate?

To such concerns and demands as these the faculty may well respond that budgets are tight, that the pressures of other tasks are great, that appreciation of and support for devoted teaching is generally lacking within the university. These responses are often justified. But better teaching and improved learning are not inherently more costly than merely adequate teaching and uninspired learning, whereas the rewards, in both student success and faculty fulfillment, are great. Department chairs and college deans will appreciate and support devoted teaching if and when those in positions of senior leadership and influence—the president, provost, and especially the trustees—recognize the need and reward the response. The need and opportunity for such leadership has never been greater.

## THE GOALS OF A UNIVERSITY EDUCATION

Many of the concerns over the undergraduate experience arise because of a lack, on many campuses, of any meaningful agreement on the goals of an undergraduate education. Reading the average college catalog reveals a remarkable degree of homogeneity between institutions, of bland generalizations expressed in a twenty-first-century version of Newmanesque rhetoric and exhortation but containing precious few particulars. One wonders how the average college applicant distinguishes one college from another, except for the carefully crafted fine print of graduation requirements. And sadly, it is in these requirements that the true nature of the particular university is most clearly seen.

No broad universal agenda for the goals of undergraduate education will be appropriate for every campus. Such goals must be a homegrown product, reflective of institutional character and purpose, the collective expertise and considered values of the faculty, and the available resources, facilities, and student body of the campus. But, at a minimum, a meaningful curriculum should address the need to nurture among all students:

- A sense of curiosity and self-confidence, together with the skills to satisfy the first and justify the second;
- A sense of proportion and context in understanding the worlds of nature and society;
- A degree of mastery in one chosen area, together with an understanding of its modes of thought, its assumptions, and its relationships;
- An openness to others, with a commitment to responsible membership in a diverse community; and
- A sense of personal direction, with the self-discipline, skills, and values to pursue it.

Others will, no doubt, suggest alternative goals, and they must be considered and pursued campus by campus. But some objectives there must be, for without some goals education withers. Developing such aims, describing their relative merits, exploring the best means of achieving them: these are the demanding but critical tasks of the faculty of every institution. Not all faculties will choose to devote themselves seriously to addressing these issues. But they must, and we need the best minds of the faculty to be engaged in the task.

## SCIENCE AS AN ESSENTIAL COMPONENT
## OF LIBERAL EDUCATION

If, then, we accept the concept of a liberal education that enables men and women to develop the capacity to understand and evaluate competing viewpoints and ultimately to embrace a cohesive worldview, a meaningful moral code, and a reasoned openness to new knowledge and alternative viewpoints, together with the commitment and competence to contribute to society, what place does or should science have in such a scheme? What role should it play?

By science, I mean not only the physical and biological sciences and mathematics, but also the applied sciences and engineering, as well as the social sciences in their broadest sense. Science serves a liberal end to the extent that it opens to us an understanding of the universe in which we dwell, of the remarkable planet on which we live and depend, of its origin and its history, of its robustness and its fragility, of its components and resources, of its variety and its unity, of its systems and its workings, of its regularity and its unpredictability. Such science introduces us to Earth's inhabitants and their evolution, to our ancestors and our teeming contemporaries, to the growth of communities and their interactions, to the effects of migration and isolation, to our behavior, to our prospects, to our cooperation, and to our competition.

In a unique sense, the sciences introduce us to ourselves, to our fellow inhabitants, and to our dwelling place. Far from competing with the insights we derive from the humanities, the sciences complement, supplement, and enrich the intimations and insights into our nature and our society that the humanities provide.

Nor is the particular insight that the sciences provide purely technical. At its best, science gives glimpses of rare beauty and fresh understanding. An artist painting a sunset, a traveler crossing a mountain range, a sculptor carving a figure, a musician creating a new composition, a writer describing a character, and a citizen voting in an election will each gain new perspective and richer understanding from within the contemplation the sciences provoke.

But courses like Physics for Poets, useful as they are, do not exhaust the educational value of the sciences. We need excellent courses like Physics for Poets, but we also need excellent classes like Physics for Physicists and Chemistry for Physicians, Mathematics for Architects and Sociology for Engineers. We need them because the sciences represent the essential foundation of so many areas of professional practice and modern life, from engineering to agriculture, from public health to regional planning, from manufacturing to medicine. And science is equally entwined with most areas of public policy, from opinion polls to conflict resolution, from communications to national defense. Everywhere, in every area, our lives not only intersect with the practice and fruits of science; they depend upon it.

So we need not only a sound public comprehension of science, but also a strong grounding in the sciences for the growing numbers whose professional careers involve the daily application of scientific principles. But this grounding, though it must be unsparingly rigorous, should also provide more than useful formulae and applicable equations. Much more, in fact: it should enrich the understanding of its practitioners just as the science offerings do for the non-scientist, providing just the same sense of relatedness, beauty, wonder, and enlightenment for the engineer as it does for the philosopher or the politician. The worst outcome of a division between general and professional science courses would be a separation between "soft" appreciation and "hard" but thoughtless application. Appreciation is as essential for those involved in the task of application as is the understanding of application for those seeking appreciation. A successful and sustainable society needs both.

Nor is this essential complementarity a matter only of educational significance. The practice of science at its most advanced level requires such a combination of approaches. Most fundamental research in science is undertaken not with an eye to its immediate usefulness or the benefits of its practical application, but with an eye to its value in satisfying personal curiosity and increasing individual understanding. Roald Hoffmann, for example, is a distinguished Cornell professor who was awarded the Nobel Prize in chemistry for his idea that chemical transformations could be approximately predicted from the subtle symmetries or asymmetries of electron orbitals in complex molecules. He was inspired in his work by the beauty of the resulting structures, not by their utility, but his work has subsequently enabled others to synthesize a whole range of useful compounds.

The burgeoning field of biotechnology, which has proven widely applicable (in agriculture and many other areas), was established on basic research conducted some thirty to forty years earlier and with little thought given to its wider application.

Less benign, but no less significant, the Manhattan Project, which hastened the end of World War II, depended on discoveries in basic physics made decades before.

A "liberal education" is too valuable to be limited to "liberal arts students"; it should be the experience of all students, whatever their chosen field of study. The realization of the relationship between our need for both enlightened understanding and useful application of knowledge is not new. The English philosopher Francis Bacon wrote in *Novum Organum* in 1620:

> from experience of every kind, first endeavor to discover the
> true cause and axioms; and seek for experiments of Light,
> not for experiments of Fruit. For axioms, rightly discovered
> and established, supply practice with its instruments, not one
> by one, but in clusters and draw after them trains and troops
> of works. (Bacon, 2005; 71)

But can a liberal approach be useful in presenting "real" science? I believe it can, though this approach should not replace or diminish either rigor or the unapologetic incorporation of the "basic facts" and "hard data."

When I was a professor of geology at the University of Michigan, I used to take my students on one or two field excursions every year. These varied from a weekend camping trip in the Appalachians for freshmen to a six-week field-mapping camp in Wyoming for geology majors. Another field excursion involved a group of thirty or so beginning students who traveled to Britain for three weeks to explore the geology of that country, where much of the initial work was done to establish the scale of geologic time. These students formed a varied group comprising arts and science majors of every kind: premed, engineering, architecture, literature, and foreign languages. Our scientific goal was to understand something of the development of the concept of the immensity of geologic time, based on the rocks, structures, and fossils we studied in the field. We explored the ancient rocks of Scotland's Northwest Highlands; the coalfields of England; the layered rocks of Wales, where Sedgwick and Murchison did battle; Hutton's Unconformity at Siccar Point, where a whole new view of Earth's history was established; and the richly fossiliferous rocks of the Dorset coast, where the remains of prehistoric reptiles and marine invertebrates bear silent testimony to the reality of evolutionary change. In addition to each day's fieldwork, each student was required to present during an evening group discussion a paper on the influence of geology and topography on some other major topic: the extent of the Roman invasion, the development of English scenery, the location of industry, the novels of Hardy, the poems of Wordsworth, the paintings of Turner, the sculptures of Moore, the pattern of agriculture, the location of breweries, the building stones and architecture of cathedrals, the materials of the Industrial Revolution, the development of railroads, the form of cities, and so on. The study of geology in the field was enlivened and enriched by this wider set of interests and relationships.

Any course, anywhere, offers comparable possibilities for linkage and enrichment. Experimental learning and linkage are among the most powerful and enduring methods of creating understanding.

Although reductionism is the lifeblood of science and its methodology, both the best teaching and the most fruitful application of science require a degree of integrative thinking. Here the arts in all their richness can provide fruitful stimulation and essential complementarity.

## SCIENCE IN THE CURRICULUM: GOALS AND CONTEXT

The goal of teaching science in the undergraduate curriculum should be to develop in all students a degree of interest in, broad understanding of, and insight into the world in which we live, in all its richness, variety, and fullness: physical, biological, and social. This is the goal for all students, whatever their scholarly interests or professional aspirations. And for those intending to pursue careers in science or science-based professions, the larger goal should be to provide an appropriately rigorous introduction to the practice of science, together with some understanding of its history, its methods, its assumptions, its relationships, its ambiguities, its challenges, and its social linkages.

These are ambitious objectives, far removed from the traditional Physics 101 and Chemistry 202 courses of most campuses. They are also demanding goals, not only for students, but still more for faculty members, not all of whom will be enthusiastic with the suggestion of such new breadth. But these aims will be good for education, good for our society, good for our students, and good for science. How else can we prepare our students for productive lives in a world where social and ethical questions loom so large and are so intertwined with scientific theory and technological practice?

But how does one achieve such goals? What sort of mix of courses should be offered? What should be required? What should be the content of such courses as these? What educational approach should they embody? The papers that follow in this volume provide striking and successful examples of such courses and approaches, but to propose the adoption of a uniform curriculum would be as unwise as it would be impractical. The curriculum has to be locally designed and developed. No curriculum can be one-size-fits-all. How could it be? Models developed elsewhere will be helpful, and experience in comparable situations will provide insight, but local faculties, working together, must create, refine, and provide the curriculum. The most distinctive thing about any institution should be, and generally is, the curriculum and how it is taught. The curriculum is where students' expectations are fulfilled, students' careers are established, and students' lives are enriched.

## METHODS OF TEACHING SCIENCE

The papers that follow represent a rich variety of effective methods of teaching science. Other workshop reports, teaching outlines, and discussions of the methods of teaching science to undergraduates are readily available. So, let me offer not a review of methods, but a few thoughts on obstacles to effective science teaching and some suggestions on style.

Four obstacles frequently discourage many non-science students from pursuing science courses: terminological submergence, factual inundation, mathematical intimidation, and laboratory trivialization.

*Terminological submergence* arises because of the avalanche of new terms and unfamiliar definitions that many introductory science courses involve. One study suggests that a first-year course in basic science can involve the mastery of more new words than does a comparable course in a modern language (Jarmul, 1996b). How can this be avoided? Can science be made accessible to non-scientists without a terminological overdose?

*Factual inundation* reflects a comparable but distinct hazard. Science does involve facts, and scientific comprehension requires an understanding of them. But science is much more than mere facts: what makes it meaningful is its glimpses into relationships, causes, effects, proportions, sequences, probabilities, and incongruities. Disarticulated facts, unrelated to meaningful context and unexamined in their significance, can destroy interest rather than enlarge understanding. How can we avoid this hazard?

*Mathematical intimidation.* The role of science is to explore or reveal the relatedness of things, and this is true not only of particular facts, but also of our larger experience. Mathematics helps us identify, quantify, and estimate such relationships. Courses in mathematics for non-scientists are frequently demanding, and mathematical intimidation is a common complaint. But can introductory science be taught without rigorous mathematical underpinnings and an accompanying mountain of facts, figures, graphs, and equations? I believe it can, though it may require a good—perhaps a great—teacher to do so. Here again, though we have no standard recipe for success, examples and illustrations can help to suggest and inspire, as do the examples described in this volume.

*Laboratory trivialization.* For too many non-science majors a lifelong aversion to science develops from what they come to regard as laboratory trivialization. Such students rebel against long hours spent in the lab, devoted to, for example, timing the movements of a pendulum in what many see as a pointless exercise to confirm a formula already grudgingly learned; or to titrating solutions of colored salts in order to establish what seem to them to be irrelevant concentrations of inconsequential compounds. Lab work *is* a part, a vital part, of all science; it reduces the immensity and complexity of the universe to manageable proportions. But it is as a method of inquiry, a particular means of comprehension, that lab work and experimentation play such a vital role in science. And lab work, conducted as meaningful inquiry, is the foundation of successful learning, especially for non-science majors.

The question here is one of substance as much as style. We should offer creative, inquiry-based labs, and examples are given in some of the papers that follow. But can we also offer an introductory science course without mathematics, without labs, without a surfeit of technical terminology? I believe this is possible, and some of the papers that follow describe successful examples.

Any discussion of teaching methods inevitably leads back to goals and purpose because effective teaching and learning involve more than course content and teaching methods. We need to ask such vital questions as how to evaluate the quality of a course itself and how to compare the relative benefits of different teaching methods, styles, and practices. We must discover how to evaluate overall student progress and performance, how to understand the particular student experience in any one course in relation to the contribution of courses in other areas of the curriculum, and to undergraduate life more broadly. All these questions and more will demand the attention of the faculty. And it is the privilege and responsibility of the faculty, individually and collectively, to address them.

A few will argue that any set of curriculum goals is too prescriptive, that free-wheeling faculty, individuality, open-mindedness, breadth of coverage, and free range of student choice are preferable to any required structure. The danger of such a view is that collective intellectual abstention and educational ambiguity so often lead to perpetual suspension of judgment on anything of consequence—a regrettable outlook to cultivate in our students. Life comes at us head on; ethical situations demand critical thinking and reasoned choice, not endlessly deferred judgment. Our society will prosper to the extent that our professionals in all science-based and science-related fields exercise their personal judgment and professional expertise based on both the "hard facts" and their broader implications. And our public life depends on an electorate that is both aware of and knowledgeable about the huge range of technical and scientific issues that confront us.

## THE ROLE, RESPONSIBILITY, PRIVILEGE, AND REWARDS OF THE FACULTY

A casual view might suggest that the prominent place of science in the university is assured and that its particular contribution to the life of the academic community is increasing. After all, new labs are under construction everywhere, research support from government and industry grows, and science graduates are eagerly recruited. Student numbers continue to increase. But increasing enrollments in science and science-based courses should not lead one to assume that all is well with science teaching in the university. As good as most science teaching undoubtedly is, good is not great. We can and should aspire to do better, to offer courses worthy in quality to the high aspirations of our scientific calling. That means a deliberate attempt to think anew about the place of science in the curriculum and a determination to rescue the curriculum itself from destructive fragmentation, unexamined growth, and disciplinary constraint. Improvement will also require us to confront the reality of unguided student choice and unreformed graduation requirements. This will be demanding faculty work; it will also be divisive at times, as sacred cows are challenged, long-established customs reconsidered, and comfortable compromises reviewed. To defer such a task is always tempting: to plead the urgency of a publisher's deadline to be met, a paper to be submitted, a joint experiment to be completed, a critical faculty vacancy to be filled. As urgent as these tasks may be, there will always be similarly pressing competing projects. Curriculum review and reform will always be next (or somewhere below next) on the list unless we recognize that its neglect year after year deprives our students of our best efforts—of any serious effort—to equip them for the changing and challenging world in which, for scientist and non-scientist alike, the role of science looms larger every day. Some 50 percent of the issues before the Supreme Court of the United States, for example, now involve some element of science.

To those faculty colleagues who argue that concern about such matters as the curriculum is "not in their job description," I am bound to ask to whom it should be entrusted: to the dean, the provost, the president, the board of trustees? To the students? Perhaps, to some public, industry, business, or other external "user" review group, or a state educational body? To propose any such alternative is to raise the battle cry of academic freedom and faculty autonomy. But the implication of this is that the curriculum—its content, its philosophy, its implementation, its embodiment—is the business of the faculty. To neglect or ignore the responsibility is to abrogate the unique and pivotal role that faculty members are privileged to play, not only in university life, but also in the larger well-being of society and in the nurturing of future generations. Decision-making regarding public issues like climate change, energy policy, and health care, as well as regarding private issues like genetic screening and organic food, requires both a scientifically literate and informed public and a scientifically skilled professional cadre.

To the claim that "this is not my particular field of expertise," one must observe that few, if any, of what are said to be the five hundred definable fields of knowledge are likely to include these macro-issues. Intellectual fragmentation, while enormously fruitful in addressing particular problems, deprives us of the comprehensive reflection and wise deliberation that come from a more extensive and nuanced consideration. Nowhere is this fragmentation more evident than in the balkanization of the universities' science departments. The University of Wisconsin-Madison, for example, was reported in 1996 to have seven hundred faculty members in the life sciences, distributed between two colleges, three schools, and thirty-seven departments (Jarmul, 1996a).

If faculty members are to assume the responsibility for this more comprehensive approach to the teaching of science, they must be encouraged, supported, recognized, and defended. They must be encouraged, especially by their department chairs and deans, to develop their teaching interests and skills. They must be supported through such things as small competitive teaching grants and adequate funding for lab supplies. They must be recognized for their contributions to departmental life. And they must be defended from narrowly based reviews and evaluations, which often equate dedication to teaching proficiency with lack of appropriate devotion to research activity. A department is best represented and students are best served by faculty members who care deeply about and are actively committed to both responsibilities.

## CONCLUSION

No meaningful education can take place without recognition of the need to develop an understanding of and a concern for the overriding issues of our larger society. By this I mean not the particular news events of the moment or the current political debate, but the macro-issues that confront our larger human population: such things as sustainability, population growth, food supply, energy resources, environmental conservation, and climate change. Even to list these topics is to recognize not only their urgency, but also the extent to which our ability to confront their implications and effects will depend on our collective scientific skills, our broader comprehension, and our wise political judgment. Above the continuing indecision of our prolonged academic debate, we need the best science we can devise, offered in this broader context, in our curriculum, in our lives, and in our society. Science may well prove to be the most significant of the liberal arts.

## REFERENCES

Anderson, M. 1992. *Impostors in the Temple: American Intellectuals are Destroying Our Universities and Cheating Our Students of Their Future*. New York: Simon & Schuster.

Bacon, F. 2005. Novum organum. In *The Work of Francis Bacon*. London: Elibron Classics.

Barba, W. C., ed. 1995. *Higher Education in Crisis: New York in National Perspective*. New York: Garland Publishing.

Barrington, L., and J. Casner-Lotto. 2006. *Are They Really Ready to Work?* New York: The Conference Board. http://www.conference-board.org/publications/describe.cfm?id=1218.

Bok, D. 2006. *Our Underachieving Colleges: A Candid Look at How Much Students Learn and Why They Should be Learning More*. Princeton, N.J.: Princeton University Press.

Bowen, W. G., M. M. Chingos, and M. S. McPherson. 2009. *Crossing the Finish Line*. Princeton, N.J.: Princeton University Press.

———, and H. T. Shapiro. 1998. *Universities and Their Leadership*. Princeton, N.J.: Princeton University Press.

Chickering, W. A., and Z. F. Gamson. 1987. Seven principles for good practice in undergraduate education. *AAHE Bulletin* 39(7):3–7.

D'Souza, D. 1991. *Illiberal Education: The Politics of Race and Sex on Campus*. New York: The Free Press.

Ehrenberg, R. G., ed. 1997. *The American University: National Treasure or Endangered Species?* Ithaca, N.Y.: Cornell University Press.

———, ed. 2006. *What's Happening to Public Higher Education?* Westport, Conn.: Praeger Publishers.

Faust, D. G. 2009. Crossroads: The university's crisis of purpose. *The New York Times*, September 6. http://www.nytimes.com/2009/09/06/books/review/Faust-t.html.

Hersh, R. H., and J. Merrow, eds. 2005. *Declining By Degrees: Higher Education at Risk*. New York: Palgrave Macmillan.

Jarmul, D., ed. 1996a. An infrastructure for change. In *Beyond Bio 101: The Transformation of Undergraduate Biology Education*. Chevy Chase, Md.: Howard Hughes Medical Institute. http://www.hhmi.org/BeyondBio101/change.htm.

———, ed. 1996b. Introductory courses. In *Beyond Bio 101: The Transformation of Undergraduate Biology Education*. Chevy Chase, Md.: Howard Hughes Medical Institute. http://www.hhmi.org/BeyondBio101/courses.htm.

Leonhardt, D. 2009. Colleges are failing in graduation rates. *The New York Times*, September 8. http://www.nytimes.com/2009/09/09/business/economy/09leonhardt.html.

Merrow, J. 2004. Grade inflation: It's not just an issue for the Ivy League. *Carnegie Perspectives*, June. http://carnegiefoundation.org/perspectives/grade-inflation-its-not-just-issue-ivy-league.

Newman, J. H. 1996. *The Idea of a University*. Ed. F. M. Turner. New Haven, Conn.: Yale University Press.

Pascarella, E. T., and P. T. Terenzini. 1991. *How College Affects Students: Findings and Insights from Twenty Years of Research*, vol. 1. San Francisco: Jossey-Bass Inc.

———. 2005. *How College Affects Students: Volume 2: A Third Decade of Research*. San Francisco: Jossey-Bass Inc.

Pattison, M. 1892. *Isaac Casaubon 1559–1614*. Oxford: Clarendon Press.

Rhodes, F. H. T. 2001. *The Creation of the Future: The Role of the American University*. Ithaca, N.Y.: Cornell University Press.

———. 2010. *Respice, Prospice Higher Education: A Decennial Review*, ed. J. J. Duderstadt and L. Weber, 3–34. London: University Research for Innovation, Economica.

Sass, S. L. 1998. *The Substance of Civilization*. New York: Arcade Publishing, Inc.

Smith, P. 1990. *Higher Education in America: Killing the Spirit*. New York: Penguin Books.

Sykes, C. J. 1988. *ProfScam: Professors and the Demise of Higher Education*. Washington, D.C.: Regnery Gateway.

# CHAPTER 3

# Science in the Liberal Arts and Sciences

## Eugene H. Levy

Science general education can and should play a much more important role in undergraduate education than has been the case thus far. In order to better serve the national interest, science general education should be rethought in its own special terms and reconstructed as a uniquely valuable part of college education, beyond its current status as a broadening requirement for liberal arts students not majoring in science or engineering. To achieve the broader educational goals set out in this essay, I propose that the content and presentation of science general education be restructured and the target audience expanded.

This volume focuses on the seemingly well-defined challenge of effectively teaching science in college and university liberal arts curricula. That is generally intended to mean teaching science to students who are not otherwise studying (that is, "majoring in") science. The science courses concerned are usually categorized under the rubric of *general education*: that part of the curriculum or course requirements designed to bring conceptual breadth to education, complementing the narrower and more intensely focused parts of the curriculum that constitute the *major*. For the purposes of this essay I will construe general education as courses focused on conceptual content rather than on developing defined skills such as writing, communication, foreign language facility, quantitative reasoning, and so on. This definition may irritate some who will point out, correctly, that the so-called skills courses can also engage significant conceptual content. The distinction is not necessarily defined by sharp and bold boundaries. Moreover, nothing is lost, and possibly much is gained, if a general education science course also helps develop skills in writing or mathematics by exercising those skills under pedagogical supervision in the content-rich context of science. Nonetheless, the distinction, as I employ it, is commonly reflected in college and university curricula.

Some form of general education is more or less universal among U.S. colleges and universities. The structures of general education curricula vary from institution to institution. The two most prevalent variants of general education are (1) the distribution requirement and (2) the core curriculum. Each is framed by its own concept of the role that general education should play in college-level education. On the one hand, a *distribution requirement* is usually built around the idea that all students should be exposed to a variety of scholarly disciplines on the principle that variety and breadth of exposure constitute the goal of general education. Typically, the variety is defined to encompass humanities, social sciences, and natural sciences. However, institutionally idiosyncratic variants exist. For example, science is sometimes, lamentably, lumped with technology or engineering. (Whatever value a course in technology qua engineering might offer to general education—and I believe a well-designed course *can* offer great value—it does not substitute for science.) The *core curriculum*, on the other hand, is built around the idea that some common core of questions, concepts, subject matter, issues, and understanding should engage all students during the course of their undergraduate education and that what they take with them from that part of their education should have lifelong value of a special sort.

Partisans defend the merits of their favored flavor of general education: distribution, core, or some hybrid variant (such as a distribution requirement in which courses must be chosen from among a defined subset of all available courses). The existence of these two distinct approaches to general education is especially useful to those who claim that change itself has inherent value. Moreover, the ability to claim credit for change can be valuable for career advancement and résumé development in university leadership positions. Thus, whichever system of general education a university employs, there is always the opportunity—and sometimes a felt imperative—to change it. In fact, I have heard it said about one university that it was past time to revise the structure of the curriculum simply because the curriculum structure had not been revised for a number of years. I have not studied the matter, but I have sometimes wondered how many colleges and universities episodically switch back and forth from a semblance of one to a semblance of the other, emulating a bi-stable oscillator, each change producing a satisfied claim that the educational experience has been improved. This is not to suggest that change itself cannot have inherent value; indeed it may, if only because it provokes reflection about the curriculum that might not otherwise take place.

For a time early in my own teaching career, I strongly favored a more or less unconstrained distribution structure for general education. My reason for favoring this approach was a common one and easy to understand: my own undergraduate general education had been structured as a distribution requirement. That structure had seemed to me fine enough at the time, and, as I reflected slightly on it at the beginning of my teaching career, it seemed an obvious and easy way to go. An unconstrained distribution structure is flexible and effective at exposing students to variety and breadth in undergraduate education; it offers a path of low resistance for faculty and departments; and its courses are relatively easy to design, implement, and staff, inasmuch as the distribution structure leaves faculty fairly free to offer their own courses, tailored to their interests, tastes, and expertise. The unrestricted structure is indeed a real advantage. We hire faculty members for their intellectual creativity and originality and expect them to focus their research and creative scholarship in self-motivated directions. Relatively unconstrained distribution curricula allow that same sense of independent creativity to extend to teaching in general education courses. This aspect has a great deal in its favor, which should induce one to think hard before proposing to give it up.

In the most extremely unconstrained systems, students are able to satisfy a distribution requirement by taking any available courses, provided they achieve the required distribution of credits over the specified areas. Relatively ambitious or gutsy students can satisfy their general education science requirement by taking regular disciplinary classes alongside students majoring in those disciplines. However, many students seek other alternatives, and most science departments respond to the large demand for general education by offering specially designed courses, sometimes even tailored—not necessarily on purpose—to attract and be accessible to the less engaged. Although many excellent courses are offered in broadly unconstrained general education systems, market forces can have the insidious potential to promote relatively low educational common denominators. In many institutions, registered student credit hours serve as a currency with which faculty positions can be justified and in some budgeting systems explicitly paid for. Departments can compete for this currency, even to the point of adjusting content and grading standards so that students will not feel disadvantaged—and perhaps even find advantage—in taking one department's courses instead of another's. As if to underscore the perception of diluted expectation, some courses have, over time, accreted designations like "Rocks for Jocks," as unfair as the implied pejorative might be to many of the students—especially the jocks—taking the courses. Strong vested interests sustain this arrangement. Faculties have been built in part on the teaching hours earned in these courses. The fact that this arrangement has persisted for decades suggests a certain satisfaction with it. Indeed, it is hard to argue that the approach is flawed. But that is not to say that the job of general education cannot be done better and that we should not try to make more effective use of the important educational opportunity that general education science presents and of the educational need that it fills.

In science, the typically sequential and hierarchical structure of the subject matter, the challenge of accessing technical aspects of the material, and often the formal or mathematical sophistication in the courses designed for majors push most general education science enrollments into the courses designed specifically for that purpose. Frequently, these courses are diluted versions of the introductory courses designed for students majoring in the subject. This latter aspect, especially, represents a lost opportunity. General education requirements shaped around a distribution structure forgo the opportunity to develop a core of common interconnected understanding and ideas with which one might wish all college graduates to become conversant, a point made eloquently by the former dean of Harvard College, Harry Lewis, a computer scientist: "At its best, general education is about the unity of knowledge, not about distributed knowledge. Not about spreading courses around, but about making connections between different ideas. Not about the freedom to combine random ingredients, but about joining an ancient lineage of the learned and wise."[1]

Early in my own teaching, I became troubled by the lost opportunity bound up in loosely structured distribution systems, with students choosing from among a variety of diluted disciplinary introductions. I came to believe that we could—and should—try to offer general education in a way structured to achieve more clearly defined and valuable ends. For me, this took the form of trying to develop, over time, a course with which I felt I could be reasonably satisfied, even if it were the only or the last science course to which a university student would be exposed. As it happened, my own development in this dimension occurred in the context of, and was enabled by, a fairly loosely structured distribution system. Had I been teaching in the context of a core curriculum, with tighter, more sharply defined curriculum objectives and structures, the opportunity to develop a course with the content—and structured in a way—that I perceived to be especially valuable might not have been as readily available. This fact engenders a cognitive dissonance to which I am particularly sensitive because I am about to advocate that general education science be structured in core-curriculum form. I assuage this personal dissonance by realizing that evolution—of ideas as well as organisms—need not be linear and completely logical. Some ideas that are pretty good in some dimensions may give way to other ideas that are better in more dimensions. After all, the dinosaurs died so that we mammals could thrive and prevail (if you will forgive the attribution of such selfless intentionality to the dinosaurs' extinction).

## WHO SHOULD TAKE GENERAL EDUCATION SCIENCE?

In most cases, students majoring in science are exempted from the general education science requirement because the presumably more elementary treatment of the general education material is considered redundant for those who are already immersed in a specialized science curriculum. Conversely, almost all students not specifically majoring in science typically are required to take some number of those courses. Students majoring in engineering, however, are sometimes exempted from the general education science requirement, presumably for the same unjustified reasons that engineering or technology courses are sometimes conflated with, and allowed to substitute for, science.

1. H. Lewis, Letter from Former Harvard Dean Harry Lewis, n.d., http://www.whatwillthey learn.com/deans-letter.

I have long argued that exempting engineering students from the general education science requirement is a mistake (a point that has offended some engineering colleagues). Engineering students should be required to fulfill the general education science requirement just as other students not majoring in science are required to do. In my experience, this proposition stimulates a variety of reactions among engineering colleagues, generally ranging from disbelief or annoyance on the part of those who are relatively receptive to the idea, to manifest outrage from those who are more hostile. My argument about the desirability of extending the general education science requirement to engineers is not intended to disparage the engineering curriculum or engineering students. In fact, I have provoked even greater indignation from my science colleagues by proposing that students majoring in science should also fulfill a core general education science requirement. My experience has been that this evenhanded and ecumenical position does not placate my engineering colleagues nearly to the extent that it puzzles and appalls my science colleagues.

This somewhat fringy position has an obvious corollary. If we were to require science majors to fulfill a general education requirement in science by taking courses alongside the students not majoring in science, then we would be obliged to design and offer courses that would make it worth the while. Our responsibility as science educators would be to develop and offer general education science in a way that would lend credibility to such a broad-scale requirement, rendering the resultant courses a valuable, education-expanding experience for science and engineering students while at the same time ensuring that the courses are accessible and valuable to French majors, musicians, and sociologists. Even if the only outcome were to improve general education science in this way, that alone, in my view, would be worth the effort. To emphasize the distinction from the more traditional construction of the term *general education science*, I will refer to what is proposed here as *science general education*.

In thinking about a constellation of science general education offerings that could fit both typical physics majors and typical bass trombone majors, for example, one might envision offering several different kinds of courses, varying, say, in technical and mathematical intensity. However, I do not believe that would be the best approach. In fact, I think such a gerrymandered approach would undercut several of the important advantages of a universal requirement. Great educational advantage for everyone could be realized from high-quality science general education that is made accessible and valuable to all undergraduate students and designed to satisfy a universal requirement. If designed and presented well, I believe such science courses would be of value not only to the liberal arts students but to science (and engineering) students as well, especially if students from the varied backgrounds were to be mixed in the same classrooms.

A skeptic might object that such courses necessarily will have to be presented in so watered down a fashion as to be superficial and trivial for the science (and engineering) students. In the physical sciences—which, for specificity, are the disciplines I will focus on here, though similar principles apply more broadly —the designations "watered down" and "superficial" are usually code for "descriptive courses with little or no mathematics." To be sure, science courses accessible to as broad a range of students as I am suggesting would employ mathematics of a fairly elementary and simple sort: these would not be calculus-level courses. However, the designations "watered down," "superficial," or "descriptive"—intended to constitute fatal criticism—need not apply. In this context, the sparse use of mathematics is not necessarily a deplorable compromise needed to pander to a mass of students, but potentially a virtue, valuable in its own right for all students, both individually and as a cohort. The goal should be not only to render the science accessible to the mathematically disinclined but also to push the mathematical adepts to confront scientific concepts and phenomena seriously without the protective cover of mathematics —that is, without having mathematics as a crutch with which to frame explanations that, while mathematically unassailable, may lack physical understanding.

Moreover, several additional values attach to science general education for the broader student body, bringing science students together with everyone else. First, this approach presents the opportunity to build the basis for ongoing productive civic dialogue about the nature, substance, and value of science. Universal science general education can help build needed bridges between the scientific and nonscientific cultures in our society and perhaps help initiate and then expand the more effective ongoing national conversation about science that is so crucial to the quality of our cultural and material life as citizens. Some national cultural debates would be well served if the scientific community and the educated laity were able to converse with a stronger base of common language and understanding. Neither science as an enterprise nor the national interest is well served if science is regarded as accessible only to initiates who share an idiosyncratic language largely beyond the ken of most others and a value system disconnected from the main. One of the shortcomings of overly descriptive courses designed for non-science majors is that the science comes across as a closed mystery for which the secrets of real understanding are available to only a small elite. Forcing ourselves to present science general education in a way that is both useful and accessible to all students would challenge us to remedy that shortcoming.

Few aspects of this idea provoke as much objection as the assertion that there is value in exposing science majors to science courses that rely on mathematical or technical tools beneath the science majors' attained or expected level of sophistication. To illustrate my point that such exposure would indeed have value, I will take as an example a common, widely studied, yet perplexing, physical system: the spinning top. As many children learn early, a top or gyroscope spinning with its axis set at an angle to the vertical on a flat horizontal surface does not fall over in the way that naked intuition almost compels one to expect. Instead, the top holds its seemingly impossible tilt and precesses with its spin axis sweeping out a cone around the vertical direction defined by the local gravity. Physics students study the theory of spinning objects during undergraduate education, typically learning in some detail about the classical precessing top. With a little mathematical manipulation, the usual explanation is straightforward—if not entirely illuminating. Already having learned about angular momentum conservation, students are instructed to take a specified vector cross product to see that by the magic of the vector arithmetic, the top can satisfy a balance condition by precessing around the local gravitational vertical. The behavior of spinning objects is fundamental to a vast range of phenomena across both classical and quantum physics. In my experience, when asked why a tilted top does not fall over, most physics students appeal to the memory of a vector cross product or an elliptic integral. But when asked to explain the phenomenon in a more intuitively accessible way, they—along with physics graduates and more than a few physics faculty—rarely give much of an answer.

While drafting this article, I had occasion to retest this perception at a small national meeting of physics educators. The question elicited several rapid responses, including one reminding all of us that the polhode rolls without slipping on the herpolhode. But none of the responses even approached a physically or intuitively accessible account of the spinning top that does not fall over. In fact, few who could recite the incantation about polhodes and herpolhodes actually remembered the definitions. Moreover, as poetic as that invocation might be for those who remember polhodes from herpolhodes, it does not, in fact, describe a spinning top that does not fall over; it describes a body in free rotational motion in the absence of external torques. Is it any wonder that a communication gap separates the cultures?[2]

The purpose of this diversion to the spinning top is not to suggest it as a subject to include in a science general education course. The point is simply to underscore one of the benefits that I attribute to the kind of science general education experience I am suggesting: that asking even science students to engage their disciplines without the usual technical and mathematical armamentarium is of potentially great value. That armamentarium, requisite to the professional practice of science, is not necessarily, by itself, a path to full understanding, even for science professionals. It is certainly not a path to the kind of understanding that can foster broader, sustained intercultural intercourse about science. To further emphasize the point that nurturing intuitive understanding is a valuable enhancement to the education of scientists, I note that once having understood the precessing top in a physical way, the causes of and relationships among the various motions, such as spin, precession, and nutation, become physically evident rather than remaining a haze of often less-than-fully transparent mathematical formulae.

---

2. The physical explanation of why the top does not fall over requires some slightly subtle reasoning and spatial visioning of the complicated three-dimensional motions of the top, for which a clearly drawn diagram can be helpful. Instead of rehearsing an explanation here, I refer the reader to the lucid treatment in the first volume of *The Feynman Lectures on Physics*; see Richard Phillips Feynman, *The Feynman Lectures on Physics*, vol. 1 (New York: Addison-Wesley, 1970).

Nothing prevents the presentation of clear physical explanations in science classes for majors. However, it is often not done. Well-designed integrated science general education courses offer an ideal opportunity to accomplish that by necessity while other valuable educational objectives are being met. At the same time, one or two semesters of science general education will not cover the broad array of disciplinary education. But covering everything is not necessary to stimulate the habits of mind that seek deeper physically intuitive explanations and, as a valuable by-product, facilitate effective communication about and understanding of science in broadly accessible terms.

The suggestion that a science general education requirement be extended to all undergraduates has several objectives intended to provide educational value to both the traditional general education science students and the science-discipline majors, albeit in somewhat different ways. First, grappling with even their own science disciplines without the supporting structures of mathematics, jargon, and assumptions so familiar that they may become unquestioned and cloak a lack of physical understanding is a valuable experience for science majors. Engaging science in conversation with those who do not share the same background and intellectual orientation can be an effective way to hone the understanding of both experts and novices. Second, there is value in broadening the scientific education of science majors as well as students not majoring in science. Many of the challenges that our society confronts involve issues that cross disciplines, engendering the need for an educated populace capable of grasping and appreciating the science, preferably at a level that goes deeper than pure description and in ways that cross both the disciplinary and cultural gulfs that divide us. We tend to categorize students as being inside or outside of science. But science itself is a broad endeavor, and science students can also benefit from classroom exposure to disciplines outside the often-narrow confines of their majors. Third, bringing together science majors and non-science majors in a common science general education core can help improve essential intercultural communication on scientific questions that frame continuing debates in our society, as well as on social and environmental issues for which an understanding of science is crucial. Fourth, the challenge to faculty to develop and teach courses that are, at the same time, accessible and valuable to both science majors and students majoring in other fields can provide an opportunity to reconstruct the science general education experience in a way that will refresh and invest new value in undergraduate education.

## WHY A CORE CURRICULUM?

Arguments for a structured core in general education are based on the proposition that a common body of ideas and understanding exists with which every educated citizen ought to be conversant. For example, it is hard to argue with the assertion that every college graduate should be conversant with the development of world civilizations, the history of ideas and events that shaped our society, and the historical and social circumstances that continue to influence world events. It is likewise hard to argue with the proposition that in our complex modern world every college graduate ought to be at least superficially familiar with the functioning of national and world economies, the armament of controls and regulations that can be brought to bear on guiding and adjusting them, and the conditions and behaviors that can drive them awry. Similarly in science, it is hard to argue with the proposition that every educated person should be conversant with a core of important understanding about the natural world, how natural phenomena work to make the world behave as it does, and how the natural laws as revealed by science are harnessed to improve the quality of our lives. This core of understanding encompasses elements of the structure and behavior of matter and the interactions of matter that generate and control the phenomena we observe in the natural world. To say that, even from a purely practical perspective, responsible citizens today need a sound basis for assimilating and taking part in the public debates that involve scientific and technological questions in such areas as environment and climate, energy, and questions involving life—ranging from such matters as genetic modification of organisms to the ultimately deleterious evolutionary implications of overuse of antibiotics—has become a platitude. Platitude or not, the proposition is true.

Another core of understanding informs and shapes a scientific worldview about the nature of our universe, our planet, and life on Earth. The involved questions range from the truly transcendent—questions about the origin of the universe and life—to more mundane but still socially vexing questions such as the time at which, and the circumstances under which, potential human life becomes, or ceases to be, actual human life. Some of these questions hover at the intersection of human values and scientific fact, infusing and confusing continuing controversies over, for example, embryonic stem-cell research and the application of medical therapies. Some of these questions and controversies have crystallized along one of the most persistent and polarized axes of discourse in our society: the divide between religious and scientific worldviews. We cannot expect to resolve all these questions in science general education, nor is it clear that we should try, but we can hope to equip our students to confront these questions with a clearer understanding of the issues than characterize much public debate.

Science general education should be designed with a seriousness of specific intent and coherence that is commensurate with the importance and significance of its highest purposes. Catching a wave or two of descriptive science in one or two disconnected general education geology, environment, physics, chemistry, or biology courses does not obviously and always fill the need. Failure to fill that educational need is not the fault of the students; it is the fault of the faculty for not shaping this most important component of education with the intent, seriousness, and specificity that it requires and merits.

## THE UNFORTUNATE ALLURE OF INTRODUCTION

I have suggested reasons to prefer a core-curriculum approach—rather than a distribution approach—to general education, an idea that is not especially contentious even if not widely implemented. I have also argued that science general education should be required of all undergraduate students and that science and engineering majors ought to commingle with non-science majors. But everything hinges on the curriculum, which leads me to consider the role of "introduction" in general education. Courses designed for general education are frequently thought of and constructed as "introductions" to their subject matter. Sometimes the courses are even specifically titled as introductions or explicitly described as such in course abstracts. These "introductions" differ from the introductory courses designed for students majoring in a scientific discipline because technical detail and mathematically oriented aspects are typically reduced or eliminated. What remains tends to be a stripped-down version of the introduction designed for majors, simplified and presumably made more accessible to a broad cross-section of students. What is frequently not stripped out is a wide array of detailed factual information and explanations of phenomena that are largely descriptive. Students are often left as confused and unknowing as before the course, except for the temporarily retained combinations of words and images memorized in anticipation of the examinations.

This outcome challenges us to rethink science general education. "Introduction," for me, carries the sense of a beginning, an entrée to a continuing relationship. An introduction is preparation in anticipation of what is expected to follow. For most students, their science general education courses are not introductions at all. These courses are, in fact, the last one or two times, probably in their entire life, that most will be exposed to a formal course in science. An introductory course for an astronomy, biology, chemistry, geology, or physics major is an opportunity to *introduce* students to the concepts, techniques, and manipulations that will form the foundation of their further conceptual work in the courses that follow and perhaps throughout their professional lives. It anticipates a continuing engaged and intimate relationship with the subject matter. In this sense, general education is not an introduction at all; it is a final exposure, a farewell of sorts. As a faculty member teaching a general education course, my goals for a class that I expect to be my students' last formal and organized exposure to science are not similar to the goals that I would set in an introductory class intended to be the start of an ongoing, open-ended formal relationship with the subject.

Astronomy courses, or courses on astronomy-related subjects such as planetary science, are widely enrolled among general education science courses at many universities and colleges. As an example of how best to use—or not use—the time in a last formal exposure to science (as opposed to in an introduction), consider that many such courses and associated textbooks cover, near the beginning, methods for locating astronomical objects in a celestial coordinate system and the associated methods for pointing telescopes to observe celestial objects. This is a somewhat complicated business. Although, for this purpose, the stars and galaxies can be considered relatively fixed on the sky, objects in the solar system move rapidly. But what truly complicates the subject is that Earth-based telescopes must be pointed from the approximately spherical surface of a planet that is itself rotating at the rate of a turn per day and orbiting the sun at a turn per year. Celestial coordinate and time-keeping systems, as well as clever telescope mounts, have been devised to make finding, pointing, and tracking tractable, even automatable. Rare is the general education student who truly absorbs the time-dependent, three-dimensional reasoning necessary to assimilate and use this knowledge. Even a practicum exercise at a telescope, guided with step-by-step instructions and fill-in-the-blank questions, is unlikely to bring many students to a useful grasp of such material, to say nothing of a sustained understanding. For a student majoring in astronomy, by contrast, telescope pointing is an essential element of the curriculum and reasonable to include in an introductory course. Indeed, for that student, a first course truly is an introduction, and pointing telescopes is an essential skill soon to be deployed in actual practice; the earlier such concepts are introduced the better. However, for many, if not most, general education students, an encounter with celestial coordinates, with the relationship between solar and sidereal times, and with the arcana of telescope pointing systems has little long-term value, except perhaps for the ethereal advantage of having glimpsed the paraphernalia and complexity of the astronomical priesthood. It is unlikely to leave, for most such students, much in the way of persistent perception beyond the sense that the subject is hard to penetrate and that they once worked through some exercises vaguely remembered.

My purpose is not to pick on astronomy—a subject I am close to and for which I have great affection—but rather to stimulate discussion about how we might most effectively spend the precious few minutes we have at our disposal to devote to the science education of our nation's next generation of citizens and leaders. I could have made a similar point about the value of dwelling on Newton's laws of motion in general education. Detailed understanding of Newton's laws is of irreducible importance to physicists as well as to scientists and engineers in numerous other specialties. A significant fraction of a physicist's educational time is spent elaborating the consequences of Newton's laws. As important as that is, it does not necessarily translate into value in making a substantial issue of Newton's laws in science general education.

I am, of course, not oblivious to the good arguments that might be offered in support of teaching about telescope pointing to general education students even if the exercise develops only limited, specific, and evanescent understanding. After all, science is an empirical subject. One of the objectives we might want to achieve is to bring our students into at least cultural contact with the realities and challenges of empirical science by teaching about the careful discipline and significant effort that underlie serious science. Fomenting contact with any aspect of real science is surely a good and valuable contribution to education. But, as teachers of science general education, it behooves us to look beyond what is merely good and valuable and to ask what might be the best and most valuable use of the limited time we have for general education. Essential skills for beginning astronomy majors are not necessarily of commensurate value for science general education students exposed to the same subject in a more superficial manner.

CONTENT

What should students be learning in science general education? Any attempt to answer this question must take into account the science education that occurs before college. That conversation is further freighted by what are perceived to be broad-scale deficiencies—or at least the extreme unevenness—in pre-college science education in schools across the nation.

The fact that science general education in college comes on the heels of a dozen years of pre-college science education induces, in my experience, two antipodal reactions among faculty. On the one hand, some seem so demoralized by what they perceive as the deficiencies in so much of pre-college science education that they argue for a ground-up approach in college science general education, including, by accentuating laboratory work, heavy emphasis on the empirical aspects of science. This can translate into a desire to try to make up in one or two semesters of college science for a half-dozen years of perceived preceding deficiencies. Others argue that general education has been taken care of in high school—and if it has not, it should have been. These partisans sometimes argue that college general education should be done away with so that students can devote all their time and energy to the major track for which they are in college in the first place—more or less the way things are done in parts of Europe.

Given such a range of views even among those who hold, as I do, that science general education is a crucial component of college education, the lack of consensus as to the most appropriate content is not surprising. In my own approach to developing a science general education course, I punted on the question of prior science education. Recognizing that students come to the class with a wide range of backgrounds and preparation, I sought to develop a course that would stand on its own, sufficiently different in approach that it would complement what science background even most well-prepared students would bring. But, at the same time, I sought to develop a course sufficiently self-contained that a student with deficient prior background in science could be expected to be able to master the material. Although I have never had the opportunity to teach in the kind of educational environment I advocate in this paper—one in which all students would take science general education together—I found that the occasional science major who did take the course without needing it to satisfy a requirement found it to be of value (at least that was the opinion of those who talked to me about the experience). Inasmuch as I never bought into the proposition that college-level science general education should necessarily require a laboratory component, I did not combine my course with any kind of laboratory or practicum sequence. In that, I was implicitly assuming that most, if not all, students had gained some appreciation of the empirical nature of science in their prior education and that, even if they had not, little additional value would be gained by a subsequent cookbook laboratory experience in college.

I sought to braid three main strings through the course. The first tries to develop students' understanding of the rational mechanical nature of the world: the constitution of matter, the ways that the constituent parts interact through the forces of nature, and how those interactions give rise to the properties and behavior of matter and to the interaction of matter and light, which informs so much of our understanding. This string entails quite a bit of physics, which is then recast and re-presented elsewhere throughout the course in the context of the phenomena of chemistry, astronomy, and planetary and earth science. The second string develops the relationship between the basic properties and behavior of matter and observable phenomena, thus sustaining a sense of connection between phenomena and the origin of phenomena in basic physics. The intent is to help students develop a sense of confidence that the world— or much of it, that part short of highly complex systems displaying emergent behavior—is comprehensible in simple terms and that they have access to that comprehension. I have found that this approach helps assure students that even if explanation eludes them, rational explanation is, in principle, accessible —an outcome that seems to me among the most desirable effects of science general education. The third string narrates a history of the universe through to the development of life on Earth and is built from the physics thread as well as observations. The third string has two motivations. The first is to weave the physics, chemistry, earth and planetary science, and biology into a memorable story that imbues the material with a sense of impact and importance. The second motivation is to leave students with a deeper scientific understanding of questions, and some answers, that have a long and persistent history of human preoccupation and significance and occupy a prominent place in contemporary public discourse and controversy. In my view, this "story" constitutes an essential cultural narrative with which all students should become conversant. The course I developed was most recently given the following description:

> This course explores the origin and evolution of the universe, planets, and life, from the beginning of time—as we now understand that concept—to the living Earth. We will explore the implications of our modern knowledge of the universe and of our scientific understanding of matter and the laws of nature to see what those tell us about answers to deep and long-standing questions about our world, about its

connection with the wider cosmos, and about its origin and evolution. These questions have occupied human thought and speculation throughout all of recorded history, threading through parts of myth, religion, philosophy, and science. We live in a remarkable time: Firm scientific knowledge, developed mainly during the past several hundred years, provides a basis for finding definitive answers to some of these age-old human questions. Basic principles and ideas will be emphasized. Among the purposes of this course is to show that many aspects of the world around us can be understood in simple ways, and to explore the boundaries between that which is confidently known and that about which firm knowledge still eludes us.

The general list and sequence of topics is not especially remarkable and overlaps with or, more commonly, can be extracted from any number of textbooks written for general education science courses. The syllabus for the most recent incarnation of the course listed its topics as:

*Matter, Force, and Energy*—Composition of matter: molecules, atoms, nuclei, and particles. Structure and behavior of matter. Forces of nature. Energy and light. Interaction of light and matter.

*The Sky*—Major objects in the universe. What is the universe made of: the composition of distant objects. The nature of stars and galaxies. Distances to distant objects and the cosmic distance scale. Expansion of the universe.

*The Origin and Development of the Universe*—The principles of cosmology. Possible universes: the expanding universe and the "Big Bang." The origin and evolution of matter. Continuing evolution of the universe.

*Galaxies and Stars*—Formation of galaxies. The nature of stars; their birth and evolution. Sources of stellar energy and the synthesis of the chemical elements. Deaths of stars: white dwarfs, supernovae, neutron stars, and black holes. The life of the sun.

*Formation of the Solar System: Sun and Planets*—Solar system structure and regularities. Characters of the planets; comets and asteroids; planetary satellite systems. Solar system matter, the origin of the solar system, and the formation of planets.

*Planets and their Atmospheres*—Primary and secondary atmospheres. Planetary differentiation, evolution, and structures. The early Earth. Planetary environments: nature and evolution of terrestrial planet environments—Venus, Earth, and Mars.

*The State of the Earth*—Earth structure, continental drift, global tectonics, and the physical evolution of Earth. Earth's atmosphere, hydrosphere, and biosphere. Earth's biological environment: the organic evolution of Earth.

*Nature and Origin of Life*—The definition of life. Basic life processes. Replication: the structure of replicating molecules —DNA. Protein synthesis and the structures of terrestrial organisms. Diversity of life: mutation and evolution. Origin of life: Chemical evolution. Cells. Evolution to "higher" species. The emergence of the human species and cultural evolution.

*Implications and Questions*—What is the likely prevalence and character of other planetary systems? How likely are there to be other planets similar to Earth? How likely is it that life existed/exists/will exist on other planets?

This list of topics contains little that is unusual for such a course. More remarkable perhaps would be a list of material and detail not covered. The course was purposely constructed to be spare of elaborate detail, defined as much by what was not covered as by what was covered. My approach has been to try to include only details that are essential to the core of understanding I seek to develop, to eschew comprehensiveness in favor of comprehension, and to cover nothing that I could not at least aspire to have the students remember several years afterward. I found over a number of years of teaching this course that the early urge to add material and topics, to tend toward the encyclopedic, eventually gave way to the elimination of material and topics, allowing deeper treatment of fewer topics. A second characteristic of the course is continual emphasis, where possible and where it can be made reasonably transparent, on relating phenomena back to basic physics. The purpose is to emphasize the connectedness of phenomena; the nature and robustness of our understanding, where it can be considered robust; and the possibility and importance of building knowledge on deep, simple, and general ideas—that is, to try to delineate the boundaries that separate strong scientific understanding from speculation, ignorance, and less systematic ad hoc approaches to knowing.


ALL TOGETHER

The national interest calls for a citizenry that has a grasp of science sufficient to engender realistic confidence in the nature, efficacy, limits, and importance of science as a modality of understanding and engaging reality. Science provides the foundation of knowledge and understanding on which our technology, prosperity, and material well-being are built. Moreover, science provides the most penetrating framework for seeking answers to questions that have occupied human beings for longer than recorded history. These questions cover matters ranging from proximate ideas about the nature of life and living systems needed to inform ethical debates and decisions to transcendent existential questions about the nature of the universe and the emergence of the human environment—and human beings themselves—from the universe. Some of these questions touch on issues that are also the subjects of religious and other belief systems that societies developed over millennia to try to grapple with the truly transcendent (and the once-seemingly transcendent) mysteries of existence. The fact that science and religion impinge on some of the same questions only underscores the persistence of these questions as subjects of human preoccupation and their importance in shaping the human self-concept.

Science general education is the only opportunity for colleges and universities to contribute broadly to meeting the national need for a citizenry appropriately conversant with science. A sustained, fluent, and effective conversation across the cultural gap that currently divides the scientific community from society at large is required to maintain such a citizenry. Reconstruction of science general education to bring all students together in a well-designed common core may offer the most effective approach. As much as students not majoring in science can benefit from suitable breadth of science appropriately presented, science majors can benefit from a carefully constructed broad presentation of science—complementary to what they experience in their major courses—without the protective cover of formalism and jargon that can, in any event, mask a lack of understanding. Meeting this need will not be easy; it will require institutional flexibility and willingness to reconsider current assumptions, practices, and educational structures in the small part of the curriculum that is involved, and it will require a significant investment of time and energy on the part of science educators for whom marginal time and energy are already in short supply. However, the need is real. The very existence of this volume testifies to the widespread perception that current educational practice falls short in equipping our students with the knowledge to effectively negotiate the increasingly scientific and technological social terrain of the twenty-first century. The investment of flexibility and effort would be justified.

# CHAPTER 4

# Scientific Literacy: A Modest Proposal

James Trefil and Robert M. Hazen

In the next day or two, science will make the news with headlines like "Swine Flu Reaches Pandemic Stage" or "Magnitude 6.5 Earthquake Rocks China."[1] Genetic engineering, water pollution, designer drugs, planetary exploration, global warming, and dozens of other topics are an essential part of the fabric of the twenty-first century. Climate change, natural resources, health, environment, energy, homeland security: these and many other scientific and technological issues directly affect us all and dominate national debates about our priorities and our future. Every citizen needs to understand these issues. To do so, every citizen must be scientifically literate.

Undergraduate science education plays a central role in this national imperative. For millions of American students, college represents the last opportunity for formal science education. Our modest proposal for achieving scientific literacy recommends reaching out to non-science majors with courses that place science—in its broadest sense—within a context that is relevant and accessible to all undergraduates.

## CHANGING ATTITUDES TOWARD SCIENTIFIC LITERACY

The quest for effective and relevant science education for the general public spans nearly a century. The influential education reformer John Dewey penned one of the first theoretical justifications for incorporating science into the general curriculum. Dewey formulated a rationale for science education that resonates in the educational establishment still today: "Contemporary civilization rests so largely upon applied science that no one can really understand it

1. This essay is adapted in part from Robert M. Hazen and James Trefil, *Science Matters: Achieving Scientific Literacy*, 2nd ed. (New York: Anchor, 2009); James Trefil and Robert M. Hazen, *The Sciences: An Integrated Approach*, 6th ed. (Hoboken, N.J.: Wiley, 2010); and James Trefil, *Why Science?* (New York: Teachers College Press, 2008).

who does not grasp something of the scientific method. . . . The formation of scientific habits of mind should be the primary aim of the science teacher in the high school" (Dewey, 1909).

During the 1920s and 1930s, these ideas captured the attention of educational philosophers and precipitated the inclusion of science in the curriculum. Implicit in this movement was the idea that a magic bullet called the "scientific method" would somehow transform students into logical, reasoning human beings. University of Wisconsin educator I. C. Davis offered a telling definition of the successful student:

> We can say that an individual who has a scientific attitude will (1) show a willingness to change his opinion on the basis of new evidence; (2) will search for the whole truth without prejudice; (3) will have a concept of cause and effect relationships; (4) will make a habit of basing judgment on fact; and (5) will have the ability to distinguish between fact and theory. (Davis, 1935)

Experience has shown that these education goals, however worthy in the abstract, are simply unrealistic. At some point, we need to ask ourselves what we can reasonably expect from the actual students who sit in our classrooms. To be sure, a small percentage of students will excel, and some will go on to distinguished careers in science and technology fields. But what about the great majority of students who will go on to become doctors, lawyers, teachers, and business leaders? What about our future politicians, who will have to vote on issues related to science and technology? What should be the role of science education in their lives? We argue that undergraduate science education should ensure that every student is scientifically literate.

## WHAT IS SCIENTIFIC LITERACY?

We define scientific literacy as *the matrix of knowledge needed to understand enough about the physical universe to deal with issues in the news and elsewhere.* This definition is based solely on considerations of how citizens actually use science. Just as one does not need to be an economist to read the business section of the newspaper or a lawyer to read about a pending Supreme Court case, one does not need to be a scientist to be scientifically literate.

What everyone *does* need to know is a mix of facts, vocabulary, concepts, history, and philosophy (Hazen & Trefil, 1991; Hirsch, 1987; Trefil & Hazen, 2007). Scientific literacy is not the specialized stuff of experts but the more general, relevant knowledge used in political discourse and everyday life. Everyone should understand the nature of science as a way of knowing, or the types of questions science can and cannot answer. They should understand the role of measurement, experiment, and mathematical analysis in science and the strengths and limitations of science in resolving complex societal debates. Scientifically literate citizens should also know core concepts and basic vocabulary related to matter, energy, forces, and motions. They should be conversant in topics such as the nature of atoms and chemical reactions, the formation of planets and stars, the processes of plate tectonics and Earth cycles, and the fundamental biological concepts of cells, the genetic code, and evolution.

The knowledge that constitutes scientific literacy is broad but not deep. Consequently, this definition of scientific literacy will seem minimal, perhaps even inadequate, to those who insist that everyone must understand science at a complex level. This attitude was expressed, for example, by the late New York University physicist Morris Shamos (1995), who distinguished between what he called cultural, functional, and "true" scientific literacy. The fundamental problem with this approach to science education is the belief that an individual cannot be "truly" scientifically literate unless he or she can independently draw conclusions about scientific issues using the same kind of reasoning that a professional scientist would employ. From Shamos's viewpoint, having enough background to understand a newspaper article on fossils or superconductors or the greenhouse effect is not enough. This position echoes John Dewey's "scientific habits of mind" yet does not recognize (as Dewey implicitly did) that such a goal is appropriate only for the small fraction of students who major in science. Such discrepancy arises over and over again in the debate about science education and deserves closer inspection.

Individuals' attitudes toward mathematics might also serve as a metric for their opinions on the nature of scientific literacy. Shamos writes, "It is unrealistic to believe that one can fully appreciate the broad reach of science without seeing firsthand the role played in it by mathematical reasoning" (Shamos, 1995). This attitude, which might be translated as, "I had to learn a lot of difficult math to become a scientist, so you should learn it, too," is taken to an absurd extreme by some faculty, who argue that everyone should study calculus at the university level *before* studying science. To deny students an understanding of science because they do not know mathematics is no more sensible than denying them *War and Peace* because they cannot read Russian.

A common fallacy in science education is that every student should "think like us." We have all encountered students who were highly intelligent individuals, accomplished in many areas, but who had extreme difficulty in grasping the quantitative thought process of science. Education psychologist Howard Gardner (2006) underscores the problem with his analysis of different types of intelligences (including linguistic, logical-mathematical, spatial, bodily-kinesthetic, interpersonal, and intrapersonal intelligence). Of these diverse capabilities, only logical-mathematical and spatial reasoning contribute centrally to the traditional scientific process. To select arbitrarily the intelligences appropriate to science and say that everyone has to excel in them makes no more sense than requiring that everyone be able to write a symphony or play sports at a professional level.

This brings us back to the definition of scientific literacy. We want citizens who are able to approach the scientific aspect of public issues with the same level of competence that they have in other areas. What, precisely, does our model citizen have to know to meet our goal?

Some would propose that everyone should be able to "apply critical reasoning" and "come to independent conclusions." By this standard, average citizens are supposed to be able to look at scientific arguments, listen to the competing experts, and use their scientific knowledge and education to decide which side is right. This is a noble ambition, but let us be blunt: this expectation is unrealistic. For one, scientific issues today and in the foreseeable future are sufficiently complex that most Ph.D. scientists are unprepared to perform this analytical task. Indeed, Ph.D. scientists themselves are often scientifically illiterate in most fields except their personal specialties. Thus, short of requiring everyone to have advanced degrees in everything, we see no way to achieve this goal.

Accordingly, we need to acknowledge the difference between scientific competence and scientific literacy. If our goal is to train a new generation of engineers, scientists, and technicians, then we want to teach people how to do science. But no matter how technological the economy becomes, most people will never need to do science for a living. Everyone, however, will need to be scientifically literate to function effectively as a citizen. The distinction between the needs of these two populations is important and largely negates arguments for scientific literacy based on topical and mathematical rigor.

Thinking "like us" does not appear to be of much help in dealing with public issues. After all, the amount of information a citizen needs to enter a public debate is minimal and not at all like that of a science specialist. A "think like us" approach does little to promote scientific literacy. In essence, we must avoid confusing the difference between *doing* science and *using* science.


A MODEST PROPOSAL

What can educators do? For the past two decades, we have promoted a science education strategy designed to bring every citizen as far along in science as he or she is capable of going, based on two simple, self-evident propositions:

1) We have to teach the students we have, not the students we wish we had.

2) If we expect students to know something, we have to tell them what it is.

Before proposing a detailed outline of the core content of a scientific literacy course, we will start off with a general discussion of these two propositions.

*Teach the Students We Have*

Much of the unhappiness we see with respect to teaching non-scientists comes from the failure to honor this first proposition. If we decide to teach non-scientists (and not everyone has to make that decision), we are going to get a mixed bag of students. A small group (probably less than a third in most classes) will be genuinely excited by the subject. A larger group of students (between a third and a half in our experience) will be less engaged but will put in the time necessary to get a good grade. And, inevitably, a final group of students will lack the ability or the ambition to succeed.

Collectively, these are the students we have to teach. Some will "get it" easily, and others will struggle, but the job of the teacher is to help each student as far along the path to scientific literacy as possible. This reality often means that some worthwhile goals have to be put on the back burner while we concentrate on the science. We cannot, for example, spend a lot of time correcting a student's English or writing skills; we do not have enough time.

More important, we probably are not going to be able to take on the twin problems of scientific illiteracy and innumeracy (Paulos, 1988) at the same time. Not only will many of our students have intelligences other than those associated with mathematical skills, but they will also suffer from varying degrees of math phobia. If we want students to engage with science, then we cannot try to communicate by using lots of equations. This constraint is not necessarily a problem because the basic ideas of science can be easily presented without equations.

Ultimately, we suspect that the problem with the first proposition is that many scientists secretly yearn for a diminished world in which Gardner's many intelligences are shrunk down to only one or two (the one or two they are good at, of course). But the essence of being a good scientist is the ability to recognize the realities of the external world—in this case, a world in which our students have many kinds of intelligence but share a common need for scientific literacy.

*Tell Students What We Want Them to Know*

The second proposition also seems self-evident but is profoundly out of line with a major school of thought in science education. This misguided school holds that something exists called the "scientific method" (or, as Dewey put it, a "scientific habit of mind") and that all we have to do is teach students this scientific process and they will grasp everything else about science on their own. This approach is most commonly manifest in ill-founded requirements that oblige every undergraduate non-science major to take an introductory, two-semester lab sequence in a single branch of science: Physics 101 and 102, for example. Such courses may illustrate the "scientific method," but they will also leave graduates ill-equipped to deal with most real-world problems such as energy resources, environmental change, and global health policy, all of which require a basic understanding of concepts in chemistry, geology, and biology, as well as physics.

This point exemplifies a long-standing issue in science education: the conflict between *method* and *content*. What we define as scientific literacy is on the content side of this dichotomy, while Dewey's paradigm is on the method side. We believe that the focus on teaching the "scientific method" is a deeply flawed approach for non-science majors. When we want to annoy our colleagues, we call it the "teach them Newton's laws and they'll derive molecular biology on the way home" school of thought. Such a thing as the "scientific method" does exist, but knowledge of this method is only a small first step on the road to our vision of scientific literacy.

Two arguments highlight the fallacy of the method school of thought. First, if we applied this argument to any other field of study, its failings would be transparent. If we argued for the existence of a "language method," such that studying French would provide easy access to Czech or Urdu, we would all recognize that the argument does not accurately describe how the learning of languages works. If we want to read Czech, we do not study French; we study Czech. Similarly, if we want to discuss stem cells, we do not study climate models; we study molecular and developmental biology.

Second, computers are producing dramatic changes in the way that science is being done. The simple experiments one can do in a university lab class—which are supposed to teach the scientific method—no longer have much relevance as far as many real problems in science are concerned. Consequently, the "scientific method" may become increasingly irrelevant to public discussions. A concentration on method rather than the actual content of scientific literacy, then, is likely to produce students ready to cope with Galileo's rolling balls in a world dominated by genome sequencing and global climate modeling.

THE GREAT IDEAS OF SCIENCE

Our approach to scientific literacy in general, and undergraduate science education in particular, focuses on content. We argue that approximately twenty "great ideas of science" (Table 1) collectively provide the foundation for scientific literacy (Hazen & Trefil, 1991; Trefil, 2008; Trefil & Hazen, 2007). Each of these ideas represents a core scientific concept that integrates a vast body of observation, experiment, and theory. Each reflects everyday experience and observations and thus can be presented in everyday language without equations or mathematical abstraction. Collectively, the great ideas span all the branches of science and provide a comprehensive view of the processes of the natural world.

The list of great ideas, while not immutable, includes overarching concepts that unify nearly all observations of the natural world made by scientists of every specialty. When the initial list of twenty great ideas was first proposed (Hazen & Trefil, 1991), *Science* conducted a survey of its readers, hundreds of whom proposed additions, deletions, or modifications to the list (Culotta, 1991; Pool, 1991). Predictably, most specialists wanted more content in their field: physicists, chemists, geologists, and biologists alike claimed that their specialties deserved a greater fraction of core concepts. Nevertheless, the principle that science rests on a few overarching concepts, including energy, matter, and evolution, was not called into question.

What follows, then, is our proposed list of twenty great ideas of science—the foundation upon which any undergraduate science curriculum should be based.

---

### Table 1: Twenty Great Ideas of Science

1) Science is a way of asking and answering questions about the physical universe.
2) One set of laws describes motions on Earth and in space.
3) Energy is conserved and always goes from more-useful to less-useful forms.
4) Electricity and magnetism are two aspects of the same force.
5) All of the matter around us is made of atoms.
6) Matter and energy come in discrete units; we cannot measure anything without changing it.
7) Atoms bind together by the rearrangement of electrons.
8) The properties of a material depend on how its atoms are arranged.
9) Nuclear energy comes from the conversion of mass.
10) All matter is really made of quarks and leptons.
11) Stars, which use nuclear fusion to convert mass into energy, must eventually burn out.
12) The universe was born at a specific time in the past, and it has been expanding ever since.
13) Every observer sees the same laws of nature.
14) Earth and other objects in the solar system formed 4.5 billion years ago from a great cloud of dust and gas.
15) Earth's surface changes constantly because of convection of hot rocks deep within the planet.
16) Earth operates in many cycles.
17) All living things are made from cells, the chemical factories of life.
18) All life is based on the same genetic code.
19) All forms of life evolved by natural selection.
20) Ecosystems are interdependent communities of living things.

---

### 1. Knowing

*Science is a way of asking and answering questions about the physical universe.* A deep truth about the universe is that it behaves in regular and predictable ways. The underlying assumption behind the scientific endeavor is that the universe obeys general laws that are discoverable by the human mind. Nevertheless, science is not the only way, nor always the best way, to gain an understanding of the world in which we live. Science complements philosophy, religion, and the arts as ways to gain insight into the cosmos and our place in it.

Discovering regularities in nature requires that we observe the phenomena around us—the first step in the idealized scientific method. Once we understand those regularities, we can devise models, make predictions about what will happen, and observe nature and perform experiments to see if those predictions are correct.

### 2. Forces and Motion

*One set of laws describes motions on Earth and in space.* The science of motions developed when our ancestors recognized regularities in the movements of objects in the sky and on land. Isaac Newton proposed his universal laws to define the relationships between motions and forces such as gravity.

### 3. Energy

*Energy is conserved and always goes from more-useful to less-useful forms.* We do work when we exert a force over a distance. Energy is defined as the ability to do work (that is, to exert a force over a distance). Two laws of thermodynamics unify the study of energy. The first law recognizes that energy comes in many forms, including motion, heat, light, and varied kinds of stored (or potential) energy. Energy can change from any one of these forms to another, but the total amount of energy in a closed system cannot increase or decrease.

The second law of thermodynamics deals with the direction of the universe. Heat left to itself flows in only one direction, from hot to cold. Similarly, systems left to themselves always become more disordered with time.

### 4. Electricity and Magnetism

*Electricity and magnetism are two aspects of the same force.* Electrical charge can be either positive or negative, and the electrical force operates in such a way that the force between like charges is repulsive, whereas the force between unlike charges is attractive. Magnets have north and south poles, and the magnetic force is such that like poles repel one another while unlike poles attract. Isolated magnetic poles do not occur in nature: whenever we find a north pole, we also find a south pole.

Electrical and magnetic forces appear to be different, but whenever electrical charges move (that is, whenever an electric current flows) a magnetic field is produced (the working principle of the electromagnet and the electric motor). Conversely, whenever a magnetic field changes near a material that conducts electricity, an electric current is produced in that material (the working principle of the electric generator).

Equations that summarize the behavior of electric and magnetic phenomena predict the existence of electromagnetic waves—energy waves that move at the speed of light. Radio, microwave, infrared radiation, visible light, ultraviolet light, X-rays, and gamma rays are examples of electromagnetic waves.

## 5. Atoms

*All of the matter around us is made of atoms.* The world holds two kinds of materials: those that can be broken down by chemical means (compounds) and those that cannot (chemical elements). Each element is composed of small units called atoms, and all other materials are made by combining atoms. Each atom has a massive, positively charged nucleus surrounded by negatively charged electrons.

## 6. Quantum Mechanics

*Matter and energy come in discrete units; we cannot measure anything without changing it.* At the scale of the atom, every property—mass, energy, spin, and more—comes in discrete bundles called quanta. At the scale of the atom, any measurement must involve a change of the quantum state of the object being measured. Therefore, we cannot measure an object at the scale of the atom without changing it in the process of measurement.

## 7. Chemical Bonding

*Atoms bind together by the rearrangement of electrons.* Everyday materials form from different combinations of atoms, which bond together by rearranging the atoms' outermost electrons. Electrons produce a bond between atoms in three ways: (1) one atom can transfer an electron permanently to another to produce an ionic bond; (2) two atoms can share a pair of electrons to produce a covalent bond; (3) each atom can give up an electron, which is then shared by all the atoms to produce a metallic bond.

## 8. Materials

*The properties of a material depend on how its atoms are arranged.* The properties of a material depend on the type of bond holding its atoms together, as well as the arrangement of those atoms. For example, electrical properties depend on how strongly electrons are locked into their bonds. In a metal, electrons are free to move when subjected to outside forces, so electrical current flows easily. Metals are thus electrical conductors. In most plastics or ceramics, on the other hand, electrons are locked tightly into covalent or ionic bonds. Such materials are called electrical insulators.

## 9. The Nucleus of the Atom

*Nuclear energy comes from the conversion of mass.* The nucleus of the atom is a dense collection of particles that carries most of the mass of the atom. In nuclear reactions, some of this mass may be converted to energy via Einstein's famous equation $E = mc^2$. Nuclei with the same number of protons but different numbers of neutrons are called isotopes of one another. Some isotopes are unstable and undergo a process of disintegration known as radioactive decay.

Energy can be derived from nuclei by fusion (the coming together of small nuclei to form larger ones) or fission (the splitting of large nuclei into smaller ones). When the mass of the final products is less than that of the initial nuclei, the difference is converted into energy.

## 10. Particle Physics

*All matter is really made of quarks and leptons.* Atoms are made of even smaller particles, including leptons (of which the electron is one example) and quarks (which combine in groups of three to make protons and neutrons).

## 11. Stars

*Stars, which use nuclear fusion to convert mass into energy, must eventually burn out.* Stars are born in the gravitational collapse of dust clouds in space. The temperature and pressure at a star's center increase until nuclear fusion reactions start, converting hydrogen into helium in the process. The energy from these reactions creates a pressure that counteracts the force of gravity and stabilizes the star. The sun and other stars spend most of their lives in this hydrogen-burning phase.

The sun will eventually consume its hydrogen fuel and will collapse to become a white dwarf star (in another 5.5 billion years). Stars much more massive than the sun can become unstable, exploding into a supernova. Debris from a supernova is blown into space, where it is incorporated into new generations of stars.

## 12. The Big Bang

*The universe was born at a specific time in the past, and it has been expanding ever since.* American astronomer Edwin Hubble discovered that matter in the universe is clumped together in large collections of stars called galaxies and that galaxies are moving apart from one another. The Hubble expansion implies that the universe began at a specific time in the past (about 14 billion years ago) and has been expanding and cooling ever since.

Studies of the expanding universe reveal that visible matter represents only a small fraction of what the universe contains. Over 90 percent of the cosmos is made of poorly understood material called "dark matter" and "dark energy."

## 13. Relativity

*Every observer sees the same laws of nature.* Albert Einstein's theory of relativity comes in two parts: special relativity, which deals with observers moving at constant velocities; and general relativity, which deals with observers who are accelerating. Among the paradoxical findings of special relativity are (1) moving clocks slow down, (2) moving objects become more massive, (3) moving objects appear to shorten in the direction of their motion, and (4) mass and energy are equivalent, as stated in the famous equation $E = mc^2$.

## 14. Planets

*Earth and other objects in the solar system formed 4.5 billion years ago from a great cloud of dust and gas.* The sun and planets of our solar system formed from the gravitational collapse of a nebula, an immense cloud in space. More than 99 percent of the mass of this nebula formed the sun, while most of the remainder formed the planets. The four inner planets closest to the sun (Mercury, Venus,

Earth, and Mars) are relatively small and rocky. The outer four planets, which formed in colder regions farther from the sun where gases could condense, are gas giants formed primarily of the elements hydrogen and helium.

## 15. Plate Tectonics

*Earth's surface changes constantly because of convection of hot rocks deep within the planet.* Earth is layered like an onion. The central core consists of dense iron and nickel; the mantle is composed of minerals rich in silicon, oxygen, and magnesium; and the outermost layer is a thin crust. Earth's surface is separated into thin, brittle, tectonic plates that move around in response to convection in the hot mantle. Continents are the uppermost layer of these plates. The continuous motion of the plates constantly changes the surface features of the planet.

## 16. Earth Cycles

*Earth operates in many cycles.* Earth's rocks, water, and atmosphere operate in cycles in which energy flows and atoms are used over and over again. Water, for example, evaporates from the oceans and falls as rain on land, eventually flowing back into the ocean, as either a surface river or an underground aquifer. Over long periods of time, more of Earth's water can be taken up in ice caps and glaciers during ice ages, or can be put back into the oceans during periods of global warming.

## 17. Cells

*All living things are made from cells, the chemical factories of life.* Life is based on chemical reactions, which take place in complex structures called cells. Cells are the fundamental unit of life, and all cells arise from preexisting cells. Each cell is analogous to a chemical factory. Chemical reactions in a cell are controlled by protein molecules that serve as enzymes, and the information for building those molecules is coded in stretches of DNA called genes.

## 18. Molecular Genetics

*All life is based on the same genetic code.* All known life forms on Earth, from bacteria to humans, use the same DNA code and the same molecular machinery to produce the proteins that run chemical reactions essential to life. This fact is the basis for genetic engineering, a technique that already plays a major role in agriculture and medicine. In genetic engineering, a gene from one organism is inserted into the DNA of another organism.

## 19. Evolution

*All forms of life evolved by natural selection.* Scientists divide the development of life on Earth into two stages: chemical evolution, which involves the development of life from inorganic materials; and evolution by natural selection, which describes the process by which the first early life form produced the diversity of modern life. Natural selection is associated with the discoveries of Charles Darwin and is what most people mean by the term *evolution.*

Evolution by natural selection depends on two familiar characteristics of living things: first, populations exhibit variations in traits (so that, for example, some rabbits can run faster than others); second, individuals compete (so that fast rabbits are more likely to survive and reproduce). Over many generations, this selection process produces new species. Evidence for evolution by natural selection comes from the fossil record and from the examination of genes in the DNA of modern life forms.

*20. Ecosystems*

*Ecosystems are interdependent communities of living things.* Ecosystems include all living things in a specific area, together with their material surroundings. Plants and animals within an ecosystem often depend on each other in complex ways, so it is not usually possible to change one part of the system without changing other parts as well. Studies of past ecosystems show that both the kinds of plants and animals present in a system and the relationships among different organisms change over time.

Human activities, such as increased burning of carbon-based fuels, may gradually change the composition of Earth's atmosphere. These changes may, in turn, alter the global climate and, hence, Earth's ecosystems in ways and extents that are difficult to predict with certainty.

## CONCLUSIONS

Science educators have implemented many approaches to engaging undergraduate non-science majors, including traditional discipline-based lab courses; seminars on broad topics such as energy, evolution, the environment, or forensics; explorations of scientific current events and public policy; and courses that explore science from historical and/or philosophical perspectives. In the hands of a dedicated and dynamic teacher, any of these strategies has the potential to captivate and enlighten students, and many of these approaches are used to great effect at colleges and universities with small classes and frequent student-faculty interactions.

The "great ideas of science" curriculum represents another undergraduate option that integrates many of the best aspects of other course strategies but that may be better suited to the needs of a large community of non-science majors. The great ideas provide students with a broad perspective on all scientific disciplines and underscore the impact of those varied fields on modern society. Each great idea can be illustrated with everyday experiences and current events, and each can be presented in a framework that recognizes a rich historical and philosophical context. The great ideas curriculum also underscores the strong linkages in concept and content among the different branches of science: forces, motion, energy, matter, atoms, evolution, and many other topics appear again and again throughout the curriculum and thus reinforce the importance of a few core ideas.

Most important, by introducing students to the full sweep of the sciences, we provide them with a firm foundation for lifelong learning in science. Students will thus have the opportunity to appreciate the role of science in their lives, to apply that understanding to personal decisions related to health and environment, to foster learning in their children, and to share in the excitement and wonder of the greatest ongoing human adventure—the adventure of scientific discovery.

## REFERENCES

Culotta, E. 1991. Science's 20 greatest hits take their lumps. *Science* 251: 1308–1309.

Davis, I. C. 1935. The measurement of scientific attitudes. *Science Education* 19:117–122.

Dewey, J. 1909. Symposium on the purpose and organization of physics teaching in secondary schools. *School Science and Mathematics* 9:291–292.

Gardner, H. 2006. *Multiple Intelligences: The Theory in Practice*. New York: Basic Books.

Hazen, R. M., and J. Trefil. 2009. *Science Matters: Achieving Scientific Literacy*, 2nd ed. New York: Anchor.

Hirsch, Jr., E. D. 1987. *Cultural Literacy: What Every American Needs to Know*. New York: Houghton Mifflin.

Paulos, J. A. 1988. *Innumeracy: The Consequences of Mathematical Illiteracy*. New York: Farrar, Straus and Giroux.

Pool, R. 1991. Science literacy: The enemy is us. *Science* 251:266–267.

Shamos, M. H. 1995. *The Myth of Scientific Literacy*. Rutgers, N.J.: Rutgers University Press.

Trefil, J. 2008. *Why Science?* New York: Teachers College Press.

———, and R. M. Hazen. 2010. *The Sciences: An Integrated Approach*. 6th ed. Hoboken, N.J.: Wiley.

# CHAPTER 5

# Science Education in the Age of Science

## Chris Impey

Discussions of science education create a sense of déjà vu. Like major astronomical alignments, reports on the state of undergraduate science teaching within the liberal arts curriculum roll around every decade or so (American Association for the Advancement of Science, 1990; Boyer, 1998; National Research Council, 1999; this volume). Revolutions are all around us, in the burgeoning fields of genomics, astrophysics, nanotechnology, and many others. Science is outstripping the ability of even its practitioners to keep up beyond their area of research. What hope of keeping up do non-technical citizens have, especially when much of the information provided by mass media is fragmentary, inchoate, or misleading? The answer—and the onus—rests with scientists who teach college courses for non-science majors. One in four Americans is a college graduate, and that number will rise as higher education continues to offer career attainment and financial success.

Fortunately, educators have at their disposal a wealth of research that they can use to improve learning and retention in the classroom, as well as new technologies that can spur learning and curiosity in science. If we are to help students become more than just passive participants in the Age of Science, we must redouble our efforts to help them understand the great intellectual adventure that is reshaping the world.

The following quotations from *A Tale of Two Cities* (Dickens, 1859) set the scene by drawing contrasts between the vitality of scientific research and the imperfect grasp of science by our students and the general public.[1] *It was the best of times, it was the worst of times . . .* Over the past fifty years, the employment of scientists and engineers in the United States has increased from two hundred thousand to nearly five million, with a corresponding growth in the number of research papers and knowledge. Yet support for academic re-

1. Data are taken from the National Science Foundation's biennial *Science and Engineering Indicators* series.

search and development (R&D) is lower in inflation-adjusted dollars than it was thirty-five years ago, and R&D as a percentage of the U.S. gross national product (GNP) is lower than at most times since 1980.

*. . . it was the age of wisdom, it was the age of foolishness . . .* The fraction of Nobel Prizes in science going to Americans increased from 63 percent in the years 1951 to 1975 to 86 percent during the final twenty-five years of the last century. The number of natural sciences graduate degrees awarded has risen by 50 percent over the last twenty years. However, the U.S. Department of Health and Human Services Office of Research Integrity estimates that about one thousand cases of scientific misconduct go unreported each year.

*. . . it was the epoch of belief, it was the epoch of incredulity . . .* Americans believe in the value of scientific research. By a margin of four to one, they think its benefits outweigh any negative effects; by a margin of ten to one, they say the government should fund basic research. On the other hand, only one in three members of the public is aware of the Big Bang model; only half believe that we evolved from earlier species of animals; and one in four is unaware that Earth goes around the sun. Susceptibility to pseudoscience and supernatural explanations also remains stubbornly high.

*. . . it was the season of light, it was the season of darkness . . .* Science and technology have raised more than a billion people out of poverty worldwide in the past fifty years. In the same period, improvements in medicine have increased life expectancy by twenty years. Hanging over this success are the shadows of human-induced global climate change, the rise of pathogens and toxins in the environment, and the fact that the major powers retain more than twenty thousand nuclear weapons—enough to kill all humans many times over.

*. . . it was the spring of hope, it was the winter of despair . . .* Science and technology are young relative to the span of the human species and are enjoying a surge thanks to the exponentially increasing capabilities of computers and networks. If we can survive our troubled adolescence, the universe is our oyster. If we are representative of technological species, Drake's equation puts a cosmic perspective on our dilemma by estimating the number of intelligent, communicable civilizations in the Milky Way. If we endure for thousands of years with our current capabilities, we are likely to have kinship among the stars. If our cultural instability is typical, we are likely to be short-lived and alone in the universe.

THE STATE OF SCIENCE EDUCATION

As with science, so with science education. In 2007, Career Cast, a major job search Web portal, evaluated two hundred jobs in terms of pay, stress, and work environment. Science and engineering jobs accounted for twelve of the top twenty and eight of the top ten most desirable positions. Yet the number of bachelor's degrees in math, physical science, and engineering has been flat or falling for twenty-five years. Less than half of high school students take biology or physics, less than 20 percent take any calculus, and a majority of public secondary schools cannot fill all their math and science teaching vacancies. Technical training in the U.S. university system is the envy of the world; a third of advanced degrees in science and more than half of advanced degrees in engineering are awarded to foreign nationals. But many of the non-scientists coming out of the U.S. system are not scientifically literate, according to the National Science Foundation (NSF) surveys that are delivered to Congress every two years (for example, see National Science Board, 2008).

Meanwhile, not much has changed in the classroom since the report *Reinventing Undergraduate Education* (Boyer, 1998) slammed research universities for giving short shrift to undergraduates studying science. The body of peer-reviewed literature on the efficacy of collaborative learning and interactive modes of engagement is growing, but science is taught mostly by pure transmission, or lecture, and is evaluated based on the testing of facts, at the lower levels of a learning taxonomy (Bloom, 1956; Mintzes & Leonard, 2006). Bloom's original schema divides learning into affective, psychomotor, and cognitive domains. Within the latter are six skills that range from low- to high-order learning: knowing, comprehending, applying, analyzing, synthesizing, and evaluating.

Compounding a traditional and ossified situation, the academy's reward system continues to embrace a pyramid of values that places research above teaching and outreach, graduate students ahead of undergraduates, and the teaching of non-science majors well below scholarship and faculty evaluation (Fairweather, 1993).

This article explores the challenges of and opportunities for teaching science to non-science majors in the context of a liberal arts education. My examples are often from astronomy, a core subject of the classical quadrivium for more than eight hundred years. Astronomy epitomizes the rationale for liberal arts: although to many it may seem useless, astronomy can in fact be used to teach critical thinking skills that are applicable across the curriculum. It also has singular features: much of the best research data are readily accessible in the public domain (images and other data from the Hubble Space Telescope are the most notable examples; more generally, the night sky belongs to everyone). In addition, whereas amateur scientists are rare or nonexistent in most fields, astronomy has innumerable active amateurs. Finally, people are familiar with the topic, which makes it accessible and nonthreatening to novice learners. However, this final benefit is offset by the fact that in popular culture, the image of astronomy is sometimes muddied by UFO "sightings" or confused with astrology. All the teaching methods discussed in this essay can be effectively used in large classes (100 to 150 students) of non-science majors with minimal additional teaching support.

# SCIENCE EDUCATION IN PRINCIPLE

*What Every Student Should Know*

The best way to engage a group of scientists in a debate on education is to start with the question of what every student should know. They all will have an opinion—often forcefully stated—and will offer up a list of essential topics in their specific discipline. The lists will have a common core of mutual agreement, along with idiosyncratic and individualistic selections. Most of the heat —and little light—will come from arguments over the non-overlapping elements.

Professional astronomers form a small scientific community of about 7,000 people in the United States and twice that number worldwide. The American Institute of Physics (2009) tabulates seventy-five institutions granting astronomy Ph.D.s, and those physics and astronomy departments have roughly 1,700 faculty members between them. Most astronomy faculty teach introductory astronomy for non-science majors. The total enrollment in such courses is about 250,000 per year, which includes 150,000 students enrolled in four-year colleges with astronomy, physics, or combined physics/astronomy departments, and 100,000 students in two-year schools, most of which are community colleges or two-year colleges with neither physics nor astronomy departments (Fraknoi, 2004). Educational leaders and teaching specialists from the community of departments offering astronomy courses gathered in the early 2000s for two workshops to answer the question, what are the goals for the teaching of Astro 101?

Although each workshop group had no knowledge of the other's discussions, their answers were remarkably similar (Partridge & Greenstein, 2004). They agreed that the goals for teaching Astro 101 should be for students to gain:

- A *cosmic perspective*—a broad understanding of the nature, scope, and evolution of the universe and where Earth and the solar system fit into the larger picture;

- An understanding of a limited number of key *astronomical quantities*, as well as some knowledge of appropriate physical laws;

- An understanding of the notions that *physical laws and processes are universal*, that the world is knowable, and that humans come to know the world through observations, experiments, and theories (the nature of progress in science);

- Exposure to the types, degrees, and roles of *uncertainty in science*;

- An understanding of the *evolution of physical systems* and some knowledge of related topics such as gravity and the formation of spectra, as well as a set of useful tools from related subjects such as math, chemistry, geology, and biology;

- An acquaintance with the history of astronomy and the *evolution of scientific ideas*, or science as a cultural process; and

- Familiarity with the *night sky* and how its appearance changes with time and with one's position on Earth's surface.

What is striking about these goals is their lack of specificity regarding content. The workshop groups did not design a curriculum or propose detailed standards. Several of their goals make only passing reference to astronomy and with the change of a few words could apply equally to physics or to a much less closely related discipline. Astronomy educators implicitly recognize that their audience has no long-term commitment to the subject: most of their students are satisfying a science requirement as part of a general education program. The goals agreed upon at the two workshops recognize that the most valuable approach to teaching astronomy is to teach broad content that applies across all scientific disciplines. The philosophy seems to be "less is more."

The workshop groups also set goals for the skills, attitudes, and values students should take away from an introductory astronomy course. They agreed that students should:

- Be exposed to the excitement of actually doing science, the evolution of ideas in science, and science's cultural backdrop;

- Receive training in the method of science, in particular the role of observations and experiments, analysis of evidence and hypotheses, critical thinking (including appropriate skepticism), hypothesis-testing (including experimental design and following the implications of a model), quantitative reasoning and the ability to make estimates, the role of uncertainty and error in science, and how to make and use spatial and geometric models; and

- Be left more confident in their own critical faculties, inspired by and about science in general and astronomy in particular, and interested in and better equipped to follow scientific arguments in the press and the media.

These goals are pan-scientific and make almost no reference to astronomy. They are as ambitious as they are overarching, and they set a high bar for teaching students who arrive poorly prepared in science, often with habits of mind ill-suited for grappling with unfamiliar subject matter and applying logic to the world around them.

### Throw the Book at Them

The most important resource for teaching non-science majors has been the textbook. In astronomy, as in all other scientific subjects, textbooks have become overstuffed behemoths scrambling to track the increase in knowledge.

**Figure 1: The Increasing Cost of Textbooks and Tuition Relative to General Consumer Prices, 1986 to 2004**

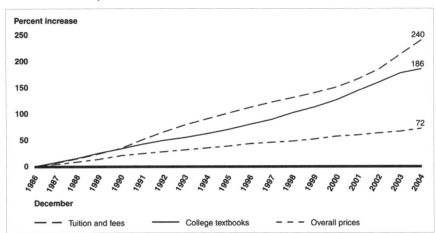

Educators are concerned about the increased cost of education, but the rapidly rising cost of science textbooks is causing students not to buy them even when they are required, to the detriment of their learning. Source: Bureau of Labor Statistics. 2005. *College Textbooks: Enhanced Offerings Appear to Drive Recent Price Increases.* GAO-05-806. Washington, D.C.: Government Accountability Office.

A survey of introductory astronomy textbooks in 2007 found two dozen titles, involving three dozen authors, serving a market of about 250,000 students per year (Bruning, 2007). A typical astronomy textbook is 600 pages long, costs $100, and includes a glossary with 500 terms. Average length and cost have increased steadily over the past few decades, with cost rising much faster than inflation (see Figure 1; Bureau of Labor Statistics, 2005).

However, the most significant limitations of textbooks as pedagogical tools are not size and cost, but the traditional and conservative way they are written and compiled. This conservatism derives not from publishers' unwillingness to include exotic and esoteric phenomena such as superstrings, gravity waves, and alien civilizations, but from their strictly "kitchen sink" approach to the content and their inability to structure books so the processes or general attributes of science have equal footing with the facts. In fairness to the authors and publishers of these books (I was one of the former for about a decade, so I know the business from three sides: as a teacher, an author, and the parent of two students using textbooks), market forces push books to become larger, to include all recent advances, and to become more similar as they copy each other's features and innovations. Publishers are moving in the direction of vertical integration, where a textbook is part of a teaching "system" that also incorporates a website, interactive tutorials and applications, and testing materials.

Student dissatisfaction with the price of textbooks and the lack of cheaper alternatives is strong and growing. A coalition of public interest research groups (PIRGs) and student government associations has captured the attention of legislatures in several dozen states (Ripoff 101, 2005). Following a U.S. Government Accountability Office report finding that prices of textbooks had tripled between 1986 and 2004 and estimating annual expenditures of $1,000 on textbooks, Congress passed a bill in 2008 requiring publishers to release more information on prices and prohibiting the practice of selling only new books bundled with software, CDs, and workbooks. In the PIRG study, two-thirds of faculty said they never used the bundled items, and three-quarters said that frequent new editions were largely unjustified.

Malaise in the textbook industry affects science education directly. High prices mean that one in four students does not buy the required textbook, and that percentage is increasing. When students buy, lease, or rent used or old books, they may forgo the latest information in fast-changing fields. In 2006, the National Academy of Science sponsored a workshop on "Reconsidering the Textbook," convening NSF and academic leaders to survey textbooks and analyze their relation to the growing set of electronic tools available for learning. The participants acknowledged signs of evolution from static printed pages of content to a more dynamic, interactive medium but were unsure whether traditional media producers could make the "jump to hyperspace." Since then, electronic publishers have taken advantage of the increasing capabilities of handheld devices (Butler, 2009).

Meanwhile, the habits of college-age students are rapidly changing with the ubiquity of computers and high-speed Internet. A study by the Pew Research Center's Internet and American Life Project found that the Internet has eclipsed television, print media, and libraries as the primary source of science news and information (Horrigan, 2006). Nearly 90 percent of online users research science information using the Internet. Depending on topic, the Internet is used more frequently than any other information source by a factor of two to six. The Pew report is a gold mine of information on the way the public now gets its information and has great relevance for the strategies of science educators (see Figure 2).

For example, the study reveals that people choose the Internet to get science information purely on the basis of convenience, as opposed to any perception of high accuracy. The Internet boosts general science awareness; two-thirds of all users say they come across science news and information when they go online with another purpose in mind. Eighty percent of those who get science information online use another resource to check those facts, although most simply use another online resource for fact-checking. The Internet is becoming a hermetic world of information, which increases the pressure on science educators to train their students in how to evaluate the credibility of online resources. At the moment, few universities have widely available or mandatory classes on information literacy.

**Figure 2: Understanding of Science—Comparing College Graduates Who Get Science Information Online to College Graduates Who Do Not**

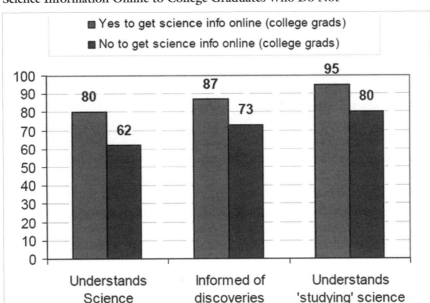

This graph shows that use of the Internet as a source of science news and information corresponds to high levels of science understanding, after controlling for different levels of education and interest. Measures of understanding the content and the method of science are based on NSF metrics. Because of the large sample size, the differences between "yes" and "no" responses for each of the categories are highly significant. Source: Horrigan, J. B. 2006. *The Internet as a Resource for News and Information about Science.* Washington, D.C.: Pew Internet and American Life Project. http://www.pewinternet.org/Reports/2006/The-Internet-as-a-Resource-for-News -and-Information-about-Science.aspx. 14.

*An Electronic Cornucopia*

With four million articles in English and an open editing framework, Wikipedia continues to grow rapidly and now dwarfs all other information resources on-line or in print. A third of all adult Americans who go online use Wikipedia as a reference, and on a typical day one in ten online users consults it. Wikipedia is routinely among the ten most-visited websites (Rainie & Tancer, 2007). The average Wikipedia user is younger, richer, and more highly educated than the average Internet user. Academic debates over whether students should use it are essentially moot; for college-age people Wikipedia has rapidly become a one-stop shop for all forms of information. The more relevant questions are "How accurate is its science content?" and "How can it be improved?"

Scientists and educators are understandably dubious of the reliability of a resource that can be anonymously edited by anyone. However, when *Nature* commissioned a head-to-head comparison between Wikipedia and *Encyclope-dia Britannica*, the result was almost a draw (Giles, 2005). Among forty-two articles on science topics, four serious errors were found in each resource, and

## Figure 3: Usability of Wikipedia Relative to NASA's Website for Information on Apollo

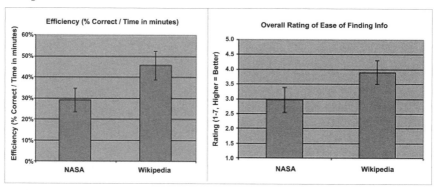

In a head-to-head usability study that asked 130 people to answer nine questions about the Apollo program, Wikipedia scored better than NASA's website in almost every aspect: task accuracy, time, efficiency, and ease of finding information. The left-hand graph shows the percentage of items that were answered correctly normalized by the amount of time taken. Overall, the scientific content of Wikipedia is accurate and comprehensive. Source: Tullis, T. 2008. Results of online usability study of Apollo program websites. Measuring User Experience. http://www.measuringuserexperience.com/Apollo/. Graphs courtesy of Tom Tullis.

a typical article had four minor errors in Wikipedia and three in *Encyclopedia Britannica*. Since then, smaller studies by a variety of bloggers and commentators confirm the general absence of major errors in Wikipedia science articles, although the writing quality is uneven. One study found that Wikipedia was more accurate and usable on a particular topic than a National Aeronautics and Space Administration (NASA) website devoted to the topic (see Figure 3). The Wikipedia Foundation has taken steps to improve reliability by identifying a cadre of expert editors whose edits cannot be undone or overridden by anyone else. I have read more than a hundred articles on astronomy and astrophysics and agree that howlers are rare; the quality and level of detail often are surprisingly good.

Wikipedia has benefited synergistically from the power of search engines, particularly Google. Over 70 percent of Wikipedia's traffic comes from search engines, half of it from Google. Wikipedia's high density of internal and external links guarantees its pages high ranking in Google's page-rank algorithm; most searches on academic topics return Wikipedia pages in the top three results. Google is also the most frequent downstream destination for users of Wikipedia, completing the cycle. The best strategy for scientists may be to accept the inevitable—the future of information is computers and networks, electrons and waves, not paper and ink—and improve the resource by reading Wikipedia articles in the topics of their expertise, editing them where they find mistakes, and developing test cases to train their students on how to skeptically evaluate the quality of online content.

The information revolution is really just beginning. Tools for navigating and organizing digital information have not been able to stay ahead of the rising tide, so finding the useful information and reliable knowledge in that ocean of bits is a challenge. In 2010, roughly $10^{19}$ bits, a staggering 1,000 exabytes, will be added to the digital universe (Gantz et al., 2007). That amount of data would fill enough books to line a bookshelf stretching from the sun to twice Pluto's distance, or thirty-six tons of books for every person on Earth.

A wealth of scientific information also exists that is not currently visible to any Web surfer. In June 2008, Google passed a milestone when it indexed its trillionth Web page. However, the crawlable Web is just the tip of an iceberg of information contained on computers and in databases that Google cannot see (Bergman, 2001). The "deep Web" is several orders of magnitude larger and contains a large amount of data relevant to science education. Examples include over 500 terabytes of data in the National Climate Data Center of the National Oceanic and Atmospheric Administration (NOAA) and 50 terabytes in NASA's High Energy Astrophysics archive. University librarians have taken an important step toward harnessing this hidden information with INFOMINE (http://infomine.ucr.edu), a virtual library that organizes Internet resources across academic disciplines. A different approach is taken by the creators of the Wayback Machine (http://www.archive.org/web/web.php), a nonprofit initiative to archive the history of the Web, currently with more than 150 billion pages stored.

Learning on the Web will improve if software engineers can solve another great challenge: building "semantic" search tools. Google has achieved revenue of over $20 billion a year based on simple keyword search, and many major players on the Web still use human labor to answer general questions. No technology yet exists to answer a question posed in natural language, although Wolfram|Alpha (http://www.wolframalpha.com) and Microsoft's Bing (http://www.bing.com) are steps along that road. The ability to perform robust semantic searches will greatly increase the power of the Internet as a learning tool.

*Lifelong Science Literacy*

In the Age of Science, what could be more natural than desiring that students in our classrooms gain some level of science literacy? Most scientists agree that people not destined for scientific or technical careers nevertheless should be familiar with the results and the process of science. All twenty-first-century citizens require a sufficient vocabulary, a basic knowledge of general concepts, and an understanding of the scientific method to better comprehend the world in which we live and to make sound decisions about scientific issues.

Beyond that broad and uncontroversial initial statement, however, are variations in philosophy that map to different strategies for teaching. One such variation might be called the argument from liberal arts, according to which business majors, for example, should study chemistry or physics to enable them to see reasoning and analytic skills applied outside their chosen field and to become familiar with the context for all knowledge (for an extreme example of this position, see Kitao, 1999). The argument from the standpoint of comprehension stresses that anyone should be able to understand the terms and concepts in a science article printed in a general newspaper or magazine (Hazen & Trefil, 1991). The argument from civics asserts that in a world increasingly influenced by science and technology, an informed citizenry is needed to guide the formulation of public policy (Miller, 2004). A minority viewpoint declares that all students should know from direct experience—practice—how scientists ask questions of nature, even if the students will not use this knowledge in their subsequent careers (O'Neil & Polman, 2004). Finally, a few contrarian experts consider the goal of broad scientific literacy to be unrealistic and ill formed (Shamos, 1995).

Surveys of the public's understanding of science, conducted over the past two decades, have framed the issue of scientific literacy and should give most scientists cause for alarm. A recent Harris Interactive poll for the California Academy of Sciences (2009) found that only one in two adults knew how long it took for Earth to go around the sun, fewer than two in three adults knew that the earliest humans and dinosaurs did not coexist, and only one in two could approximate the percentage of Earth's surface that is covered with water. Just one in five got all three questions right. These questions are a subset of a larger set of questions from a longitudinal study of American adults conducted by the NSF on behalf of the National Science Board (see Figure 4; NSB, 2010, and references to previous volumes therein). Based on three criteria—giving a sufficient answer to the open-ended question on what it means to study something scientifically, recognizing that astrology is not scientific, and correctly answering six or more out of nine science content questions—just 25 percent of the public is considered to be scientifically literate.

This statistic raises a series of questions, most of which do not have neat or even agreed-upon answers. How should science literacy be defined? What level of performance is considered adequate, and how is it justified? What is the functional utility of science literacy, and how is it evaluated? What is the trade-off between breadth and depth, either in terms of coverage of the science disciplines or topics within a discipline? Are some facts or concepts so central that *everyone* should know them? In what follows, I avoid these questions. Scientists do not occupy particularly high ground in the debate over scientific literacy because they tend to be quite uninformed in specialties beyond their own (Collins & Evans, 2007). The lack of breadth in the science knowledge of scientists casts an interesting light on the definition of scientific literacy for non-scientists.

In the NSF biennial surveys of the public understanding of and attitude toward science and technology (NSB, 2010), educational achievement and, in particular, the number of college science courses taken are the strongest predictors of civic scientific literacy (Miller, 2004). The NSF findings invite consideration of whether existing science requirements in general education programs are providing the college-age population the societal benefits hoped for by educators and scientists. (About 10 percent of undergraduates in the

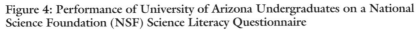

## Figure 4: Performance of University of Arizona Undergraduates on a National Science Foundation (NSF) Science Literacy Questionnaire

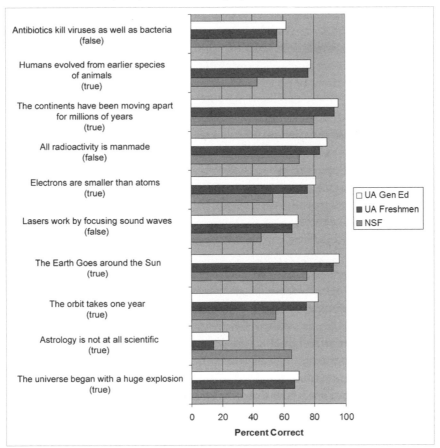

Responses to a series of statements on biology, geology, physics, and astronomy administered to the general public in a phone survey conducted by the NSF and in a questionnaire administered to both first-year students at the University of Arizona (UA) who had not taken any college-level science courses and UA students (typically juniors and seniors) enrolled in general education science classes. The samples sizes are 1,864 for NSF, 1,275 for UA first-year students, and 828 for UA general education students. Data are from 2006 for NSF and 2004 to 2008 for UA. The anomalous result on astrology—the low performance of the college-age cohort compared with the general public—seems real because responses to a Likert-scale measurement from the same overall survey instrument (a five-choice scale from strongly agree to strongly disagree) are consistent. Source: National Science Board. 2008. *Science and Engineering Indicators*. Arlington, Va.: National Science Foundation.

United States take a general education astronomy course during their undergraduate career [Fraknoi, 2001].) For twenty years I have conducted a continuing study of scientific literacy at the University of Arizona. Nearly ten thousand undergraduates enrolled in science classes have been asked science content questions that overlap with those used in the NSF's *Science and Engineering Indicators* series (see http://www.nsf.gov/statistics/indicators). Data for my study are just beginning to be published (Impey et al., 2010), but several of the initial findings are intriguing:

- Scientific literacy among entering freshmen is only marginally higher than that of the general public, with the exception of larger differences in knowledge of evolution and the Big Bang. Gains in knowledge on any particular item by graduation are only 10 to 15 percent, despite the fact that students have taken two or three science courses (see Figure 4).

- There is a small but highly significant gender effect in favor of better performance by men on the scientific knowledge questions. The study has not detected any improvement in scientific literacy for either men or women over twenty years, while the gender gap has persisted.

- Of students who have completed their science requirements, one in three believes that antibiotics kill viruses as well as bacteria; one in four thinks lasers work by focusing sound waves; and one in five thinks atoms are smaller than electrons and is unaware that humans evolved from earlier species of animals and that Earth takes a year to go around the sun.

- Only one in five undergraduates says that astrology is "not at all" scientific, though that fraction increases from 17 percent to 34 percent as students move through the university. Equally worrying, half of all science majors say that astrology is "sort of" or "very" scientific (see Figure 5).

- Education majors—the cohort of future teachers—perform worse than average on almost all the individual questions and in terms of their overall scientific literacy.

- General education teaching for non-science majors has been credited with impressive gains in public science literacy over the past twenty years (Miller, 2004). The University of Arizona data do not support that hypothesis. Most people seem to gain what basic scientific knowledge they have during high school. Subsequent college classes may be ineffectual in improving science literacy much beyond the level of a high school graduate for reasons that are unclear, but there are several possibilities. One is that the science knowledge students gain in high school is fragmentary and may barely prepare them for college-level science classes. Another is that college-level science courses lack a comprehensive science syllabus, and the result is substantial gaps in student knowledge. A third explanation may be that science courses are taught with ineffective teaching methods.

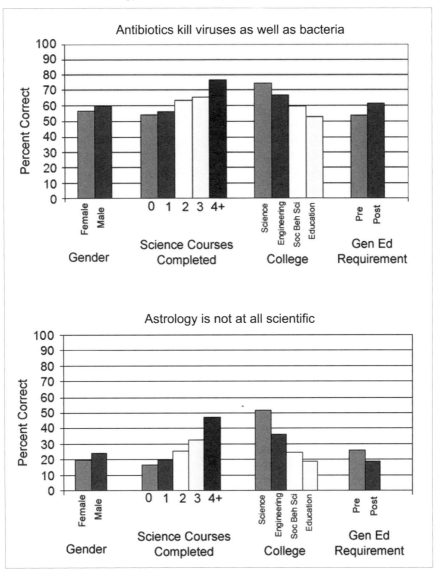

The analysis of 9,200 true/false reactions to a statement about antibiotics and 6,300 true/false reactions to a statement about astrology shows a small but statistically significant gender effect. The percentage of students who correctly answer each question increases with the number of science courses taken, although the improvement is greater (and starts from a lower base) with the astrology question. Most students who have taken four or more science courses are science majors. The distinction between pre- and post-general education requirement connotes students who have taken less than two and two or more science classes, respectively. Among majors in the colleges of science, engineering, social and behavioral sciences, and education, those students preparing to be teachers perform the poorest. Source: Impey et al. 2010. A twenty year survey of science literacy among college undergraduates. *Journal of College Science Teaching.*

- In sum—and if the University of Arizona undergraduate population is typical of most large public research universities—students graduate with substantial gaps in their scientific knowledge. Our instruction is not raising students to the level we would expect for educated citizens who must vote or express their opinions on many issues that relate to science and technology.

Knowledge is one part of the terrain of science literacy; beliefs and attitudes are another. Students (and people in general) often hold mutually conflicting beliefs. As long as they are not faced with a situation where the tension must be resolved, there is no problem. The second part of my twenty-year, ongoing study at the University of Arizona requires undergraduates to respond to twenty-four statements about science and technology on a five-item Likert scale, with choices ranging from "strongly agree" to "strongly disagree." Students are generally well disposed to technical endeavors; for example, 93 percent agree or strongly agree with the statement, "Overall, the progress of science and technology has been beneficial to our civilization."

However, students' responses to statements about the limitations of science and examples of pseudoscience are illuminating (see Figure 6). Undergraduates do not view science as all-encompassing in its explanations: 80 percent agree or strongly agree with the statement "There are phenomena that physical science and the laws of nature cannot explain." Without further interrogation, one cannot tell whether the students in their responses are alluding to phenomena that science cannot explain *even in principle* (in which case they are not rationalists) or phenomena such as dark energy or the mind-brain problem that science *has not yet* successfully explained (in which case they have a realistic sense of science's current boundaries). In addition, 40 percent believe the positions of the planets affect everyday life, the same percentage think some people have psychic powers, one in six believes that aliens visited ancient civilizations, one in four thinks faith healing is a legitimate alternative to conventional medicine, and a quarter think that some numbers are lucky for some people (whether the rest think that some numbers are unlucky is not clear).

This unparalleled data set will be used for a comprehensive study of science knowledge and beliefs among undergraduates. The study will use overlapping NSF questions to bring in the general population and will use the demographics of the University of Arizona's student body to bring in twenty-one million college students nationwide. The modest gains in scientific literacy that seem to accrue from college science classes suggest our pedagogy has room for improvement. Moreover, undergraduate susceptibility to pseudoscientific beliefs leaves these young people open to charlatans and scams of many kinds. A general education course in skepticism would be a useful addition to the curriculum at my university and probably at many others.

## Figure 6: Responses from Nearly Ten Thousand Undergraduates to Statements about Pseudoscience

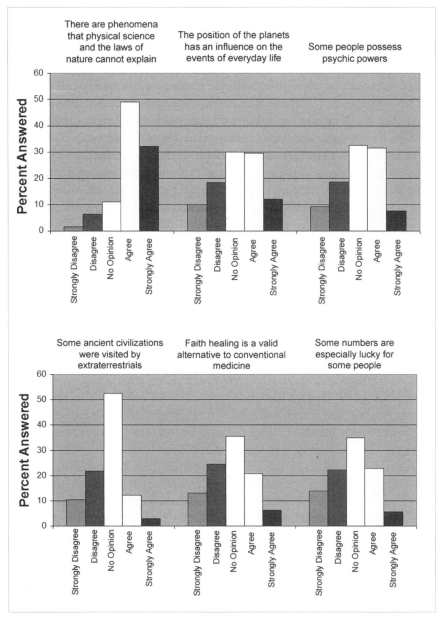

Overall responses by nearly ten thousand undergraduates over twenty years to six statements about pseudoscience and nonscientific beliefs. These beliefs coexist with solid performance when answering the questions in the science knowledge portion of the survey. Source: Impey et al. 2010. A twenty year survey of science literacy among college undergraduates. *Journal of College Science Teaching.*

*How People Learn*

A review of the vast literature from neuroscientists and behavioral psychologists on how people learn is beyond the scope of this paper. The science instructor can most usefully assimilate that information from a number of collections that take the research and apply it to the classroom. Two notable volumes published by the National Academies Press (Bransford, Brown & Cocking, 2000; Donovan & Bransford, 2005) emphasize three key findings:

- Students are not blank canvases on which we paint knowledge. They come to the classroom with preconceptions about how the natural world works. If their prior understanding is not properly diagnosed and engaged, they may fail to learn new information and concepts, or they may revert to their prior understanding outside the classroom.

- To develop competence in a scientific subject, students need facts that fit into a conceptual framework, and they need to organize those facts themselves in a way that facilitates retrieval and application.

- Research favors a metacognitive approach, or explicit recognition by students of how they learn. Students who are aware of how they learn will be more engaged because they can set learning goals and monitor their own progress.

Ignorance is sometimes bliss, because knowing these findings raises the bar on how we teach. We have to work with the preconceived notions students bring into the classroom (in fact, the word *education* alludes to this reality: its root is the Latin word for "drawing out" something potential or latent). We must not only teach students facts but also provide multiple contexts for developing their understanding of those facts. We should determine how to inject the teaching of metacognitive skills into the curriculum; use the tools and technology of the classroom to center on the learner more than the instructor; use assessment to guide the choice of pedagogy; and balance the "lenses" of instruction, including the fact that students learn in multiple communities: the classroom, their department, their future profession, and friends and family.

The three principal conceptual frameworks for learning are behaviorism, cognitivism, and constructivism. Let us imagine (or at least hope) we have progressed beyond the radical behaviorism formulated by psychologist B. F. Skinner. Even though molding classroom behavior and meshing student effort with grading schemes involve more than a hint of operant conditioning, the classroom is much richer than a large Skinner box. Cognitivism arrived in the 1930s with an assumption that prior knowledge plays an important role in learning, and cognitivists use memory models to understand the role of "chunking" and cognitive load in classroom settings (Sweller, 1994). Constructivism began with developmental psychologist Jean Piaget and has propelled many waves of

## Figure 7: Different Conceptual Models of Learning and Their Media and Technology Counterparts

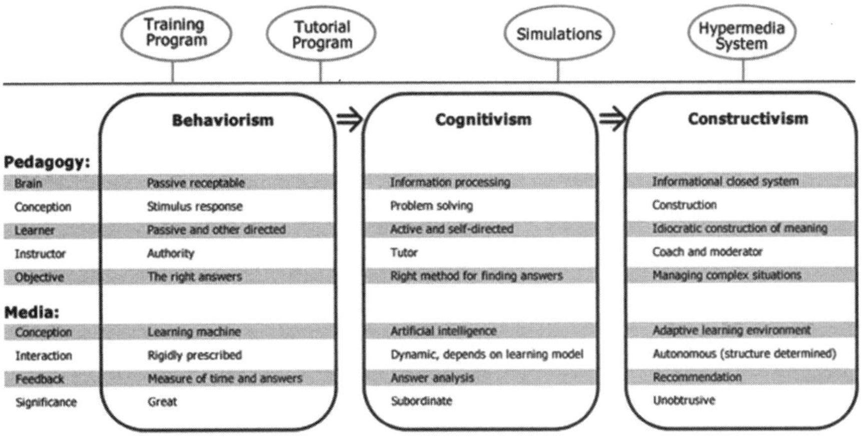

| Training Program | Tutorial Program | | Simulations | Hypermedia System |
|---|---|---|---|---|

| | Behaviorism ⇒ | Cognitivism ⇒ | Constructivism |
|---|---|---|---|
| **Pedagogy:** | | | |
| Brain | Passive receptable | Information processing | Informational closed system |
| Conception | Stimulus response | Problem solving | Construction |
| Learner | Passive and other directed | Active and self-directed | Idiocratic construction of meaning |
| Instructor | Authority | Tutor | Coach and moderator |
| Objective | The right answers | Right method for finding answers | Managing complex situations |
| **Media:** | | | |
| Conception | Learning machine | Artificial intelligence | Adaptive learning environment |
| Interaction | Rigidly prescribed | Dynamic, depends on learning model | Autonomous (structure determined) |
| Feedback | Measure of time and answers | Answer analysis | Recommendation |
| Significance | Great | Subordinate | Unobtrusive |

The principal theories of learning all make different assumptions about how the brain processes and retains information, and each posits a different role for the instructor. Teaching technologies are available that map to each of the conceptual frameworks. Source: Figure created and provided by author.

education reform. The many hues of this philosophy are united by an emphasis on the student's free exploration within a pedagogical framework, whereby a professor moves from being the "sage on the stage" to being the "guide on the side." This approach in its purest form has attracted some criticism (Mayer, 2004).

Figure 7 shows how these three theories map onto pedagogy and instructional media. The "continuum" of instructional technology displayed along the top is developed in more detail with the ways media are used in the classroom on the lower part of the diagram. The pedagogical principles implied by the three theories and the ways they apply to learning are shown in the top part of the diagram. Moving from left to right, each theory corresponds to a greater degree of autonomy and engagement of the learner and higher degrees of adaptability and flexibility for the instructor. Modern education theory strongly favors constructivist approaches.

A popular instructional model based on constructivism is called the "Five E's." It can be used at all ages, from young child to adult. In practice, the first two stages are often merged.

- Students *engage* a topic by making connections between present and past learning experiences. For example, in a lesson on the cause of the seasons, students might work in pairs to compare how each of their experiences relate to the seasonal cycle, such as how the cycle relates to their observations of the variation in the highest elevation of the sun in the sky. They can also compare what they know about Earth's orbit and its distance from the sun.

- In the *explore* phase, students develop concepts from a common base of experiences. Students might use a collimated light beam to observe how intensity varied with distance from the light source or angle of the radiation. Exploration can be open-ended but is more often guided.

- The *explain* phase allows teachers to introduce formal terms and explanations and permits students to verbalize their conceptual understanding. Thus, the instructor might present the inverse square law and the way light intensity on an area changes as the arrival angle varies. Students would then explain how these concepts relate to their earlier exploration of light intensity.

- The *elaborate* phase helps extend student understanding and allows them to apply their skills. The instructor might remind students that seasons are opposite in the northern and southern hemispheres, which creates a tension with the idea that seasons are caused by the varying Earth-sun distance. The students' challenge is to see how that information relates to the two ways light intensity can vary.

- As students *evaluate* the issue they have been given, they assess their own understanding. For seasons, they might decide whether the variations in Earth-sun distance are sufficient to cause seasonal variations on Earth. In doing so, they confront one of the most omnipresent misconceptions in astronomy.

Cognition research may one day underpin our understanding of how people learn, with consequences for teaching strategies. But cognitive science is still a new academic field, with the first Ph.D. awarded in 1991 (Thagard, 2005). The last few decades have seen progress in neuroscience and computational theory, although some philosophers have questioned the supposition that human brains work solely by representation and computation. One of the most mature theories, Adaptive Control of Thought-Rational (ACT-R), is a symbolic framework that divides knowledge into declarative and procedural representations, which can be coded and implemented using a computer programming language (LISP) interpreter. Carnegie Learning's Cognitive Tutor software incorporates LISP and is currently used to teach math in thousands of schools across the United States (Anderson & Lebiere, 1988; Anderson & Schunn, 2000).

## SCIENCE EDUCATION IN PRACTICE

The traditional large lecture class is poorly suited to the goals of the science course: to transfer long-term knowledge to students, convey a general sense of how science works, and influence their worldview. Some of the structural problems that inhibit the widespread adoption of good principles of teaching and learning are particular to the sciences. Faculty in research-intensive units may experience a reward structure that favors research over teaching, or institutions may place little emphasis on mentoring for teaching. Faculty members in a small department are likely to have high teaching loads, increased contact hours, and slender financial support. In most settings, few faculty members are up to date on best pedagogical practices.

The graying professoriate has a growing disconnect with the technology and computer habits of its undergraduates. In most large lecture classes, professors have limited support (one graduate teaching assistant for a class of one hundred or more is not uncommon) and limited opportunity to break the class into small groups. How do we engage students and encourage learning in these conditions? One can easily become discouraged, but renewed national attention to the problem is cause for optimism. For example, the Reinvention Center at SUNY Stony Brook was founded with a goal of promoting and furthering the recommendations of the Boyer Commission (Boyer, 1998). Those recommendations propose that research universities:

- Make research-based learning the standard;

- Have an inquiry-based freshman year;

- Build on the freshman foundation;

- Remove barriers to interdisciplinary education;

- Explicitly link communication skills and course work;

- Creatively use information technology;

- Have a capstone experience;

- Educate graduate students as apprentice teachers;

- Change the faculty reward system; and

- Cultivate a greater sense of community on campus.

Instructors can draw on many tried-and-tested tools and strategies, such as think-pair-share questions, lecture tutorials, polling about misconceptions, and peer-led debates (Bain, 2004; Davis, 1993).

### Learner-Centered Teaching

Professor-centric lectures, no matter how well crafted and how entertaining, can go only so far in helping students learn (Bridges & Desmond, 2000). A body of research published thirty years ago shows that even motivated adult

**Figure 8: Schematic Summary of Student Attention Level in Lectures**

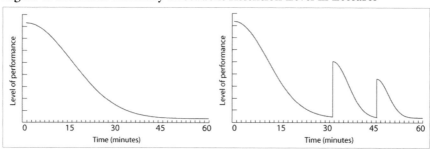

These two graphs measure students' relative level of performance as the fraction of students paying attention at any time as determined by twelve lecturers over an average of ninety lectures. The level of attention and performance during any lecture shows an almost immediate decline, and at the end of a class period of normal length (sixty minutes) attention is down to a very low level (left-hand graph). Interrupting the lecture for activities, quizzes, or asides helps (right-hand graph), but engagement never returns to what it was at the start of the class. Source: A schematic representation of the conclusions drawn by Johnson, A. H., and F. Percival. 1976. Attention breaks in lectures. *Education in Chemistry* 13:49–50.

learners have an attention span of no better than fifteen to twenty minutes (Johnson & Percival, 1976). Today's multitasking, hyperkinetic cyberyouth are even less inclined to sit and listen to a lecture. Indeed, the lecture is social technology dating back to the Middle Ages, a time when electronic distractions did not exist (see Figure 8). On the other hand, people routinely watch a movie that lasts two hours or more while following the plot and with minimal lapses of attention, suggesting that a strong narrative, emotional engagement, and variation of sensory input are the keys to sustained attention.

If that is not convincing, then consider this striking example from physicist Carl Weiman of the University of British Columbia; he pioneered education reform while at the University of Colorado. In an introductory physics class for non-science majors, he gave a cogent mini-lecture on the physics of sound and then brandished a violin. He explained that the strings do not move enough air to create the sound from the violin. Rather, the strings cause the back of the violin to move via the sound post, and thus it is the back of the violin that actually produces the sound. Fifteen minutes later he asked a multiple-choice question about where the sounds from a violin came from, and only 10 percent said the back; almost everyone else said the strings. This low level of retention of a counterintuitive fact after only fifteen minutes also applies to faculty and graduate students. Does this mean that all lecturing is bad? No, but it means that lectures have to be carefully designed with principles of cognition in mind (Schwartz & Bransford, 1998).

The most effective courses are learner-centered courses in which learning goals are clearly stated and are commensurate with methods of evaluation (Dancy & Beichner, 2002); interactive techniques are used to continually engage students; and assessment is used to tune the strategies to the particular context of each course, each professor, and each set of students (Angelo & Cross, 1993; Hake, 1998). "One size fits all" has no place in learner-centered education.

Most professors are familiar with the unspoken pact that can develop in the classroom. The professor agrees to deliver a highly structured presentation, not to ask students to think outside the box, and to evaluate them according to the material in the textbook with objective tests, usually multiple choice. In return, the students agree not to be disruptive, to act as tidy receptacles for information, and to regurgitate that information when it is time for a test. All of this is implicit. As long as nobody questions the premise, and the grades connect to the content that is being taught, everyone is fairly happy. This description is a caricature, but not by much.

Weiman and Perkins (2005) describe the failure of traditional methods of physics instruction, noting that:

> Students receiving traditional instruction master on average less than 30% of the concepts that they did not already know at the start of the class. The result is largely independent of lecturer quality, class size, or institution. . . . After instruction, students, on average, are found to be less expert-like in their thinking than before. They see physics as less connected to the real world, less interesting, and more as something to be memorized without understanding.

Learner-centered techniques challenge faculty to relinquish some authority and control in the classroom. Peer learning shifts the locus of and responsibility for learning toward the student, which is a positive development (Mazur, 1996; Crouch & Mazur, 2001). Unfortunately, the use of innovative teaching techniques can result in lower student evaluations (Emery, Kramer & Tian, 2003) because these methods often require more effort and engagement from students who might be disengaged if they are non-science majors taking a required science class. This disincentive underscores the imperative that both faculty and department heads be committed to the larger goal of improving learning. Once a professor has experienced the exhilaration of a student-run debate or a group activity where the entire classroom is buzzing with animated discussions, he or she will almost never want to go back to that safe place behind the imaginary fourth wall that "boxes in" the lecturer. Remember: the locus of learning depends on the educator but ultimately rests with the students and the work they do.

### Student Misconceptions

Even when they are encountering a subject for the first time, students are not blank sheets of paper. Particularly in the sciences, students often hold strong misconceptions:

> Students come to the classroom with preconceptions about how the world works. If their initial understanding is not engaged, they may fail to grasp new concepts and information

presented in the classroom, or they may learn them for purposes of a test but revert to their preconceptions outside the classroom. (Donovan, Bransford & Pellegrino, 1999)

Sometimes the dissonance is explicit. I have had students tell me they believe in astrology or a six-thousand-year-old Earth, give the answers I want to hear to do well on the quizzes, and no doubt continue with their prior beliefs after the close of the semester.

Some of the most profound misconceptions relate to the way science works, and they affect learning in any discipline. Non-scientists tend not to have a deep understanding of the tentative nature of scientific theories and the important role of assumptions; nor are they fully aware of the limitations imposed by observational errors and finite data. They tend to believe that scientific laws are perfect and absolute and that scientific calculations are error-free and precise. Their reaction if scientists disagree with one another is to question the validity of the entire enterprise. As psychologist James Alcock (2005) has noted, our brains are "belief engines," constantly processing information from our senses and generating beliefs about the world without any particular regard for what is true or not. This system evolved to ensure not truth, logic, and reason, but survival. That superstition and irrationality abound in the Age of Science is not surprising.

Preconceptions are not the same as misconceptions, though, and therein lies a complication. Children know that it gets hotter as they approach a burner on the stove, they know that a car's horn sounds louder when the car is approaching, and they know that a car headlight gets brighter when it drives toward them. In each of these situations *close means more*, and that becomes a strongly held preconception about the way the world works. But this knowledge may not be helpful in a quite different situation. Summer in the northern hemisphere is not hotter because Earth is closer to the sun (see Figure 9), and the brightest stars in the sky are not the hottest. In these cases, suitable knowledge must be constructed in brand new circumstances, and therefore must first address the student's preexisting basis for physical intuition (Bailey & Slater, 2003; Comins, 2001; Hufnagel, 2002; Novak, 2002).

*Pedagogical Principles*

Even with the temptations for instructors and students to buy into a teaching model based on passivity and regurgitation of information, an abundance of evidence indicates that traditional methods are not working. Students generally find traditional science courses to be boring, irrelevant, and incongruous with the stated goals (Tobias, 1991). Research into learning and cognition confirms that knowledge is associative and thus linked to already-developed conceptions of how the world works, which may be naive and not based on scientific principles (Gabel, 1994). Research also shows that learning is context dependent—what students learn depends on the educational setting—and that

**Figure 9: Concept Map for a Major Misconception about the Cause of Seasons**

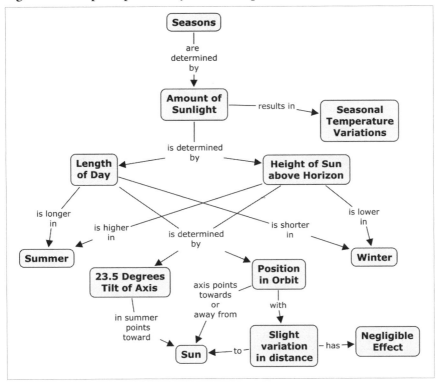

Prior knowledge has to be addressed in teaching because that knowledge tethers to intuition or direct experience even when it is erroneous. In this example, students would have to get direct experience from hands-on activities relating to the amount of sunlight falling on a surface to be able to correct the misconception. Source: Novak, J. D., and A. S. Cañas. 2008. *The Theory Underlying Concept Maps and How to Construct and Use Them*. Technical Report IHMC CmapTools 2006-01. Pensacola: Florida Institute for Human and Machine Cognition. http://cmap.ihmc.us/Publications/ResearchPapers/TheoryCmaps/TheoryUnderlyingConcept Maps.htm. Figure courtesy of Alberto J. Cañas.

students require social interactions to learn deeply and effectively (Clark, 2002; Lazarowitz et al., 2006; Duschl, 2008). Finally, the unavoidable truth is that constructive learning requires mental effort—proper pedagogy can be taxing for both faculty and students!

Teaching may be considered in terms of a progression of four models of pedagogy (see Figure 10). At one extreme is the traditional behaviorist model whereby information flows solely from the instructor and the textbook. Next is the cognitive model, in which students are active participants, often self-directed, and the instructor acts more like a facilitator. A classroom operating this way would have a lot of hands-on labs or experiments, group discussions, and peer instruction. Much of the time is devoted to problem solving. Such a course has structure, but students shape the small-scale learning environment. A Chinese aphorism is relevant: "Tell me and I'll forget; show me and I'll remember; involve me and I'll understand."

# Figure 10: Four Schema for Pedagogy with Different Roles for Student and Instructor

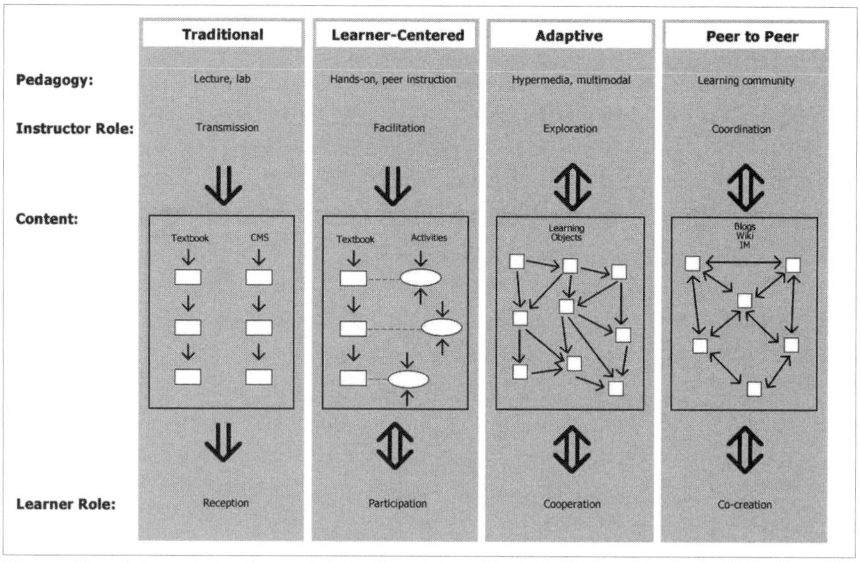

Moving from left to right, the models go from hierarchical to democratic. In the "Traditional" model, CMS is a course management system. The nature and organization of course content mirrors the philosophy of the instruction. Effective teaching avoids pure transmission but can draw judiciously from all the silos. Peer-to-peer models do not remove the authority of the instructor but adapt the progress of the course according to student performance and feedback. Source: Figure created and provided by author.

Higher education has struggled mightily to move between the first and second models of learning; however, two other transitions can be contemplated. The third pedagogical model might be called an adaptive learning environment, whereby the tools of instruction and even the shape of the course are molded by students. The content is made up of reusable learning objects that can be arranged in different sequences, in contrast to the linear flow of a textbook. A reusable learning object is a self-contained chunk of content that occupies two to fifteen minutes of class time, can be delivered in multiple learning contexts—including online—and is tagged with metadata so it can be found in an electronic search (Northrup, 2007). This type of instruction is characterized by active exploration and cooperation, and its basis in learning theory is constructivism. A final step in this direction would be peer-to-peer learning, the extensive use of blogs and wikis, and the creation of learning materials by students working with one another under guidance. The instructor becomes a coordinator and defines goals and standards in this approach. Somewhere between the "fascism" of traditional instruction and the "anarchy" of a pure peer-to-peer environment lies the sweet spot of effective instruction.

Good pedagogy is often a matter of common sense. I wish that when I was starting out as an assistant professor someone had shared the following with me:

- Set the tone of the classroom early. Professors will find that recovering a fruitful learning environment is difficult if chatter, cell phone use, tardiness, and discourtesy take hold in the first few weeks.

- Make the syllabus as thorough and unambiguous as possible. The syllabus is a professor's contract with the class, and a clear syllabus will prevent many potential problems later on. Students crave structure and transparency.

- Use repetition, with variation and diverse examples.

- Create manageable chunks of information, and never lecture more than ten minutes without interruption.

- Use reinforcement and praise routinely.

- Treat students as individuals and engage their diverse learning styles; learn their names if possible. (I can do that in a class of 100, but 150 still defeats me.)

- Remember that a big class is a complex, nonlinear social experiment. Have a plan but be prepared to adapt or alter it at any time. Being the expert and the professor confers authority, but do not be afraid to show passion!

One final tip will be familiar to any parent: avoid sending mixed messages. "Do what I say, not what I do" occurs far too often in classrooms. Professors are modeling professional behavior, and students cannot be expected to be punctual and organized if the professor is not. Students notice when professors claim to be open to questions and discussion but do not allow long enough time for the former and structure class to make the latter difficult. Professors who glance at their watch during class might intend only to judge the timing of the class session so as to cover as much material as possible; students will see the glance as a sign of impatience or desire to be somewhere else.

Perhaps the most disastrous mixed message professors can send is to tell students we want them to understand general principles and how science works while testing them on facts and specifics. Evaluation and pedagogy must be carefully aligned.

*Inquiry-Based Methods*

In contrast to traditional methods, active engagement and active learning approaches produce significant and long-lasting learning gains (Bybee, 2002; Committee on Undergraduate Science Education, 1997; National Science Teachers Association, 2002). Active learning occurs when students have to take responsibility for their own learning by engaging in critical reasoning about the ideas presented in the class. Some active learning techniques can result in apparent "failure," but the failures are often informative, and those who do not occasionally fail as a teacher may not be succeeding as well as those who take more risks in order to encourage active learning. To engage students and facilitate critical thinking:

- Ask students questions to frame a discussion. Raise a controversial or topical issue from the news. Use discussions or interactive lecture demonstrations that engage students as participants.

- Give surprise quizzes (they do not need to be graded to be effective). But always screen questions to test higher-order thought processes in the traditional Bloom taxonomy.

- Use personal responders (also called "clickers") for misconception testing or opinion polling. Note cards or other low-tech methods are equally effective. Involving all students is easy because the polling can be anonymous and the feedback to both students and instructor is immediate (Duncan & Mazur, 2005).

- Assign short, in-class writing assignments. Students could be asked to address the "muddiest point" or summarize the day's main points. Collect the responses and learn from what the students write. Instead of grading these assignments, award participation points.

- Provide video clips, songs, or references to popular culture to ground material in students' everyday lives and to engage different learning styles. YouTube is an excellent, ever-growing resource for relevant material.

- Use peer instruction methods such as think-pair-share (Lyman, 1987), where an open-ended question is posed to students working in pairs. Students discuss the question and write down their answers before sharing them with the class. Grading can be based on participation.

- Encourage interactions in small groups of three to four students by using tools such as concept tests and lecture tutorials (Prather et al., 2005). Students gather bits of instruction and then engage the material as a group by responding to one or more questions that focus on common misconceptions (Millis & Cottell, 1998).

- Employ undergraduates as preceptors who take a leadership role by helping with in-class activities and extra-credit events, as well as by assisting other students with their learning in and out of class—a role students can fulfill at most universities for credit or a modest stipend. If preceptors are properly prepared and trained, instructors need not fear that the "blind will be leading the blind," and because preceptors are close in age to the typical student in the class, they are likely to understand his or her learning difficulties.

- Conduct debates, either between individuals or in student groups. Use role-playing; students can be asked to act as particles, genes, planets, or stars. Whole-class discussions are effective if used judiciously.

- Have students construct "concept maps" that define relationships between all the concepts associated with one topic from the course.

- Use portfolio assessment. Require students to build a suite of written work over the course. Give feedback and interim grades (or at least comments) on each part. Some of the components of the portfolio can be customized to students' particular interests. A writing-intensive science course carries a higher grading load, but the reward is much deeper insight into what students do and do not know (Danielson & Abrutyn, 1997).

Presented with such a litany of recommendations, any scientist would be forgiven for demanding to be shown the data! In each of the scientific disciplines, education research is a small niche compared to the discipline's overall research. Studies on teaching and learning in astronomy are inspired by the larger community of physics education. The online peer-reviewed journal *Astronomy Education Review* was started in 2002 and is currently supported and operated by the American Astronomical Society. A small but growing cadre of Ph.D. scientists is engaged in education research and is beginning to have an impact on teaching practice around the country via workshops, publications, and the dissemination of tools and strategies. The Center for Astronomy Education drives much of this activity.

Gathering reliable data on the efficacy of the methods discussed above is not easy because of the necessity for pre- and post-testing and careful experimental design. Evaluation and assessment tools are also central to this research (and are two topics that are beyond the scope of this review). These obstacles aside, lecture tutorials are one model that has proven to be highly effective in large astronomy classes of one hundred to three hundred students. Lecture tutorials are based on the topics that faculty cover most frequently and require fifteen-minute time chunks that can be easily inserted into a lecture. Designed to elicit misconceptions or naive mental models, they are highly interactive forms of Socratic dialogue. When pre-testing on eight core topics is compared to testing after lecture and testing after lecture tutorials, the lecture tutorials show substantial gains that benefit all students equally (see Figure 11). Improvements over straight lectures are similarly large for lecture tutorials and ranking tasks (Prather et al., 2005; Hudgins et al., 2006).

**Figure 11: Learning Gains for Lecture Tutorials and Ranking Tasks**

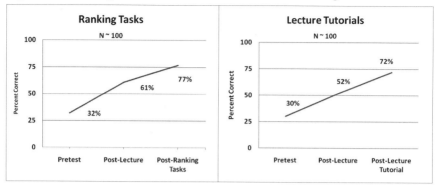

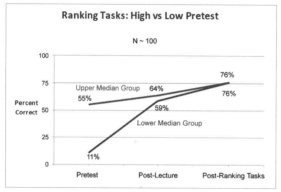

The use of ranking tasks or lecture tutorials in an introductory astronomy class produces gains over lecture, when each is measured with a pre-test and a post-test. Ranking tasks are conceptual exercises in which a student is presented with four to six physical situations, usually in graph or diagram form, and is asked to order them based on some resulting effect. The study found no significant gender effect. The lower graph shows that, for ranking tasks, students in the lowest pre-test group are elevated to the same level as the high pre-test group. Source: Prather, E. E., T. F. Slater, J. P. Adams, and J. M. Bailey. 2004. Research on a lecture-tutorial approach to teaching introductory astronomy for non-science majors. *Astronomy Education Review* 3(2):122–137. Hudgins, D. W., E. E. Prather, D. J. Grayson, and D. P. Smits. 2006. Effectiveness of collaborative ranking tasks on student understanding of key astronomy concepts. *Astronomy Education Review* 5(1):1–22. Graphs courtesy of Edward Prather.

Support for the value of interactive instruction in astronomy is growing (Prather et al., 2008). For a nationwide study, astronomy professor Edward Prather and colleagues chose "light and spectra" because these areas are the most important and commonly taught topics in most introductory astronomy classes. Pre- and post-testing were performed on nearly four thousand students taught by thirty-six instructors at thirty-one two-year and four-year institutions in the United States. Normalized gain scores were measured after testing on the Light and Spectra Concept Inventory (Bardar et al., 2006). Interactivity was measured by the amount of time each class spent outside lecture mode in group work, activities, labs, recitation sections, or one-on-one modes of engagement. Classes with more interaction showed larger gains (see Figure 12).

**Figure 12: Learning Gains on Light and Spectra Concepts versus Level of Classroom Interactivity**

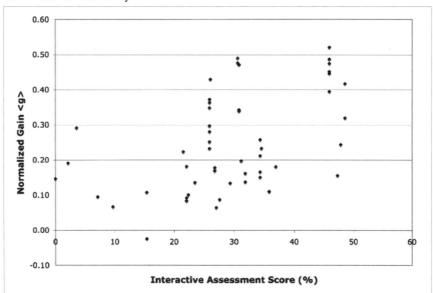

The Light and Spectra Concept Inventory (Bardar et al., 2006) was administered to nearly four thousand students across the country. The normalized gains were mostly between 0.1 and 0.2 for classes with low degrees of student interactivity and nearly three times higher for classes with high degrees of interactivity. The wide range in gains suggests some dependence on instructor and institution. Source: Prather, E. E., A. L. Rudolph, G. Brissenden, and W. M. Schlingman. 2008. A national study assessing the teaching and learning of introductory astronomy, Part I: The effect of interactive instruction. *American Journal of Physics* 77:320–330. Graph courtesy of Edward Prather.

These materials are now readily available for astronomy teachers, often in conjunction with textbooks. One book of feedback questions and discussion prompts is intended for introductory astronomy courses (Adams, Prather, and Slater, 2004). The same group has collected many strategies for teaching large astronomy classes (Pompea, 2000; Slater and Adams, 2003). Ranking tasks and peer instruction methods have also been documented (Green, 2003).

Even if lectures remain the primary delivery vehicle, they can be easily adapted to include these techniques so that inquiry-based instruction can be introduced incrementally. The advantages of any of these techniques are that student misconceptions are explicitly identified, the instructor is better paced, and students are more engaged with the class. For instance, an interactive demonstration could be preceded by a short quiz with clickers or note cards to identify the most common misconceptions about the topic. Alternately, the class could be asked to write on a card their expectations for an upcoming demonstration. The cards can then be passed around to mix them up, and sample responses can be read out before the demonstration begins.

Simple show-and-tell is highly effective if it makes students think more deeply about the material. In astronomy, an iron meteorite—an example of a messenger from trillions of miles away and billions of years ago whose material was ejected from a star before Earth was born—can be used to spark discussion. In biology, a package of dental floss in a plastic Easter egg can serve as a scale model of the nucleus of a eukaryotic cell and can be used to convey the vast information content of DNA. Pass the egg around the class and unravel the floss: in this enlarged scale model, 5 kilometers of dental floss would equal the length of the unraveled DNA in the nucleus of a human cell. Students could then imagine information written on this flossy "book of life": a sentence would be the length of a gene, and the smallest unit of information, a base pair, would be a fraction of a millimeter.

Even a simple think-pair-share question can facilitate deep learning if it is contained in a suitably structured activity. Consider this question, which I have used in a sophomore-level astrobiology class: "When a seed grows into a tree, where does most of the mass come from?" Students will animatedly discuss this for as long as I allow. Measured using clickers, initial answers split equally among four responses: water, the air, dirt and soil, and "the mass is already in the seed." The last choice represents a view of life that predates the Industrial Revolution. Students can easily show that plants are not made of the same chemicals as soil. But even after a mini-lecture on photosynthesis most students are not certain whether the correct answer is water or air, so the debate continues. After a proper accounting of transpiration, they can see that the answer is air, and knowing that the stuff of mighty redwoods is built using carbon snatched from thin air makes a deep and long-lasting impression.

## The Role of Technology

Plato was right: the best form of instruction is the Socratic dialogue. Since the time of the ancient Greeks, only two real revolutions have occurred in the delivery of instruction. The first occurred in 1969, at the time of the Apollo moon landings, when overhead projectors began to supplant the traditional blackboard. The second began with the maturation of personal computing and the Internet in the mid-1990s and continues today with a bewildering array of multimedia tools and technologies. Moore's law—the doubling every two years in the speed and circuit board density of microprocessors—and its analogue in the increase of Internet bandwidth are transforming the economy. Higher education is riding this wave of exponential change.

The so-called Net Generation is able to multitask and expects a high degree of engagement with technology (Oblinger & Oblinger, 2005). However, technology itself does not guarantee good instruction. Too many examples of instructional technology are best categorized as "shovelware," old content dressed in new clothes without any enhancement in function. Academia has long been trying to come to grips with the best ways to teach students using technology (Brown, 2000; Palloff & Pratt, 2001; Garrison & Anderson, 2003). Most professors are bewildered by the sea change in student habits away from email and TV to texting and online video, and by the wildfire spread of social phenomena like Facebook and Twitter. Signposts are provided annually by *Horizon Reports* from the New Media Consortium and the EDUCAUSE Learning Initiative (Johnson et al., 2010; see http://wp.nmc.org/horizon2010).

Many companies and individuals have developed resources that can help increase student engagement and learning. Some are associated with prominent textbooks and thus are free to adopters of the books, while others are available on the Web. The best example is the Multimedia Educational Resource for Learning and Online Teaching (MERLOT), an open-access collection of several thousand peer-reviewed and annotated learning resources supported by a large consortium of universities (Cafolla, 2006; see http://www.merlot.org). Activities linked to specific textbooks are often excellent because publishers, who see them as a way to gain comparative advantage in a competitive marketplace, make major investments in applets and interactive tutorials.

Sophisticated Java applets for introductory physics and astronomy courses allow students to behave more or less like real scientists: taking realistic but synthetic data with plausible errors, varying the parameters, and fitting models. Examples include detecting extrasolar planets with Doppler velocity data that include realistic noise and time sampling (Greg Bothun, University of Oregon) and modeling changes in chemical composition of planetary atmospheres and the effect of such changes on climate (Dick McCray, University of Colorado). Greg Corder (2005) has studied the benefits of this technology for science learning.

Existing ideas like concept maps make an excellent fit with computers, and vendors have started to produce software that lets students construct maps through a flexible interface. Another exciting avenue for learning science that provides a bridge between the worlds of formal and informal learning is "citizen science." These projects use networks to harness the power of the masses by distributing real scientific data to trained volunteers who add value to that data. As part of the Galaxy Zoo project, one hundred thousand "civilians" have classified more than forty million galaxies, with accuracy as good as the experts (Lintott et al., 2008). These projects have obvious and still-untapped applications with college students.

The first generation of digital instructional technology in the 1980s and 1990s was limited to fixed content and a linear flow of presentation and often failed to provide a rich learning experience. Electronic textbooks are a good example of such shovelware. As the technology has advanced in the past decade, it is moving toward more customizable interfaces. New teaching techniques should be able to take advantage of these changes. Some instructors have experimented with wiki-type projects, and the increasing ubiquity of Web-capable cell phones and smartphones allows instructors to push both general and customized content to students. Voice recognition and interpretation technology may soon permit students to interact with an artificial intelligence tutor and a database using text-to-speech software.

Implementing collaborative or adaptive learning environments on computers and the Internet is challenging, but the technologies exist. In a schematic view of this instructional environment (see Figure 13), the content would consist of reusable learning objects that are multimedia elements, such as hyperlinked text, interactive figures, video clips, and sound files. Their high-level organization would be shown by a concept map (Novak, 1998). Online navigation is flexible and could be directed according to a map or a tree, by keyword search, or by recommendations from other learners (examples are in the shaded box). The navigation and the interface are adaptive to the preference of the individual student user and the patterns of past users. As shown on the left of the diagram, the instructors select content and modify their interface according to learning goals, while, as shown on the right, students interact with the content either individually or collaboratively with their peers. Instructional technology has yet to incorporate these elements; at present, it is "vaporware." However, developed with care, this framework could enhance learning and student engagement.

Several transformational technologies will soon have tremendous influence on society and, inevitably, on the ways in which we teach. They are so new that as yet there is no research literature with evaluations of them in an instructional setting, and their modes of most effective use are hard to predict.

- *Mobile learning* (as opposed to distance learning using a desktop) will take off. In 2009, more than a billion cell phones were sold, with smartphones the fastest growing sector of that market. The early generation of PDAs and Pocket PCs has been eclipsed by highly capable small-format computers such as the netbooks, iPhones, and the very recent iPad (Schmitt, Rodriguez & Clothey, 2009). In 2009, for the first time more devices connected to the Internet wirelessly than through wired connections.

- The *semantic Web* will transform knowledge retrieval just as search engines transformed Web page retrieval. If a student can get a natural-language query answered in real time, most likely by intelligent agents scouring the deep Web, then retention of scientific knowledge will be superfluous for most people, just as the skill of navigation is waning with the spread of devices that take advantage of the Global Positioning System.

- In a revolution years in the making, Internet bandwidth will finally allow the network to "become" the computer and we will enter an age of *ubiquitous computing*. All textbooks and academic information will fit on a USB flash drive or an even smaller solid-state device within a phone. The spread of Gmail and Google Docs on campuses means that educational information is increasingly stored in the "cloud." Soon, students

**Figure 13: Hypothetical Learning System Utilizing Social Media and Student Feedback**

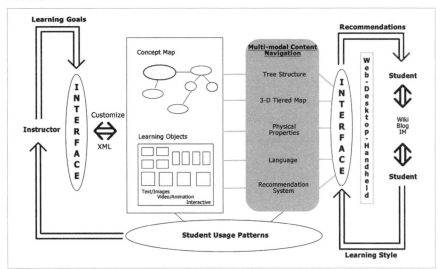

This is a schematic diagram of the components of a hypothetical adaptive learning system. The content "atoms" in such a system are reusable learning objects, linked and presented to students in a way that builds on past choices and learning preferences. To the left, the instructor provides a high-level framework for use of the content according to specified learning goals. To the right, the student user customizes his interface by learning style (text-heavy, visually rich, or audio). Some tasks are open to other learners, co-opting the architecture of social networks. Delivery would be wireless to laptops or handheld devices. This vision could be realized in the near future. Source: Figure created and provided by author.

will be able to do all their work anytime and anyplace. The boundary between formal and informal learning will blur even further.

- The use of *social networks* will increase, and their capabilities will grow. Already, most undergraduates are members of more than one social network. Educators seeking to co-opt the social graph—the map of friends of friends of a student—will be able to propagate learning tools like a virus. Facebook consumes large amounts of student time and attention for purposes that are purely social, but it is potentially a potent platform for informal and social learning. Highly interactive apps and gaming metaphors will be the most successful strategies.

- *Virtual worlds* like Second Life provide a rich 3-D environment for learning and constructing exhibits and models. More than 250 universities already have a presence in Second Life. For science educators, Second Life offers the capability of creating persistent models and simulations and letting students create their own projects and exhibits (Brown & Adler, 2008).

Alongside Wikipedia, the other omnipresent Internet appendage for students is Facebook. With more than four hundred million users, one hundred million of whom are in the United States, Facebook is the most popular social networking site in the world. Nearly 90 percent of all undergraduates use Facebook, and most students check the site several times a day, suggesting it has their loyalty and rapt attention. A year ago, Facebook abandoned its support of internal features that allowed students to see all the people at their university taking the same courses as them. In principle, this opened the door for a developer to create collaborative learning tools and online learning communities, though it has not happened yet. Among more than one hundred thousand Facebook applications, only a few hundred are educational, and for the most part, the educational apps do not encourage deep learning. Nonetheless, social networks are a frontier for education.

Another exciting wave of the future is the use of virtual 3-D worlds such as Second Life as social learning spaces and places where instructors and students can co-create educational experiences (Cheal, 2007; Kelton, 2007). With roughly fifteen million users, Second Life is the most popular of a set of realistic, graphically rendered virtual worlds where people move and talk and interact in the form of their electronic alter ego, or avatar. Access and avatar creation are free, but owning virtual land costs real money. On average, seventy thousand people are "in world" at any given time, or about one million over any thirty-day period. Linden Labs, the private company that operates the virtual world, oversees an economic activity with a GNP equivalent to about $1 billion, with $1.5 million in transactions every day and a convertible currency called the Linden that trades at about 260 to the dollar (Terdiman, 2008). Second Life is a technical tour de force. A server farm with three hundred terabytes of storage capacity generates a world of islands and archipelagos that extends about eight hundred (virtual) square miles. The programming is moving toward open standards, and its Havoc 4 physics engine creates realistic dynamics and visual effects.

The number of science "builds" in Second Life has steadily increased and includes virtual planetariums and science centers, as well as installations run by NASA and NOAA. For the past three years I have maintained a personal island—sixty-five thousand square meters, or sixteen acres, with a building capacity of fifteen thousand primitive geometric objects, or "prims"—for teaching and outreach purposes. With education technology specialist Adrienne Gauthier as the lead developer, and using preceptors and other paid undergraduates as content creators, this island has been successfully used in general education classes for non-science majors. Substantial support is required to familiarize students with Second Life, but the reward has been some clever and creative projects, the best of which can become permanent exhibits on the island. Conventional teaching is not well suited to a virtual world, but cooperative learning, model-building, and 3-D visualization of science concepts work well. Five years ago, nobody could have anticipated the explosive growth and varied uses of Second Life and Facebook. All that can be said for certain today is that the future of instructional technology will be exciting and difficult to predict (Alexander, 2009). Educators should fasten their seat belts for a thrilling ride.[2]

REFERENCES

Adams, J. P, E. E. Prather, and T. F. Slater. 2004. *Lecture Tutorials for Introductory Astronomy*. Upper Saddle River, N.J.: Pearson Education.

Alcock, J. 2005. *Animal Behavior: An Evolutionary Approach*. Sunderland, Mass.: Sinauer Associates.

Alexander, B. 2009. Apprehending the future: Emerging technologies, from science fiction to campus reality. *EDUCAUSE Review* 44:19–28.

American Association for the Advancement of Science (AAAS). 1990. *The Liberal Art of Science: Agenda for Action*. Washington, D.C.: AAAS.

American Institute of Physics (AIP). 2009. *Focus on Astronomy Faculty: Results from the 2008 Survey of Physics and Astronomy Degree-Granting Departments*, ed. R. Ivie, A. Ephraim, and S. White. College Park, Md.: AIP.

Anderson, J. R., and C. Lebiere. 1988. *The Atomic Components of Thought*. Mahwah, N.J.: Erlbaum.

———, and C. D. Schunn. 2000. Implications of the ACT-R learning theory: No magic bullets. In *Advances in Instructional Psychology: Educational Design and Cognitive Science*, vol. 5, ed. R. Glaser, 1–34. Mahwah, N.J.: Erlbaum.

Angelo, T. A., and K. P. Cross. 1993. *Classroom Assessment Techniques: A Handbook for College Teachers*. San Francisco: Jossey-Bass.

Bailey, J. M., and T. F. Slater. 2003. A review of astronomy education research. *Astronomy Education Review* 2:20–45.

2. I am especially grateful to my University of Arizona colleagues Ed Prather and Gina Brissenden for teaching me various learner-centered techniques over the years and for doing the research that demonstrates the effectiveness of many of the pedagogical ideas explored in this paper. I also thank Adrienne Gauthier for many conversations about technology and instructional design, Sanlyn Buxner and Jessie Antonellis for excellent science literacy efforts, and Erika Offerdahl and Audra Baleisis for helping me get my hands dirty with portfolio evaluation. I have learned much about inquiry-based instruction from Dick McCray and Doug Duncan at the University of Colorado, Greg Bothun at the University of Oregon, and Eric Mazur at Harvard University. The ideas in this paper came together during a visit to the Aspen Center for Physics, whose hospitality and convivial work environment are appreciated. My research in education has been supported over the past two decades by several small grants from the University of Arizona and by the National Science Foundation through its Astronomical Sciences and Undergraduate Education divisions, its Distinguished Teaching Scholars award program, and its Informal Science Education and Small Grants for Exploratory Research programs.

Bain, K. 2004. *What the Best College Teachers Do*. Cambridge, Mass.: Harvard University Press.

Bardar, E. M., E. E. Prather, K. Brecher, and T. F. Slater. 2006. The need for a light and spectra concept inventory for assessing innovations in introductory astronomy survey courses. *Astronomy Education Review* 2(4):20–27.

Bergman, M. K. 2001. The deep Web: Surfacing hidden value. *The Journal of Electronic Publishing* 7(1):1080–1090.

Bloom, B., ed. 1956. *Taxonomy of Educational Objectives*. Repr., Upper Saddle River, N.J.: Pearson Education, 1987.

Boyer, E. L. 1998. *Reinventing Undergraduate Education: A Blueprint for America's Research Universities*. Stony Brook: SUNY Press.

Bransford, J. D., A. L. Brown, and R. R. Cocking. 2000. *How People Learn: Brain, Mind, Experience, and School*. Washington, D.C.: National Academies Press.

Bridges, G. S., and S. Desmond, eds. 2000. *Teaching and Learning in Large Classes*. Washington, D.C.: American Sociological Association.

Brown, D. G., ed. 2000. *Interactive Learning: Vignettes from America's Most Wired Campuses*. Bolton, Mass.: Anker Publishing.

———, and R. P. Adler. 2008. Minds on fire: Open education, the long tail, and learning 2.0. *EDUCAUSE Review* 43(1):16–32.

Bruning, D. 2007. "Survey of Introductory Astronomy Textbooks." *Astronomy Education Review* 6:80–113.

Bureau of Labor Statistics. 2005. *College Textbooks: Enhanced Offerings Appear to Drive Recent Price Increases*. GAO-05-806. Washington, D.C.: Government Accountability Office.

Butler, D. 2009. Technology: The textbook of the future. *Nature* 458:568–570.

Bybee, R. W., ed. 2002. *Learning Science and the Science of Learning*. Arlington, Va.: NSTA Press.

Cafolla, R. 2006. Project MERLOT: Bringing peer review to Web-based educational resources. *Journal of Technology and Teacher Education* 14(2):313–323.

California Academy of Sciences. 2009. American adults flunk basic science. Press release. http://www.calacademy.org/newsroom/releases/2009/scientific_literacy.php.

Cheal, C. 2007. Second Life: Hype or hyperlearning? *On the Horizon* 15:204–210.

Clark, B. 2002. *Growing Up Gifted: Developing the Potential of Children at School and at Home.* Upper Saddle River, N.J.: Merrill Prentice Hall.

Collins, H., and R. Evans. 2007. *Rethinking Expertise.* Chicago: University of Chicago Press.

Comins, N. F. 2001. *Heavenly Errors: Misconceptions about the Real Nature of the Universe.* New York: Columbia University Press.

Committee on Undergraduate Science Education. 1997. *Science Teaching Reconsidered: A Handbook.* Washington, D.C.: National Academies Press.

Corder, G. 2005. Interactive learning with Java applets: Using interactive, Web-based Java applets to present science in a concrete, meaningful manner. *Science Teacher* 72(8):44–50.

Crouch, C. H., and E. Mazur. 2001. Peer instruction: Ten years of experience and results. *American Journal of Physics* 69:970–977.

Dancy, M. H., and R. J. Beichner. 2002. But are they learning? Getting started in classroom evaluation. *Cell Biology Education* 1:87–94.

Danielson, C., and L. Abrutyn. 1997. *An Introduction to Using Portfolios in the Classroom.* Alexandria, Va.: Association for Supervision and Curriculum Development.

Davis, B. G. 1993. *Tools for Teaching.* San Francisco: Jossey-Bass.

Dickens, C. 1859. *A Tale of Two Cities.* Repr., New York: Signet Classics, 1997.

Donovan, M. S., and J. D. Bransford, eds. 2005. *How Students Learn: Science in the Classroom.* Washington, D.C.: National Academies Press.

———, J. D. Bransford, and J. W. Pellegrino, eds. 1999. *How People Learn: Bridging Research and Practice.* Washington, D.C.: National Academies Press.

Duncan, D., and E. Mazur. 2005. *Clickers in the Classroom: How to Enhance Science Teaching Using Classroom Response Systems.* Upper Saddle River, N.J.: Pearson Education.

Duschl, R. 2008. Science education in three-part harmony: Balancing conceptual, epistemic, and social learning goals. *Review of Research in Education* 32(1):268–291.

Emery, C. R., T. R. Kramer, and R. G. Tian. 2003. Return to academic standards: A critique of student evaluations of teaching effectiveness. *Quality Assurance in Education* 11(1):37–46.

Fairweather, J. S. 1993. Faculty reward structures: Toward institutional and professional homogenization. *Research in Higher Education* 34(5):603–623.

Fraknoi, A. 2001. Enrollments in Astronomy 101 courses. *Astronomy Education Review* 1:121–123.

———. 2004. Insights from a survey of astronomy instructors in community and other teaching-oriented colleges in the United States. *Astronomy Education Review* 3:7–16.

Gabel, D. L., ed. 1994. *Handbook of Research on Science Teaching and Learning.* New York: Macmillan.

Gantz, J. F., D. Reinsel, C. Chute, W. Schlichting, J. McArthur, S. Minton, I. Xheneti, A. Toncheva, and A. Manfrediz. 2007. *The Expanding Digital Universe: A Forecast of Worldwide Information Growth through 2010.* Framingham, Mass.: IDC. http://www.emc.com/collateral/analyst-reports/expanding-digital -idc-white-paper.pdf.

Garrison, D. R., and T. Anderson. 2003. *E-learning in the 21st Century: A Framework for Research and Practice.* New York: Routledge.

Giles, J. 2005. Internet encyclopedias go head to head. *Nature* 438:900–901.

Green, P. J. 2003. *Peer Instruction in Astronomy.* Upper Saddle River, N.J.: Pearson Education.

Hake, R. R. 1998. Interactive engagement versus traditional methods: A six-thousand-student survey of mechanics test data for introductory physics courses. *American Journal of Physics* 66:64–78.

Hazen, R. M., and J. Trefil. 1991. *Science Matters: Achieving Science Literacy.* New York: Doubleday.

Horrigan, J. B. 2006. *The Internet as a Resource for News and Information about Science.* Washington, D.C.: Pew Internet and American Life Project. http://www.pewinternet.org/Reports/2006/The-Internet-as-a-Resource -for-News-and-Information-about-Science.aspx.

Hudgins, D. W., E. E. Prather, D. J. Grayson, and D. P. Smits. 2006. Effectiveness of collaborative ranking tasks on student understanding of key astronomy concepts. *Astronomy Education Review* 5(1):1–22.

Hufnagel, B. 2002. Development of the astronomy diagnostic test. *Astronomy Education Review* 1:47–51.

Impey, C. D., S. Buxner, J. Antonellis, E. Johnson, and C. King. 2010. A twenty year survey of science literacy among college undergraduates. *Journal of College Science Teaching.*

Johnson, A. H., and F. Percival. 1976. Attention breaks in lectures. *Education in Chemistry* 13:49–50.

Johnson, L., A. Levine, R. Smith, and S. Stone. 2010. *The 2010 Horizon Report.* Austin, Tex.: The New Media Consortium.

Kelton, A. J. 2007. Second Life: Reaching into the virtual world for real-world learning. *EDUCAUSE Center for Applied Research Bulletin* 17 (August 14). http://www.educause.edu/ECAR/SecondLifeReachingintotheVirtu/161863.

Kitao, T. K. 1999. The usefulness of uselessness. Keynote address at the Institute for the Academic Advancement of Youth's Odyssey, Swarthmore College.

Lazarowitz, R., R. Hertz-Lazarowitz, and J. H. Baird. 2006. Learning science in a cooperative setting: Academic achievement and affective outcomes. *Journal of Research in Science Teaching* 31(10):1121–1131.

Lintott, C. J., K. Schawinski, A. Slosar, K. Land, S. Bamford, D. Thomas, and M. J. Raddick. 2008. Galaxy Zoo: Morphologies derived from visual inspection of galaxies from the Sloan Digital Sky Survey. *Monthly Notices of the Royal Astronomical Society* 389:1179–1189.

Lyman, F. 1987. Think-pair-share: An expanding teaching technique. *MAA-CIE Cooperative Views* 1:1–2.

Mayer, R. E. 2004. Should there be a three-strikes rule against pure discovery learning? *American Psychologist* 59:11–14.

Mazur, E. 1996. *Peer Instruction: A User's Manual.* New York: Pearson.

Miller, J. D. 2004. Public attitudes toward, and understanding of, scientific research: What we know and what we need to know. *Public Understanding of Science* 13(3):273–294.

Millis, B. J., and P. G. Cottell. 1998. *Cooperative Learning for Higher Education Faculty.* American Council on Education Series on Higher Education. Phoenix: Oryx Press.

Mintzes, J. J., and W. H. Leonard. 2006. *Handbook of College Science Teaching.* Arlington, Va.: NSTA Press.

National Research Council. 1999. *Transforming Undergraduate Education in Science, Mathematics, Engineering, and Technology.* Washington, D.C.: National Academies Press.

National Science Board. 2008. *Science and Engineering Indicators.* Arlington, Va.: National Science Foundation.

———. 2010. *Science and Engineering Indicators.* Arlington, Va.: National Science Foundation.

National Science Teachers Association (NSTA). 2002. *Innovative Techniques for Large-Group Instruction.* Arlington, Va.: NSTA Press.

Northrup, P. 2007. *Learning Objects for Instruction: Design and Evaluation.* Hershey, Pa.: Information Science Publishing.

Novak, J. D. 1998. *Learning, Creating and Using Knowledge: Concept Maps as Facilitative Tools in Schools and Corporations.* Philadelphia: Lawrence Erlbaum Associates.

————. 2002. Meaningful learning: The essential factor for conceptual change in limited or inappropriate propositional hierarchies leading to empowerment of learners. *Science Education* 86:548–571.

————, and A. S. Cañas. 2008. *The Theory Underlying Concept Maps and How to Construct and Use Them.* Technical Report IHMC CmapTools 2006-01. Pensacola: Florida Institute for Human and Machine Cognition. http://cmap.ihmc.us/Publications/ResearchPapers/TheoryCmaps/TheoryUnderlying ConceptMaps.htm.

Oblinger, D. G., and J. L. Oblinger, eds. 2005. *Educating the Net Generation.* Washington, D.C.: EDUCAUSE. http://www.educause.edu/educatingthenetgen.

O'Neil, D. K., and J. L. Polman. 2004. Why educate "little scientists"? Examining the potential of practice-based scientific literacy. *Journal of Research in Science Teaching* 41:234–266.

Palloff, R. M., and K. Pratt. 2001. *Lessons from the Cyberspace Classroom.* San Francisco: Jossey-Bass.

Partridge, B., and G. Greenstein. 2004. "Goals for Astro 101: Report on Workshops for Department Leaders." *Astronomy Education Review* 2(2):46–89.

Pompea, S. M. 2000. *Great Ideas for Teaching Astronomy.* 3rd ed. Florence, Ky.: Thomson Learning.

Prather, E. E., A. L. Rudolph, G. Brissenden, and W. M. Schlingman. 2008. A national study assessing the teaching and learning of introductory astronomy, Part I: The effect of interactive instruction. *American Journal of Physics* 77:320–330.

————, T. F. Slater, J. P. Adams, J. M. Bailey, L. V. Jones, and J. A. Dostal. 2005. Research on a lecture-tutorial approach for teaching astronomy for non-science majors. *Astronomy Education Review* 3(2):122–136.

————, T. F. Slater, J. P. Adams, and J. M. Bailey. 2004. Research on a lecture-tutorial approach to teaching introductory astronomy for non-science majors. *Astronomy Education Review* 3(2):122–137.

Rainie, L., and B. Tancer. 2007. Data memo. Washington, D.C.: Pew Internet and American Life Project. http://www.pewinternet.org/~/media/Files/Reports/2007/PIP_Wikipedia07.pdf.pdf.

Ripoff 101. 2005. *How the Publishing Industry's Practices Needlessly Drive Up Textbook Costs.* 2nd ed. Washington, D.C.: State Public Interest Research Groups.

Schmitt, C., J. Rodriguez, and R. Clothey. 2009. *Education in Motion: From iPod to iPhone.* Proceedings of World Conference on Educational Multimedia, Hypermedia, and Telecommunications. Chesapeake, Va.: AACE, 2308–2313.

Schwartz, D. L., and J. D. Bransford. 1998. A time for telling. *Cognition and Instruction* 16:475–522.

Shamos, M. H. 1995. *The Myth of Scientific Literacy.* Piscataway, N.J.: Rutgers University Press.

Slater, T. F., and J. P. Adams. 2003. *Learner-Centered Astronomy Teaching: Strategies for Astro 101.* Upper Saddle River, N.J.: Pearson Education.

Sweller, J. 1994. Cognitive load theory, learning difficulty, and instructional design. *Learning and Instruction* 4:295–312.

Terdiman, D. 2008. *The Entrepreneur's Guide to Second Life: Making Money in the Metaverse.* Indianapolis: Wiley.

Thagard, P. 2005. *Mind: Introduction to Cognitive Science.* Cambridge, Mass.: MIT Press.

Tobias, S. 1991. They're not dumb, they're different: Stalking the second tier. *American Journal of Physics* 59:1155–1157.

Tullis, T. 2008. Results of online usability study of Apollo program websites. Measuring User Experience. http://www.measuringuserexperience.com/Apollo/.

Weiman, C., and K. Perkins. 2005. Transforming physics education. *Physics Today* 58:36–41.

# CHAPTER 6

# Physics for Future Presidents

Richard A. Muller

## PHYSICS IS THE LIBERAL ARTS OF HIGH TECH

*Physics for future presidents?* Yes, that is a serious title. Energy, global warming, terrorism and counterterrorism, health, Internet, satellites, remote sensing, ICBMs and ABMs, DVDs and HDTVs: economic and political issues increasingly have a strong high-tech content. Misjudge the science, make a wrong decision. Yet many of our leaders never studied physics and do not understand science and technology. Even my school, the University of California, Berkeley, does not require physics. Physics for Future Presidents (PffP) is a course designed to address that problem. Physics is the liberal arts of high technology. Understand physics, and never again be intimidated by technological advances. PffP is designed to attract students and teach them the physics they need to know to be effective world leaders.

Is science too hard for world leaders to learn? No, it is just badly taught. Think of an analogous example: Charlemagne was only half literate. He could read but not write. Writing was a skill considered too tough even for world leaders, just as physics is today. And yet now most of the world is literate. Many children learn to read before kindergarten. Literacy in China is 84 percent according to the Organisation for Economic Co-operation and Development. We can—we must—achieve the same level with scientific literacy, especially for our leaders.

PffP is based on my several decades of experience presenting tough scientific issues to top leaders in government and business. My conclusion is that these people are smarter than most physics professors. They readily understand complex issues even though they don't relax by doing integrals. (I know a physics professor who does.) PffP is not Physics for Poets, Physics for Jocks, or Physics for Dummies; it is the physics one needs to know to be an effective world leader.

Can physics be taught without math? Of course! Math is a tool for computation, but it is not the essence of physics. We often cajole our advanced students, "Think physics, not math!" You can understand and even compose music without studying music theory, and you can understand light without knowing Maxwell's equations. The goal of this course is not to create mini-physicists. The goal is to give future world leaders the knowledge and understanding they need to make decisions. If they need a computation, they can always hire a physics professor. But knowledge of physics will help them judge, on their own, if the physicist is right.

## AN IDEAL STUDENT

Liz, a former student of my class, came to me during office hours, eager to share a wonderful experience she had had a few days earlier. Her family had invited a physicist over for dinner, someone who worked at the Lawrence Livermore National Laboratory. Over the course of dinner he regaled them with his stories of controlled thermonuclear fusion and its great future for the power needs of our country. According to Liz, the family sat in awe of this great man describing his great work. Liz knew more about fusion than did her parents because we had covered it in class.

There was a period of quiet admiration that followed the physicist's stories. Finally Liz spoke up. "Solar power has a future, too," she said.

"Ha!" the physicist laughed. (He did not mean to be patronizing, but this is a typical tone physicists affect.) "If you want enough power just for California," he continued, "you'd have to plaster the whole state with solar cells!"

Liz answered right back. "No, you're wrong," she said. "There is a giga-watt in a square kilometer of sunlight, and that's about the same as a nuclear power plant."

Stunned silence from the physicist. Liz said he frowned. Finally he said, "Hmm. Your numbers don't sound wrong. Of course, present solar cells are only 15 percent efficient . . . but that's not a huge factor. Hmm. I'll have to check my numbers."

Yes! That is what I want my students to be able to do. Not integrals, not roller-coaster calculations, not pontifications on the scientific method or the deep meaning of conservation of angular momentum. Liz was able to shut up an arrogant physicist who had not done his homework! She had not just memorized facts; she knew enough about the subject of energy that she could confidently present her case under duress when confronted by a supposed expert. Her performance is even more impressive given that solar power is only a tiny part of this course. She remembered the important numbers because she had found them fascinating and important. She had not just memorized them, but had thought about them and discussed them with her classmates. They had become part of her, a part she could bring out and use when needed, even a year later.

PffP is not watered-down physics; it is advanced physics and covers the most interesting and important topics. Students recognize the value of what they are learning and are naturally motivated to do well. In every chapter they find material they want to share with their friends, roommates, and parents. Rather than keep the students beneath the math glass ceiling, I take them far above it. "You don't have the time or the inclination to learn the math," I tell them. "So we'll skip over that part, and get to the important stuff right away." I then teach them things that ordinary physics students do not learn until *after* they earn their Ph.D.

The typical physics major, even the typical Ph.D., does *not* know the material in this course. He (and increasingly she) knows little to nothing about nukes, optics, fluids, batteries, lasers, infrared and ultraviolet light, X-rays and gamma rays, MRI, CAT, and PET scans. Ask a physics major how a nuclear bomb works, and you'll hear what the student learned in high school. For that reason, at Berkeley we have now opened this course to physics majors. It is not baby physics; it is advanced physics.

I did make one major concession to my students. They are eager to learn about relativity and cosmology, subjects superfluous to world leadership but fascinating to thinking people. So I added two chapters to the end of the course. They cover subjects that every educated person should know, but that will not help the president make key decisions.

The response to the course has been fantastic. Enrollment grew mostly by word-of-mouth, from thirty-four students in Spring 2001 to more than five hundred by Fall 2006. The class now fills up the largest physics-ready lecture hall at Berkeley. About half of these students previously hated or dreaded physics; many had sworn (after their high school class) never to take it again. But they are drawn, like moths to a flame, to a subject they find fascinating and important. My job is to make sure their craving is fulfilled and that they do not get burned again. These students come to college to learn, and they are happiest when they sense their knowledge and abilities growing.

My greatest award for creating this course came in 2008 when the student newspaper, *The Daily Californian*, surveyed all students on campus. PffP was voted the "best class" at Berkeley. The course received the honor again in 2009. This is an astonishing achievement for a physics class.

Students do not take the course because it is easy; it is not. PffP covers an enormous amount of material. But every chapter is full of information that is evidently important. That is why students sign up. They do not want to be entertained. They want a good course, well taught, that fills them with important information and the ability to use it well. They are proud to take this course, but more important, they are very proud that they enjoy it.

Figure 1 shows the history of enrollment in the "qualitative physics" course at Berkeley. In the 1980s, when physics or chemistry was required for

## Figure 1: Enrollment in Physics 10 at the University of California, Berkeley

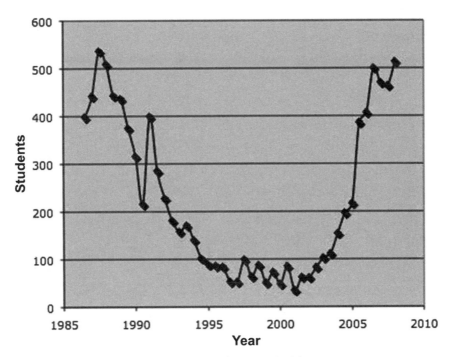

In 2001, the course was reinvented as Physics for Future Presidents.

all students, enrollment was as high as 500 students per semester. But as alternatives became available, enrollment dropped, reaching a low of thirty-four students in Spring 2001. Although Berkeley still had a "physical science requirement," it could be filled by a wide diversity of less intimidating classes, including courses in physical anthropology, geology, oceanography, and ecology.

When the approach of the course was changed, in Fall 2001, the enrollment began to grow. In 2008, it peaked at the maximum capacity of the lecture hall: 512 students each semester. (Berkeley has larger rooms available, but this is the largest one that can support the demonstrations.)

## PEDAGOGY

PffP is fun to teach and fun to take, but it is unlike other courses in qualitative physics. I use several ideas that are unusual. Instructors for a course such as PffP may find it helpful to understand these ideas.

### Immersion

I teach by total immersion. Physics majors take one to four years to get a sense of what energy means. They do not learn it from the definition. So in PffP I start using the term, with many, many examples. Students feel as if they are walking into a foreign language class in which the teacher starts speaking Spanish immediately. After a semester of using the word *energy* every class, students begin to understand what physicists mean by the term.

## Motivate and Intrigue

Many students in PffP are afraid of physics, sometimes because of a bad experience in high school. The first step is to stimulate their interest so that they forget their fear. Chapters usually begin with a story, anecdote, or puzzling facts. The purpose is to make the student wonder, "How can that be?" Important and intriguing applications are mentioned at the beginning rather than appended to the end.

The order of topics and the structure of chapters in PffP are not traditional. There is no need to put "modern physics" last, following historical order. Students are eager to learn new, exciting things, and in total immersion they do not need to wait. I introduce atomic and nuclear physics early. My goal is to motivate students by putting the most fascinating topics first. Energy is in Chapter 1, explosions in 2, spy satellites in 3, radioactivity in 4, nukes in 5. (See page 122 for the table of contents for the PffP textbook.) The students get hooked early. By the time we get to waves, light, and integrated circuits, students are warmed up and ready to find those exciting, too.

## Reading

When I began teaching this course, I decided that it had to be made more attractive to non-science majors. I surveyed my students, focusing on two key questions: What kinds of homework do you enjoy in your other classes? What work would fit in naturally with your study style? Many students said that for other courses they learned by spending a lot of time reading. Based on this feedback, I wrote notes that started out as Web page summaries but evolved into a textbook[1] *to be read*. That may sound silly, but the core idea was to have something that is fun to read and reread. The resulting textbook does not use the standard physics pedagogy of following an intense abstract section with a short "test your understanding" quiz. I did not want to break the flow, so I decided to write about each physics subject in the way a novelist might. I tried to make a textbook that is a page-turner. I encourage students to read quickly and then read again (and again), rather than work through the text slowly.

## Images and Figures

I cannot overemphasize the importance of motivation. The images and figures in the PffP textbook are chosen to be intriguing. When the students thumb through the book, the images should stir their curiosity. "What is that?" "That's

---

1. Richard A. Muller, *Physics and Technology for Future Presidents* (Princeton, N.J.: Princeton University Press, 2010).

amazing!" "I'd love to understand that." Not all the images and figures meet this standard, but I tried to include as many as possible that would stir student interest.

### Physics as a Second Language

When I first taught this course, I had students find examples of the misuse of key terms such as *energy, power, speed,* and *velocity.* I do not use that exercise anymore because it leads to a nonproductive arrogance. Most physics terms existed before physics gave them precise definitions. I ask my students to learn physics as a second language and to be able to use physics terms in their specialized physics sense when talking to other physics-literate people. This approach avoids passing on the arrogance that physicists often affect. When you know how to use specialized language, you can communicate more effectively with other experts.

### Math: Multiple Levels

PffP classes can be large and include students with a wide variety of interests and abilities. Majors in English, music, math, and physics all take the course. Some want more math, which I provide, but not before letting students know that the math portion of the lecture is not required. Those who are not interested can sleep for five minutes while I explain, for example, how the relativistic energy equation reduces to Newtonian kinetic energy, satisfying the correspondence principle. Remarkably, the students who "hate" math continue paying attention. They find the math fun as long as they are not required to reproduce it. The PffP textbook takes the same approach, explicitly stating when something is optional.

### Don't Cover Everything in Lecture

In liberal arts classes, the lectures make no attempt to cover all the material. Students who enroll in PffP are accustomed to learning things on their own. I spend the lectures on the most subtle material or the most interesting (and therefore most motivational), but I tell students that they are required to learn on their own everything in the textbook that is not marked as optional.

### Homework

To make this course attractive, I surveyed my students to find out what kinds of homework they were assigned in the non-physics courses they liked. The answer was simple: reading and writing. To address the former, I tried to write a textbook that is fun to read. I wanted the students to read through the chapter without being distracted by standard physics pedagogy (for example, the chapter-ending "check your understanding" quizzes). Then, to study, they should read it again.

Many of my students are freshmen, and to make sure they do the reading on time, I give frequent short multiple-choice quizzes. These are meant to be easy for anyone who has read (but not yet studied) the chapter but hard to guess for those students who have not. Similar questions appear at the ends of the chapters.

I was surprised to discover that most of my students did not normally read newspaper articles about science and technology. To break this bad habit, many of the homework assignments consist of the following: find a newspaper article that has physics or technology content, and write two paragraphs summarizing the content. Students can earn a high score even if they do not understand the article, as long as they state what it was that they did not understand. (Once students clearly identify what they do not understand, they are 90 percent of the way toward understanding it.) A common semester-end comment from students was: "I didn't know articles like that were for me!"

I tell students that most homework will get a grade of 2—meaning nice job and we did not have time to grade in more detail. Homework that has spelling or grammar errors earns a grade of 1. If a paragraph is so well written that the teaching assistant notices and enjoys reading it, it might earn a rare 3.

For the first homework, a large fraction of the papers are sloppily written and earn a 1. Within a few weeks, the writing improves dramatically. Some seniors have told me that they wrote more in PffP than in any other course, and even though the grading was not detailed, the regular practice improved their writing.

### Exams

My exams are 50 percent essay and 50 percent multiple-choice questions. My goal is to make students knowledgeable and articulate about the physics and technological aspects of important issues. I give examples of suggested essay questions at the end of every chapter in the textbook. If you don't have the resources to grade essays, you can give exams consisting solely of multiple-choice questions. The average student at Berkeley gets 75 percent of these correct, earning a B in the course. A sample exam is shown on page 126.

### Numbers

It is important for the student to be able to understand the use of large and small numbers, but I do not require that they be able to manipulate such numbers themselves. We review scientific notation in the first discussion sections, but I ask only that they be able to follow the numbers while I perform the manipulation. The highest priority is not to teach computation. I want them to know what is important, what is negligible, and how physics illuminates complex phenomena. I want them to be able to tell when something they are hearing is probably wrong.

## Policy and Politics

I emphasize physics and try hard to eliminate policy and politics. I try to cover the technical aspects that one must understand in order to make wise decisions, and I try to avoid most of the nontechnical aspects of the issues. One of my proudest teaching moments occurred in 2006 when a student asked permission for a personal question. He wanted to know my "politics." I was proud that in a class that discusses energy, nukes, the technology of war, global warming, and high tech, he could not figure out for whom I had voted. (And I did not tell him.) It is important to show that physics questions do not have a political spin. We can all agree on the physics. When tricky issues are raised (such as the plutonium economy), I try to give the strongest arguments on all sides. Then the students can think about the subject and decide their own positions.

The students try but can't put me in a category of, for example, pro-nuke or anti-nuke. I don't care what their opinion is. I teach them the plusses and minuses of nuclear power, and let them choose themselves.

## Lectures Online

My lectures are available for free online at University of California Television (http://www.uctv.tv), Google Videos (http://video.google.com), YouTube (http://www.youtube.com), and as podcasts on iTunes. Links can also be found on my Web page, http://www.muller.lbl.gov. In one lecture, I asked anyone who was watching or listening outside of Berkeley to email me. The response astounded me. As of this writing (2010), I have received email from ninety-three countries, including Malaysia, Mali, Tibet, Turkey, Kenya, Saudi Arabia, and Iraq.

## Respect

Respect for the student is essential. I treat each student in my class with the expectation that he or she will someday be president—if not of the United States, then at least of a major company. Educating future leaders is not just fun; it is a duty. I avoid cartoons and other images that suggest students are "just kids." Pictures and writing should approximate those that adults like and might expect to see in a magazine such as *The Economist*. This really is physics for future presidents.

## What I Do Not Teach

I do not teach problem-solving; it is not possible to do so in one semester. If the students in PffP ever need to calculate the velocity of a roller coaster, they will hire a physicist.

I don't explicitly teach the scientific method, for two reasons. The first is that students find it patronizing and boring. The second (if a second one is needed) is that I don't consider the usual scientific method, as taught, to be correct. Few advances are made by testing hypotheses. Most discoveries are made by people who have learned the right level of self-skepticism and are careful enough that when something unusual happens, something that they cannot explain by other means, they pay attention.

I believe in the dictum of the novelist: show, don't tell. After a semester of seeing real science, covering the most important and urgent topics, students get a real sense of what science knows and does not know.

*Question Periods*

I always take the first ten minutes of class to answer questions on any topic, whether something advanced ("What do you think of string theory?"), technical ("Am I anonymous on the Internet?"), or urban legend ("Do cell phones ignite gasoline at filling stations?"). My willingness to admit when I do not know the answer and to make educated guesses based on physics demonstrates the honesty that is at the core of the scientific method. The material is always interesting and topical, and they can listen without the stress of thinking that they will be tested on it.

*Commencement*

PffP is not meant to be a complete survey of physics, and the PffP textbook does not try to cover every important aspect of the issues it discusses (an impossible and unreasonable task); nor is it meant to be used as a comprehensive reference text. Rather, PffP approaches the teaching of physics as a commencement, a way of leading students into a life full of the understanding and appreciation of science. Ultimately, what students learn in the course matters less than that they learn a lot. If the course introduces students to physics and demonstrates that advanced material is not beyond their reach, then they will learn far more in the years that follow than they could possibly learn in one semester.

*Memorizing*

Unlike physics students, liberal arts students do not mind learning numbers and facts. They are empowered when they know things, such as what really happened at Chernobyl, how many people died of cancer at Hiroshima, what spy satellites can really do (and not do), what Moore's Law is (most students have never heard of it), and what the differences are between MRI, CAT, and PET scans. I tell them that whatever their point of view, knowledge will help them. They will be able to win arguments with their friends and parents. They seem to be particularly happy about the latter. Of course, it is also conceivable that as they learn the facts, some students will change their minds on some technological issues.

*Fun*

Learning is one of the greatest joys in life. Give a child a choice—say, the chance to learn how to ride a bike or unlimited ice cream for an hour—and most children will pick the former. To learn is to feel great. Perhaps the only greater joy is using that learning to contribute something to others.

Yet most students have had the joy of learning beaten out of them, perhaps by bad teachers. Yes, learning is hard, just like playing baseball or playing a video game is hard. The trick is not to mind that it is hard. As students rediscover the joy of learning, they will learn with much less effort. They will be able to devote half as much time to studying, while learning twice as much.

The material in PffP is fascinating. Students *should* find it riveting. If that does not happen, it's because they've lost sight of the joy of learning. Tell them that the trick to learning the huge amount of material presented in the course is to find it interesting. That should be easy, because it is. When students recognize that fact, the automatic learning mechanism turns on. How can they forget things that are interesting, fascinating, intriguing, and important? Encourage students to discuss the material with their friends. Have them present interesting facts to physics majors (choose facts the physics majors probably do not know). Tell the students to discuss nuclear power, radioactivity, energy, lasers, computers, UFOs, earthquakes—everything in the course—with their parents and friends. Any material they discuss with others in this manner (that is, not for the purpose of studying, but to inform others) will be material that they will never forget.

# The Table of Contents from the Physics for Future Presidents Textbook

**Chapter 1. Energy and Power, and the Physics of Explosions.**

Calorie, joule, and kilowatt-hour. Energy in various substances. Surprises: TNT and cookies, gasoline and batteries, electric car hype, hybrid non-hype. Fuel cells. Hydrogen as a means of transporting energy. Uranium, gasoline, and TNT. Cheap coal. Forms of energy. Power. Conservation of energy. Horsepower. Human power. Solar power. Exercise and diet. Wind power. Cost of energy. Kinetic energy. Anti-ballistic-missile systems: smart rocks and brilliant pebbles. The demise of the dinosaurs.

**Chapter 2. Atoms and Heat.**

Quandaries. Atoms and molecules and the meaning of heat. Periodic table. Speed of sound and light. Energy in heat. Hiss and noise. Temperature. Laws of thermodynamics. Hydrogen escape from atmosphere. Cold death. Temperature scales: F, C, K. Thermal expansion. Global warming and sea level rise. Thermometers. Space shuttle tragedy. Solid, liquid, gas, and plasma. Explosions. Ideal gas law. Airbags, sautéing, fire walking. Heat engines. Wasted energy. Refrigerators and heat pumps. Heat flow. Entropy and disorder.

**Chapter 3. Gravity, Force, and Space.**

Gravity surprises. The force of gravity. Newton's third law. "Weightless" astronaut. Key orbits: LEO, MEO, and HEO. Rock and sling. Geosynchronous. Spy satellites. GPS location. Oil exploration. Manufacturing in space. Escape velocity. Gravity in science fiction. Falling to Earth. The X Prize. Automobile air resistance and efficiency. Force and acceleration. The g-rule. Rail gun. Circular acceleration. Escape to space. Black holes. Momentum. Rockets. Balloons. Skyhook. Ion rockets. Flying: airplanes, helicopters, balloons. Floating on water. Air pressure. Hurricanes and storm surges. Convection, thunderstorms, and heaters. Angular momentum and torque.

**Chapter 4. Nuclei and Radioactivity.**

Paradoxes and puzzles. The nucleus and its explosion. Protons, electrons, neutrons, quarks, and gluons. Isotopes. Radiation. Cloud chamber. Radiation and death: the rem. LD50. Poisoning and cancer. Linear hypothesis. Chernobyl. Hiroshima cancer. Denver exposure. Tooth and chest X-ray doses. Ultrasound. Radiation to cure cancer. Dirty bomb. Alpha, beta, gamma rays, and more. Natural radioactivity. Half-life rule. Power for satellites from RTGs. Radioisotope dating: potassium-argon and radiocarbon. Environmental radioactivity. Why aren't all atoms radioactive? Optional: tunneling and the weak force of radioactivity. Forensics: neutron activation. Watch dials. Plutonium. Fission. Fusion. Power from the Sun.

## Chapter 5. Chain Reactions, Nuclear Reactors, and Atomic Bombs.

Chain reactions and the doubling rule (exponential growth): examples from chess, nuclear bombs, fetal growth, cancer, population (and Malthus), mass extinction recovery, PCR, germs, computer viruses, urban legends, avalanches, sparks and lightning, compound interest, Moore's Law, folding paper, and tree branches. Nuclear weapons basics. Critical mass. Uranium gun bomb. Uranium enrichment: calutrons and centrifuges. Plutonium implosion bomb. Thermo-nuclear "hydrogen bomb." Boosted bombs. Atomic bombs. Fallout. Nuclear reactors. Plutonium production. Breeder reactors. Dangers: cancer and the plutonium economy. Depleted uranium. Gabon natural reactor. Fuel requirements. Nuclear waste. Yucca Mountain. China syndrome. Three Mile Island. Chernobyl. Paradoxes. Present stockpile.

## Chapter 6. Electricity and Magnetism.

Compared to gravity. Charge. Current: amps. Wires and electron pipes. Resistance. Conductors, semiconductors, and superconductors. Fuses and circuit breakers. High-temperature superconductors. Volts. Static electricity. Electric power. Frog legs and Frankenstein. House power. High-tension lines. Electricity creates magnetism: magnets, N & S, permanent, rare-earth, electromagnets. Monopoles? Short range. Electric and magnetic fields. Iron. Magnetic recording, hard drives. Curie temperature. Submarine location. Electric motors. Magnetism creates electricity: electric generators. Dynamos. The Earth and its magnetic flips. Geology applications. Transformers. The Edison/Tesla competition: AC vs. DC. Magnetic levitation. Rail guns again. Automobile battery. Flashlight batteries.

## Chapter 7. Waves.

Mysterious uses of waves: UFOs near Roswell, New Mexico, and SOFAR rescuing of pilots in World War II. What are waves? Wave packets and quantum physics. Sound. Sound speed. Transverse and longitudinal. Water surface waves. Tsunamis. Period, frequency, and wavelength. Bending. Sound channel in the ocean and atmosphere. SOFAR and Roswell explained. Whale songs. GPS again. Ozone layer. Earthquakes. Magnitude and epicenter. P, S, L waves. Estimating distance rule. Liquid core of the Earth. Bullwhips. Waves cancel, reinforce. Beats. Musical notes. The ear. Noise-canceling earphones. Doppler shift. Huygens's principle.

## Chapter 8. Light.

High-tech light. Electromagnetic waves. Light communication and information theory: the bit and the baud rate. Color and color perception. Rods and cones. White and pseudo-white. Color blindness. Multispectra. Printed color. Oil slick. Images. Pinhole camera. Eyes. Mirrors. Magic with mirrors. Retro-reflectors. Corner reflector. Stealth. Slow light. Index of refraction. Mirages. Diamonds, dispersion, and fire. Prism. Counterfeit diamonds. Other illusions: swimming pools and milk glasses. Rainbows. Lenses. Eyes again. Variable lens. Nearsighted and farsighted. Red eye and stop signs. Microscopes and telescopes. Spreading light. Diffraction. Blurring and spy satellite limits. Holograms. Polarization. Polarized sunglasses. Crossed polarizers. Liquid crystals and LCD screens. 3-D movies.

### Chapter 9. Invisible Light.

Anecdote: illegal immigrants seen in the dark. Infrared. Thermal radiation and temperature. Red, white, and blue-white hot. Brown paint for cool roofs. Power radiated by warm object: 4th power. Tungsten inefficiency. Heat lamps. Dew on sleeping bags. Remote sensing of temperature. Weather satellites. Military special ops: "we own the night." Stinger missiles, pit vipers, and mosquitoes. UV and "black lights." Whiter than white. Sunburn. Germicidal lamps. Wind-burn. Ozone layer. Freon, CFCs, and the ozone hole. Greenhouse effect and carbon dioxide. Seeing through dust and smoke, firefighting. Electromagnetic spectrum. Radio, radar, microwaves, X-rays and gamma rays. Radar images. Medical imaging: X-rays, MRI (NMR), CAT, PET (antimatter), thermography, ultrasound. Bats. X-ray backscatter. Picking locks.

### Chapter 10. Climate Change.

The temperature record. IPCC. Carbon dioxide and the acidification of the oceans. A brief history of climate. Warming from 1850 to present. Paleoclimate: the end of the last ice age. Cycles of ice and their astronomical causes. Carbon dioxide increase since 1800 and the greenhouse effect. Role of water vapor as an amplifier. Hurricanes and warming. Analysis, compensating for systematic biases. Tornadoes. The melting of Alaska. Dangers of exaggeration, distortion, and cherry-picking of data. Possible solutions to global warming. Alternatives to fossil fuels. Cost of energy. Fisher-Tropsch process: coal to liquid. Capture and storage: sequestering. Energy conservation and energy efficiency.

### Chapter 11. Quantum Physics.

High tech is largely based on quantum physics. Electron waves. Spectra and remote sensing. Einstein discovers photons. Laser: a quantum chain reaction. Laser applications: supermarkets, cleaning, weapons. Controlled thermonuclear fusion using lasers. Lasers and eyes. LASIK surgery. Solar cells and digital cameras. Image intensifiers and night vision. Xerox machines and laser printers. Compact discs and DVDs. More on gamma rays and X-rays. Fiber optics limits from quantum physics. Are photons real? Semiconductor electronics. Light-emitting diodes (LEDs); traffic lights and stadium TV screens. Diode lasers.

Diodes to turn AC into DC. Transistor amplifiers and transistor radios. Computer circuits. Superconductors again. Electron microscope. Quantization of waves. Uncertainty principle. Tunneling and alpha radiation. Tunnel diodes. Scanning tunneling microscopes (STMs). Quantum computers.

**Chapter 12. Relativity.**

The nature of time. Fourth dimension. Time dilation. Twin paradox. The Einstein gamma factor. Time depends on velocity. Not all motion is relative. Length (Lorentz) contraction. Relative velocities. Invariance of the speed of light. Energy and mass. $E = mc^2$. Converting energy to mass. Antimatter engines. Zero rest mass of a photon. Massless particles have no time. Mass of neutrinos. Why you cannot get to light speed. Atomic bomb and relativity. Tachyons. Simultaneity. Pondering time.

**Chapter 13. The Universe.**

Puzzles. How can the universe expand? What came before the beginning? The solar system. Companion star? Planets around other stars. The Milky Way. Galaxies. Dark matter. WIMPs and MACHOs. Extraterrestrial life and Drake's equation. SETI. Looking back in time. Expansion of the universe. Hubble's Law. The beginning. Dark energy. The Big Bang. The 3K cosmic microwave radiation—created in the Big Bang. Gravity and relativity. Twins in gravity. Black holes again. Finite universe? Before the Big Bang. A Theory of Everything. "The Creation" (a poem).

# An Example of a Physics for Future Presidents Midterm Exam

PffP First Midterm Exam

26 Feb 2009

Row_____ Seat_____

Last name_____ First_____ SID_____ GSI_____

**Essay questions** (20 pts): pick **one** and only one to answer; **circle** the one you choose. Write a page **on the back of this sheet**. This side is for your personal notes only. Cover the important points in a clear and concise manner—as if you have only a few minutes to tell the President, your roommate, or your parent what that person needs to know. *Clear, effective writing is important.* If English is a new language for you, state so at the top of your essay. If you need to re-write the essay, ask for a new copy of this page.

1. Critics of solar power argue that the power in sunlight is so weak that it will never be a competitive source of power. Are they right? What are the possible future uses of solar power? Could it be used on the roof of a car, to power the auto? What about a solar-powered airplane? Could a large solar power collector provide power of a gigawatt? Give examples and numbers whenever possible.

2. "Even a high school student can build an atomic bomb." That statement has appeared in books and magazines, but is it true? What is involved in building an atomic bomb? What are the most difficult steps? What steps are the "easiest"? What countries have recently built atomic bombs, or are in the process of doing so, and what approaches are they taking?

**Short questions** (1 point each, 20 points total). Read the questions carefully so that you don't misinterpret them (e.g., by missing a word such as "not"). Each question has only one correct answer.

Compare the energy in a pound of gasoline to the energy in a pound of a modern computer battery:

    ( ) The gasoline has about the same energy as the battery
    ( ) The battery has 10x more energy
    ( ) The gasoline has 10x more energy
    ( ) The gasoline has 100x more energy

Sea level rise in the last 50 years is primarily due to

    ( ) warming sea water
    ( ) melting ice
    ( ) increased rainfall
    ( ) decreased evaporation

Three gases are at the same temperature. The molecules that are moving the fastest are:

    ( ) hydrogen
    ( ) oxygen
    ( ) nitrogen
    ( ) they all have the same velocity

A "heat pump" is

    ( ) similar to a refrigerator working backwards
    ( ) a kind of automobile engine
    ( ) a device used in a hot air balloon
    ( ) used in auto air bags

A change in temperature of 1° C is about equal to a change of

    ( ) 1° F
    ( ) 0.5° F
    ( ) 2° F
    ( ) 300° F

The most common altitude for a spy satellite is:

    ( ) LEO
    ( ) MEO
    ( ) HEO
    ( ) between MEO and HEO

If the sun turned into a black hole, its gravity near the Earth would
        ( ) be unchanged
        ( ) become infinite
        ( ) go to zero
        ( ) increase by about 10%

Small differences in gravity have been used to
        ( ) search for oil
        ( ) detect nuclear materials
        ( ) detect nuclear explosions
        ( ) create antimatter

Alexander Litvenko was assassinated using
        ( ) plutonium
        ( ) botox
        ( ) anthrax
        ( ) polonium

If you are exposed to 1 rem, the probability that you will get radiation sickness (note: the question is NOT about cancer) is:
        ( ) zero
        ( ) 1/100
        ( ) 1/300
        ( ) 1/2500

A Tokamak (such as ITER) is used to
        ( ) store nuclear waste (if it is certified)
        ( ) create more fuel than it uses
        ( ) destroy nuclear waste
        ( ) make fusion

Which was named after the University of California?
        ( ) a device for reprocessing
        ( ) a device for enrichment
        ( ) a method for measuring DNA
        ( ) a location for nuclear waste storage

Fallout kills primarily due to the radioactivity of
        ( ) plutonium
        ( ) uranium
        ( ) tritium
        ( ) fission fragments

According to the text, the world population
   ( ) will double in the next 50 years
   ( ) growth has recently stopped
   ( ) is still growing, but will peak in the next 40 years or so at
       9 billion people
   ( ) doubles every 18 months

When a liquid boils, the increase in volume is typically a factor of
   ( ) 2
   ( ) 10
   ( ) 100
   ( ) 1000

Which fuel is cheapest, for the same energy delivered?
   ( ) oil
   ( ) natural gas
   ( ) coal
   ( ) AAA battery

A large nuclear power plant typically produces how much electric power?
   ( ) 1 megawatt
   ( ) 1 gigawatt
   ( ) 100 gigawatts
   ( ) 1000 gigawatts

Smart rocks are
   ( ) a new design of nuclear fuel
   ( ) meant to destroy nuclear missiles
   ( ) the highest quality of coal
   ( ) a method for purifying uranium

A typical fuel for fusion is
   ( ) uranium or plutonium
   ( ) radium
   ( ) deuterium and tritium
   ( ) C-14

The Chernobyl accident happened when
   ( ) the chain reaction grew out of control (a "reactivity" accident)
   ( ) the fuel lost its coolant (the "China Syndrome")
   ( ) A fire from outside the reactor spread to the reactor, setting it on fire
   ( ) A helicopter crashed into the reactor

# CHAPTER 7

# Learning Astronomy through Writing

Martha P. Haynes

Most astronomy courses at colleges and universities in the United States are geared toward the non-science major and are often used to fulfill general science distribution requirements. Many students have some basic curiosity about the universe around them, which makes astronomy a popular introductory subject. But enrollment in introductory astronomy courses may be these students' only exposure to science at the college level. Under these circumstances, science courses must emphasize the scientific method and the process of scientific research and discovery as much as factual content. In the Google Age, teaching how to pose a scientific question may be more important than teaching how to find its answer.

Many non-science majors seem resistant to problem solving and quantitative approaches. Some claim boredom when faced with the traditional science class. An alternative approach designed to provide these students comfort is to immerse them in familiar surroundings—essay writing, some of it creative— while still challenging them to think quantitatively and scientifically. Cornell University's Astronomy 2201 course, "Our Home in the Universe," is designed specifically to engage those students who enjoy writing, especially those who are stimulated by the chance to express their creativity while being exposed to the scientific concepts required to meet the content expectations of distribution requirements.

## CORNELL'S WRITING IN THE MAJORS PROGRAM

Like many colleges and universities in the United States, Cornell University requires most of its undergraduate students to enroll in courses that are designed to improve their writing skills. In the College of Arts and Sciences, students must complete two freshman writing seminars; students with Advanced Placement credit in English literature can opt out of one class, but not both.

Other colleges require only one writing seminar, but faculty can assume that all students will have had some college-level instruction in the art and practice of writing. At Cornell, the freshman writing seminars are taught not only in the English department but across the academic disciplines, often by advanced graduate students under faculty supervision. Recently, three of my graduate students have taught the freshman writing seminar Astronomy 1109, which fully meets the writing distribution requirements while also giving students a broad introduction to astronomy and cosmology. All three of these young educators are excellent scientists as well as dedicated teachers, and each valued the opportunity to gain experience leading a composition course. The demand for freshman writing seminars taught in the sciences is high. One year, 250 incoming freshmen tried to elect Astronomy 1109, but like all freshman seminars, its enrollment was capped at 18.

For many years, Cornell has emphasized the importance of writing and fostered its inclusion across the curriculum through the John S. Knight Institute for Writing in the Disciplines. Among the Knight Institute's activities, the Writing in the Majors (WIM) program encourages faculty to incorporate writing into discipline-oriented courses where writing is not the tradition. In the humanities, written essays and course papers are standard course requirements. Science classes, however, tend to focus on problem sets and short-answer or multiple-choice tests. For the student who finds writing an essay to be natural —even enjoyable—a science class organized around verbal expression and the synthesis of acquired knowledge, rather than repeated testing of that knowledge, will seem more familiar and user-friendly. More important, such students are likely to be just as successful as in more traditional science courses. At Cornell, the goal is to teach non-science majors in a way they will find comfortable, but without reducing the level of science content. Under the auspices of the WIM program, Cornell now offers several one-semester astronomy courses— including Astro2201, which I teach—intended for students who like to write. Most enrollees use the class to fulfill a science distribution requirement in their undergraduate college.

## WRITING COURSES WITHIN THE ASTRONOMY CURRICULUM

Most astronomy departments offer large lecture-based survey courses to hundreds of students. The faculty who teach these classes are often the most gifted and high-profile lecturers. The course material usually closely tracks the material in the adopted textbook; the written work consists of problem-oriented homework, multiple-choice or short-answer tests, and, possibly, lab exercises; and the design of the course reflects an approach to science education with which most students are already familiar. Such courses are generally predictable to students, who need only study (memorize) the material covered in the textbook. Despite the high student-to-instructor ratio, grading students in these courses is typically quick and straightforward. A common occurrence, however, is for class attendance to flag, though the recent introduction of in-class interactions and the use of "clickers" have been successful in alleviating problems of unnecessary absence.

By contrast, in a smaller class the professor will know all of his or her students, and assignments will require them to synthesize material presented in class. At Cornell, Astro2201 is promoted as a more intimate and user-friendly way to study astronomy, at least among those students for whom writing comes naturally. To catch students' attention, the course syllabus focuses on a handful of popular themes: the development of astronomical thinking, black holes, dark matter, the life and death of stars, and the history of the universe. A complementary course taught by my colleagues centers on the solar system. Their curriculum covers water on other planets, the diversity of planetary systems, the search for exoplanets, and killer asteroids, but still incorporates more traditional topics—from general physics concepts such as Newton's laws and the electromagnetic spectrum to astronomical topics such as stellar evolution and nucleosynthesis. Not all students will want to enroll in a class that emphasizes writing, but for a particular segment of the undergraduate population, such a course framework holds a strong attraction.

## PRACTICAL ASPECTS OF ASTRO2201

The advantage of a course without strictly required content is that it can be designed around those topics of greatest interest to students. In order to meet our college's expectations for the content of a science class, we strive to strike a balance between a few specific themes (such as black holes and cosmology) and adequate discussion of the fundamental physical laws and astrophysical concepts. In this way, students master a broad sweep of introductory astronomy and astrophysics, albeit without covering all possible topics. Because Astro2201 is often taught as two separate sections by different instructors who try to coordinate activities (in order to avoid questions about equality of rigor, required work, and so on), we have attempted to maintain some semblance of generality while also maintaining the individuality of the syllabus relative to other courses the department offers. As a result, Astro2201 is quite different in scope and depth from the more traditional survey course.

### Writing Assignments

Our approach is based on the premise that students required to write about science will be forced to develop scientific knowledge and understanding in order to complete their writing assignments. Over the years, we have experimented not only with the nature of the assignments but with their frequency and length. We have found that regular (almost weekly) assignments are the best way to maintain student engagement. The shorter assignments are a maximum of 500 words in length. Longer papers, including a final paper, are required at three- to four-week intervals and vary in length from 900 to 1,500 words (the final). We have found that longer papers produce less originality and more regurgitation of books and websites. Therefore, we try to focus students' papers on limited topics and the discussion of issues that are not entirely new; assignments to a large extent draw on classroom content and discussion, but might ask students to apply their knowledge in a different context or to address a different audience. Some assignments are written as memos or briefings in a hypothetical work situation. Others call for explanations written for children or in response to questions from former teachers. In each case, the student is asked to assume a well-defined role of a writer addressing a particular audience. This focus helps students communicate their mastery of science content without becoming bogged down or distracted by the writing itself.

### Making the Context and Audience Clear

Designing assignments for a writing-based science class requires establishing a balance between testing the acquisition of knowledge and fostering creativity in writing. The modern information age has given rise to a practical challenge: students today have trivially easy access to huge quantities of written words of widely varying scientific quality. Constructing assignments that are educational, somewhat fun, and not easily answered by Internet search engines becomes the trick. Our approach is to exploit a somewhat extraordinary scenario for individual assignments and to define specifically and carefully that context and the intended audience. Placing students in an ancient era, for example, forces them to think about what scientific knowledge was *not* available in earlier times. In one assignment, we ask students to imagine

> The year is 1280 A.D. You are a young scholar in the court of Alfonso X, king of Castile and Leon, also known as Alfonso the Wise. An avid astronomer, you spend your nights viewing the skies and your days reading whatever histories of observations and discourses on cosmological thinking that you can find. You have read *all* the ancient Greeks and of course know Ptolemy's "Almagest" practically by heart. You are a member of the team compiling the planetary tables "Tablas" from observations being conducted at Toledo and from various accumulated astronomical records, particularly ones from the Arab world.

The assignment then places the writer in the role of Alfonso's great nephew; it mentions that the king has been curious about celestial events since he witnessed a total solar eclipse during a "vacation in Madrid when he was your age." The assignment notes that a total solar eclipse was visible from Madrid in 1239 A.D. but that the student cannot be sure if Alfonso actually saw it. He or she can, however, assume that Alfonso is familiar with the Ptolemaic explanation for the motions of the celestial bodies. More precisely, the student must imagine that:

Lately, you've come to the conclusion that the Ptolemaic system is wrong and that the heliocentric universe makes more sense. Because you realize that such ideas might be viewed as heretical by your more senior colleagues, you decide to write your thoughts about the nature of the universe in a letter to Great Uncle Alfonso.

Keeping in mind that your letter comes more than 200 years before Copernicus and that all you have available are the records of naked-eye observations and the writings of the ancient Greeks through Ptolemy, make your letter as scientifically convincing as possible. Also be sure to summarize the basic tenets of each viewpoint as well as the pro's and con's, since Alfonso may have forgotten the details.

Your quill will run out of ink at about 1000 words. Because Alfonso's eyesight isn't as sharp as it used to be, please be sure to double space the letter.

By setting a word limit, we force students to concentrate on the information that is relevant and necessary to respond to the prompt. This assignment requires students to understand the logic behind the heliocentric and geocentric universe concepts; it also raises for their consideration how scientific discovery leads to scientific understanding. Some students immerse themselves in the role of the writer, producing enjoyable letters to "Uncle Alfonso." (Modern word processing packages even allow students to print their assignments as if they were written with a quill.)

Another character used in Astro2201 assignments grew out of my personal experience. Some years ago, I spent several months of a sabbatical working in Washington, D.C., as the interim president of Associated Universities, Inc., a nonprofit corporation that manages national astronomy research facilities funded by the National Science Foundation. During that period, I visited a number of congressional offices and met with staff to discuss the programs under the corporation's purview. In every one of those offices, one of the staff members was a Cornell graduate, albeit rarely in a scientific discipline. That experience prompted me to realize that some of the articulate—if occasionally scruffy—young people who enroll in Astro2201 might end up in a congressional office and, more important, that their appreciation of science and scientific research may be rooted in their Astro2201 experience. From my encounters in Washington emerged a character described as a staff adviser to "Senator Wisdom, of Great Prairie State, an influential member of the Senate Appropriations Committee's Subcommittee on Commerce, Justice, Science, and Related Agencies," who was introduced as an ongoing player in Astro2201 assignments. In almost every class, at least one student harbors political ambitions and therefore identifies with this story.

## Revisions

Over the years, we have experimented with assignments that require at least one round of revisions based on the professors' comments. We generally choose this approach with a conceptually difficult assignment that allows us to use the revision process as a way of insisting that students master the concepts. Our favorite of these assignments is a briefing to Senator Wisdom in which the student/staffer is tasked with summarizing and providing the context for large astronomy facilities—either in existence or under construction—that receive funding from the federal government. For example, we recently asked students to explain the scientific rationale for, and technical differences between, the James Webb Space Telescope and the Atacama Large Millimeter/submillimeter Array (ALMA). Why is one destined for space and the other for the ground? Why could ALMA not be built in Great Prairie State? Are any of the senator's constituents interested in these projects? This context requires that students appreciate the different capabilities of actual astronomical instrumentation, the technical challenges of building telescopes to operate in different portions of the electromagnetic spectrum, and the scientific questions that can be addressed by different instruments. Both the first draft and a revision based on our comments receive grades, and we carefully point out that our expectations for precision and clarity increase significantly for the revised version. Our comments often address students' use of terms they clearly do not understand. The process of revision forces them to explain concepts *in their own words*, something they generally cannot do unless they fully understand those concepts. We thus use revision to push students' scientific thinking beyond what they might be able to demonstrate after only a single round of essay development.

## Group Assignments

In every second or third class, we spend part of the period engaged in group activity: working through a problem, interpreting the information contained in an image, discussing an astrophysical circumstance, or designing and conducting a simple experiment. Each student retains his or her own copy of the exercise; the groups hand in the result of work done in class; and work not completed in class is expected to be finished outside of class. Group exercises are not graded, but problems posed in them often reappear in the essay assignments. The exercises are not elaborate, require almost no equipment, and are intended mainly to compel students to apply, in an active and immediate way, the most important formulas, facts, and concepts covered in the lecture. Group exercises call on students to develop their own identification and understanding of critical concepts and give professors an opportunity to observe which aspects are a struggle for students. Because the discussions and in-class exercises in many cases cannot be re-created, we state at the beginning of the semester that attendance is required. Missed in-class assignments cannot be done outside of class, but they can be excused for valid reasons. While we do not keep a regular list of attendance, keeping track of who is present is easy. Regular, unannounced in-class exercises that count toward the final grade provide a strong incentive to attend class.

## The Portfolio

Each assignment is geared toward the understanding of specific concepts covered in the preceding classes. Some assignments build on others completed earlier in the semester, and in order to emphasize continuity, we require that students keep a portfolio of their graded work as well as the shorter group exercises done in class. The portfolio is collected twice during the semester for review and helps earn points for the conscientious student who attends class and participates. Because we have found (surprisingly) that many students do not seem predisposed to note-taking, the accumulation of in-class work in the portfolio reinforces the need for recording information in the absence of having a formal laboratory component—that is, to some extent, the portfolio serves as a lab notebook. Additionally, it provides a useful way to organize and give weight to the in-class assignments, especially those we refer to some weeks after they are initially completed.

## Appreciating Peer Review

The awarding of telescope time, the funding of grants, and the evaluation of submitted manuscripts make astronomers appreciate the value of peer review. Therefore, we give students an opportunity to explore how peer review works and also to experience the grading process themselves. We have them read, rank, comment on, and assign grades to a collection of four short essays of varying quality completed by their classmates earlier in the semester. Because we do not want students to read their own papers, we ask them to read papers written by students in a different section of Astro2201. (If we did not offer multiple sections of the course, we would assign different collections of papers to different groups within a class, ensuring that no correlation existed between a group's members and authorship of the papers the group was assigned to review.) Although they dislike ranking the papers and assigning grades, students are, frankly, often more critical than we are. The exercise teaches them about the process of peer review; it also gives them a better appreciation of how difficult grading is and hence wins us quite a bit of sympathy.

## The Graduate Teaching Assistant Experience

Class assignments are read by the graduate teaching assistant (TA) and (usually) the faculty member. The TA receives special training in how to read, comment on, and grade writing assignments. When graded work is returned to students, the graduate assistant discusses during the class period the correct answers and comments generally on the exposition. Written comments are provided on each paper so that students can reflect on how to improve as the semester progresses. The TAs are strongly encouraged to enroll concurrently in the graduate-level Writing in the Majors Seminar (WRIT 7101) taught by Keith Hjortshoj, who has been director of the WIM program since 1992. Through this seminar, our astronomy graduate students receive formal instruction in the theory of teaching writing and benefit from the years of experience that the staff of Cornell's writing program can offer them.

### Grades and Grading

Unfortunately, students object when they do not understand how each point is assigned. Explaining the grading scheme for structured tests (such as multiple choice) is much easier than doing so for written work (as is grading such tests). In Astro2201, grades are based on the accumulation of points awarded for the quality of a series of writing assignments, as well as for class attendance and participation. The maximum point award for each assignment depends on its length and difficulty. By reviewing the current point distribution at various times during the semester, we are able to give students a review of basic statistics, such as the meaning of *mean*, *median*, and *standard deviation*. Because Cornell publishes the median grade awarded in each class, we presume they already know what to expect.

We devise writing assignments that require clear answers, then establish and stick to criteria that can be tied to a quantitative grading scale. This method is important. Creativity and exposition should count, but scientific content must be emphasized. A beautifully written essay that is weak in scientific content should receive a low grade—as should a poorly written essay that is scientifically strong. Each writing assignment must receive a comment that is specific and personal enough that each student can understand how his or her grade was assigned and what he or she needs to do to improve the assignment.

An important practical aspect of designing writing assignments is providing clear guidelines about the grading scheme. Students are more comfortable if they know whether they have accomplished the goal. One of my favorite contexts for assignments illustrates this approach. The assignment asks the student to identify errors in the scientific basis of a screenplay:

> In this assignment, you are a movie script editor in Hollywood. Your producer has asked you to proofread the screenplay of the next megahit on the adventures of Ithaca Jones, the famous adventurer-academic from Cornell University. The story opens as follows:
>
> *Opening scene.* In his office, Ithaca Jones studies an ancient papyrus found accidentally folded within a book at a used book store in Dryden, NY, and hence called the "Dryden Codex." The document has a map of the necropolis of Giza, in Egypt, and hieroglyphs which IJ deciphers with admirable

ease. The camera zooms on the mystified but handsome face of IJ, as he says: *"The millennium eclipse . . . the mask of Khufu!"* IJ grabs his inseparable hat and rushes across campus to the office of his astronomer friend. From him, he learns that a solar eclipse is due in northern Africa in late March of the year 2009. Scene cuts on IJ's emphatic exclamation: *"Yes!!"*

The remainder of the assignment describes a series of events that take place in Giza and elsewhere on the day of the supposed solar eclipse. The instructions for the assignment are then given:

> Having taken Astro2201, you of course notice that this script draft is astronomically full of holes. Several (at least six) major problems of general astronomical nature could seriously embarrass its makers and mar the show. You thus decide to inform the producer, and do so concisely but fully, by means of a memo of 500 words or less in which you explain the reasons behind each problem you identify. As far as we know, a solar eclipse will not take place in northern Africa on March 22, 2009. This should not be considered an error, but rather artistic license.

Students who identify fewer than six problems with the astronomical content of the screenplay are awarded fewer points for the assignment. Because students are asked to explain the background of each problem, they must propose an alternative. Asking them to limit their memo to five hundred words helps teach them to use words judiciously and to confine their responses to relevant information rather than wandering off subject. Because the memo format is repeated in several other assignments throughout the semester, we have opportunities to comment on how successfully students meet the requirements of a given format. We generally see significant improvement in students' writing over the course of the semester.

A particular challenge of the writing class in a nontraditional discipline is to avoid having the writing aspects interfere with the acquisition of curricular content. Because of the somewhat unconventional nature of the writing assignments, some students initially have difficulty understanding what we are asking of them. Common errors early in the semester include deviating from the topic, bringing in irrelevant information, using terminology that the audience would not (and probably the writer does not) understand, and failing to provide enough specificity. However, these flaws are usually quickly overcome once the student understands what we are looking for.

## SOME LESSONS LEARNED FROM ASTRO2201

Not every lesson plan or course syllabus for Astro2201 has proved equally effective, and we have learned on the job what works and what does not. While "one size does not fit all," some of the lessons we have learned may be of use to others considering a similar course.

### Teach through Images

Astronomy is a science principally practiced by observing the night sky, usually with powerful telescopes. Images of astronomical objects wind up scattered across everyday life: we have a line of automobiles called "Saturn," a candy bar called "Milky Way," a cleaner called "Comet," and a professional soccer team called the "Galaxy." Children's bedroom ceilings are adorned with glow-in-the-dark stars. My own very unscientific mother bought me a bedspread depicting the moon, stars, and Saturn. Today's images from the Hubble Space Telescope or the Very Large Array may be more detailed and colorful than images produced by earlier telescopes, but even older ones can still be intriguing and even beautiful. The scientific objective of interpreting astronomical images involves deducing information about the physical characteristics and conditions of the object, its place within the cosmic hierarchy, and its evolutionary history. Encouraging students to think beyond the mere appearance of celestial objects, to consider the origin of their colors and structure and the physical processes that produce the radiation we detect in an image, is a good way to engage them in the methods of astronomy and the tools astronomers use to deduce information about the cosmos.

### Encourage Interaction Early and Often

To facilitate in-class discussions and group activities, enrollment in Astro2201 is capped at thirty-five. We guessed wrong on preenrollment once and ended up with forty students. Group activities were only barely manageable, and, with only one TA, grading was a challenge. Once we tried formatting the class as a lecture course with weekly section meetings. All seventy-five students attended the lectures; the class was then split in half for the section meetings. However, this format did not engage students in the same way, and the extra hour per week that the group sections required was expensive in terms of instructor time and was unattractive to students. The faculty also found that the higher enrollment resulted in a class in which conducting a productive discussion was much more difficult. These challenges changed the nature of the class, making it far less enjoyable.

The lecture itself must be small enough that students feel comfortable (eventually) and are forced to talk frequently. The intimacy afforded by a smaller class size seems to be a requirement for engaging the non-science major in adopting a scientific role. Nonetheless, each class is different depending on the number of talkative, engaged, bright students who speak up from day one. Engaging students in discussions and introducing discussions and public thinking as a regular feature of class in the first few class meetings is imperative. At the beginning of the semester, we can reinforce the idea that lack of knowledge is not embarrassing in a classroom and that thoughtful ideas and questions are welcome even if they prove wrong. Fortunately, the history of astronomy is full of initial conclusions that proved entirely wrong. Our classroom is adorned with a color image of a planetary nebula, which, I point out in the first class, has nothing to do with planets. We discuss the origin of the term (through small telescopes, planetary nebulae often appear to the eye as green, fuzzy objects: green like the planet Neptune and fuzzy as in "nebulous"). We point out that an astronomer who bases a conclusion on available evidence later proved wrong by new evidence is not considered to have been "wrong." Questions are encouraged or else deliberately sought. In this way, the class develops early an interactive but unthreatening tempo that will continue to thrive throughout the semester.

*Crutches May Be Helpful*

Most modern textbooks are big and heavy and contain far more material than the average student can possibly absorb. So why bother to adopt a textbook at all for a nonsurvey course? The answer is because (some) students seem to appreciate having a first place to look; however, an early lesson must explain how to use the textbook without getting lost in or being limited by it. I have also developed a simple website (http://www.astro.cornell.edu/academics/ courses/astro2201) that follows the syllabus but takes the form of "frequently asked questions" and is not all-inclusive. Readings are assigned, but are limited and directed. Students in Astro2201 likely do not grasp all the facts contained in an introductory astronomy book, but they do know where to look should they need to know. By repetition of certain basic physical concepts under the different themes discussed in the class, we try to help students recognize that some things are inextricably linked: gravity is important on many scales and fundamental to understanding the solar system and the wider universe; our comprehension of stellar evolution leads to methods for determining the ages of galaxies; and so on.

Perhaps we will forgo the textbook crutch within the next few years. At least some, perhaps most, students today prefer to search for information digitally. Thus, we now feel obliged to discuss with students how to judge a website's scholarly content. Today's students are quickly overwhelmed with information; our job is to help them develop their quality-control skills. Pointing them to bogus websites early in the semester can help reinforce the need for critical appraisal, but this need must be reinforced throughout the semester. We also try to teach students when citation is appropriate, what plagiarism is, and what constitutes creative scholarship. We hope that these discussions have value far beyond the confines of Astro2201.

*Science Is Not Straightforward*

One of the most important lessons we try to teach is that posing the proper scientific question is as important as its answer. Astronomers are really detectives who are trying to reconstruct a cosmic event or circumstance based on limited information. What does the color of an object tell us about its physical conditions? What does an optical image of a galaxy convey about its mass? Some of the in-class group activities are designed to lead groups to the wrong answer or to get students to realize that they cannot deduce the answer from the information they have been given. Putting them in a situation of doubt reinforces the notion that science is not about answering the questions at the end of the chapter and that the path from question to answer is not always straightforward.

For example, in one of the first class meetings (about one week into the semester), we divide students into groups of three or four. Each group is given one of several images showing an astronomical object (see Figures 1a and 1b for two examples; they are best viewed in full color) but no other information. Each group is asked to write a description of and raise questions about the image assigned to it: What is conveyed by the white, pink, and blue-green colors in the upper image? What is the bright object at its center? Why is the latticework seen in the lower image dark? What causes part of the object to be blue while other areas seem orange? Are the colors real? These are good questions, given that at this point students have no information about the two objects other than the images. Nor have they studied how astronomers observe and what they can deduce from different types of observations. The exercise is the students' first lesson in asking what information an astronomical image conveys.

When each group has completed that part of the assignment, the entire class views the collection of images. A representative for each group summarizes the description and the questions related to his or her group's assigned image. Students are then asked to order the objects by their distance from Earth and to explain their reasoning for that order. Because this exercise takes place on only the second or third class meeting, most students have no idea what each object is or how to measure its distance, which puts them in a tough position. They have been given an impossible task, but one that perhaps makes them more sympathetic to the ancients' attempts to explain naked-eye phenomena and more curious about how astronomers actually do determine distances.

During the remainder of the semester, whenever one of the images used in this first assignment becomes relevant, it is reintroduced, and students are able to update their understanding of it. The interpretation of images plays a critical role in astronomy. By developing their own ability to look at an astronomical image and understand what information it conveys, students learn an important lesson about how astronomers explore the universe.

**Figure 1a: Hubble Space Telescope Image of the Planetary Nebula Known as M2-9 (the "Butterfly Nebula")**

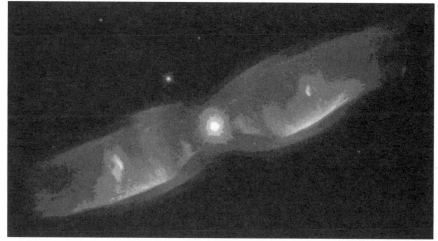

Source: B. Balick et al., WFPC2, HST, and NASA. 1999. http://antwrp.gsfc.nasa.gov/apod/ ap990321.html.

**Figure 1b: Composite Hubble Space Telescope Image of the Planetary Nebula Known as IC 4406**

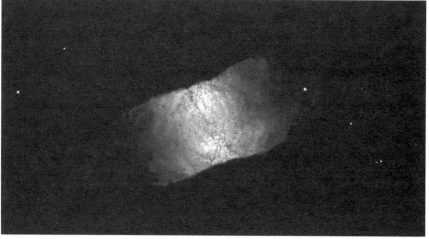

Source: C. R. O'Dell et al., Hubble Heritage Team, NASA. 2008. http://antwrp.gsfc.nasa.gov/ apod/ap080727.html.

*Smart People Can Be Wrong*

Early in the semester, we discuss the development of modern astronomical thinking. An important lesson comes from Aristotle, who rejected the heliocentric universe because parallax, the apparent annual motion of a nearby star amid the background of more distant stars as a result of Earth's motion around the sun, had not yet been measured. The flaw in his logic was the fact that he did not understand the scale of the universe and the vast distance to even the nearest stars. (Indeed, stellar parallax was not measured until 1838, by Friedrich Wilhelm Bessel.) Aristotle did not have adequate information. Thus, while his logic was well founded, his assumptions were wrong. Throughout the course of science, and astronomy in particular, lack of knowledge has led to misconceptions and misunderstanding. The lesson to be gained is the importance of expanding the frontiers of knowledge. Throughout the semester, we revisit other cases in which new knowledge led a revolution in our understanding: for example, the recent discovery that the universal expansion is accelerating. Because we cannot yet explain what either dark matter or dark energy is, we have to prepare students for our own lack of knowledge. That scientists do not know all the answers is a natural part of science.

*Our Home in the Universe*

The title of Astro2201 being what it is, the course at times focuses on how unique Earth and the solar system are, and how conditions elsewhere would differ. In successive assignments, students take on the role of a member of the script-writing team for a weekly science fiction series. They are told, "In the next episode, the intrepid explorers of intergalactic space whose adventures are followed in the series will travel to a planet inhabited by a civilization comparable at least in achievement to that found on Earth in the year 2009 and located on an Earth-like planet." In order to get students thinking about how circumstances and the eventual development of life and civilization on an Earth-like planet would differ from Earth, we give the parent star of the planet either a different luminosity, radius, mass, and surface temperature than our sun or place it in an orbit quite different from that of Earth. Furthermore, we tell students to:

> Assume that the planet's rotational period is 24 hours, that its rotation axis is inclined by 40 degrees with respect to its orbital plane, and that its orbit around the star is circular. At the same time, do *not* assume that the planet is located at 1 A.U. from the star. Rather, place the planet at the appropriate distance so that the star's apparent brightness is the same as that of the Sun as seen from Earth. Do not assume that the planet's inhabitants are human-like.

Students are then asked to develop a synopsis of the conditions on this hypothetical planet and how those conditions might favor the development of civilization, agriculture, and life-forms. The assignment forces them to think not only about these issues but about Kepler's laws, Wien's Law, and concepts such as luminosity, brightness, and surface brightness. In this instance, how the seasons on the planet differ from those on Earth opens up a host of questions about their agricultural, economic, and social implications for the planet. In different examples, the parent star might be a red supergiant, or even a pulsar, or might be found near the center of a globular cluster or near the galactic center. Encouraging students to think about how conditions would be different (multiple "star-rises," for example) engages (some of) them in discussing the likely diversity of planetary systems and how important the circumstances of Earth are to us. Their essays are also often presented in an entertaining and creative way, which makes them fun to read.

## Use Obviously Bad Science to Teach Science

Everyone who has stood in line at a grocery store has been confronted with the wacky science of yellow journalism. In one Astro2201 assignment, Senator Wisdom runs across the following article:

> *Russian Cosmonauts Travel to the Andromeda Galaxy and Discover Giant Black Hole that Threatens to Destroy Earth*
>
> Looking old and haggard but otherwise well on their return from a journey in a nuclear-powered spacecraft launched in 1965 at the heyday of the Soviet space program, a trio of cosmonauts reported today that they witnessed the extraordinary vision of a giant black hole, located near the center of the Andromeda galaxy, consuming at a prodigious rate all matter surrounding it. Stars, planets and gas, previously seen harmoniously orbiting at large distances from the center of Andromeda, are now disappearing into a dark spot which continues to shrink in size. The Solar System is thought to be threatened, according to a famous Swiss astrophysicist who reports to our correspondent that Earth will be gobbled up before the year 2017, unless "the appetite of the beast" is satiated by forcing its mass to exceed the so-called "Schwarzschild limit," beyond which the condensation ceases to be a black hole.

The assignment continues, laying out the context for the memo the senator's staffer must write:

> Having sworn in 1957 never to let the Russians get ahead again, the Senator is seriously disturbed by this report and wonders whether the situation calls for emergency legisla-

tion getting pushed through Congress. Ever the farsighted tactician, the Senator also foresees a possible opportunity for political gain, but is nonetheless concerned about maintaining a reputation of high scientific understanding.

Students are then asked to write a brief memo pointing out what is wrong with the scientific content of this clearly crazy article. Unfortunately, the context is not wholly unbelievable to students. They know what newspapers the fictitious article refers to. Sometimes a student will even bring a copy of one of these papers to class to reinforce the point.

*Science in the Arts and Humanities*

Sometimes we incorporate examples from literature, art, and history that might be interesting to a subset of our students. For example, a few students may be familiar with, or at least interested in, medieval churches and their use as astronomical solar observatories as described in J. L. Heilbron's *The Sun in the Church*.[1] Occasionally, a student will have visited the Basilica of San Petronio in Bologna and seen its famous meridian line. In the assignment, we describe a hypothetical meridian, giving its location and describing some of its geometry. We then ask students to write a memo to a professor of art history explaining how the meridian works and, for example, what the horizontal distance should be along the meridian line between the center of the solar image on the floor of the church at noon on the day of winter solstice and the center of the solar image at noon on the day of summer solstice. This assignment requires the student to demonstrate a mastery of the celestial sphere, the solstices, and the motion of the sun, but the context is one that the more intellectually curious students might find engaging.

In other assignments, we incorporate a passage from a book or poem, using it as a means to introduce the subjects up for discussion. For example, the poem "Fire and Ice" by Robert Frost discusses the fate of the universe. Dante, in *Il Paradiso*, seems to understand the constancy of surface brightness, and Beatrice proposes that differences in brightness of separate areas on the moon are related to its nature and composition. One assignment introduces a passage from Italo Calvino's *Cosmicomics* in which a narrator named Qfwfq observes the universe and notes: "One night I was, as usual, observing the sky with my telescope. I noticed that a sign was hanging from a galaxy a hundred million light years away. On it was written: I SAW YOU."[2] The Astro2201 assignment continues, "Somewhat startled, Qfwfq consults his diary and is 'seized by a ghastly presentiment: exactly two hundred million years before, not a day more, not a day less, something had happened to me that I had

1. J. L. Heilbron, *The Sun in the Church: Cathedrals as Solar Observatories* (Cambridge, Mass.: Harvard University Press, 1999).
2. From the short story "The Light Years," in Italo Calvino, *Cosmicomics* (*Le Cosmicomiche*) (New York: Harcourt, Brace & World, 1968), 127.

always tried to hide.'" The assignment asks students to explain the logic behind the date Qfwfq checks ("exactly two hundred million years ago"), as well as to explore several other cosmological questions.

*Using Images to Provide Focus*

After a semester of looking at images, thinking about what information they convey, and learning how to ask questions about them, students are ready, in their final assignment, to be given some images that lead to a discussion of fundamental cosmology. Because hundreds (probably thousands) of websites provide summaries of modern cosmology, we strive to create a context that requires students to take their own approach. Several assignments from earlier in the semester had placed the writer in the context of working for a publishing company, writing brief paragraphs about selected images for popular "coffee table" books, or writing about black holes for children. The final paper builds on those contexts:

> With the publication of the book "Images of Nature" behind you with great success and rave reviews, you head to the hills of the province of Parma, Italy for some inspiration as you sketch out ideas for a second one to be called "Hubble Reveals More than Meets the Eye." At the stone farmhouse where you are staying, you eat a sumptuous meal in the garden and fall asleep in the sunshine over a bottle of fine sparkling wine. Shortly thereafter, you are awakened by the clinking of glasses to discover that you have unexpected company. An elderly gentleman is leafing through the folder which includes an outline of your book proposal and three images, illustrated below [see Figure 2], which you were planning to include in it. Your guest identifies himself as Fritz Zwicky, the great astronomer, who, with the help of Albert Einstein, has figured out how to travel through time and has landed, on his first trip into the future, in your garden. You, of course, are shocked and excited to be in the presence of so great a man, albeit one who died in 1974, and explain to him that you are well familiar with his brilliance and fame, particularly as a result of your recent enrollment in Astro2201. In particular, you are extremely curious to find out how he has managed this feat of time-travel, and Zwicky, in return, is extremely curious to learn more about the images in your proposed book.

> You and he agree that he will tell you the secret of time travel after you fill him in on details of what the images are and how they reveal "More than Meets the Eye." He is also

**Figure 2: Images for Astro2201 Final Paper**

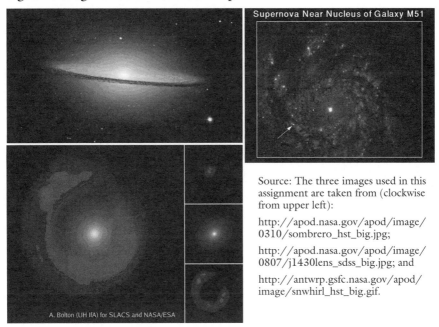

Supernova Near Nucleus of Galaxy M51

A. Bolton (UH IfA) for SLACS and NASA/ESA

Source: The three images used in this assignment are taken from (clockwise from upper left):

http://apod.nasa.gov/apod/image/0310/sombrero_hst_big.jpg;

http://apod.nasa.gov/apod/image/0807/j1430lens_sdss_big.jpg; and

http://antwrp.gsfc.nasa.gov/apod/image/snwhirl_hst_big.gif.

very curious about the "Hubble" in the book title; he knew Edwin well since he spent most of his career at Caltech and the Mount Wilson Observatory.

You may write this paper as an essay or a dialog, but remember that Zwicky is your audience. He is a brilliant and highly educated man and is fully familiar with what was understood about cosmology 40 years ago. However, his understanding of physics and astronomy depends on different terminology than is used today and, since this is his first journey forward in time, he is not familiar with anything that has happened since 1974. It's your job to explain to him what each of the three images conveys of relevance to the topic of "More than Meets the Eye," and in particular how our understanding of cosmology has changed since his lifetime. Be sure to connect your discussion to each image, leading Zwicky to understand what each image shows and how to interpret its features and colors (where relevant). Since Astro2201 space-time is getting short, give your explanation in less than 1200 words.

While it is important to relate the images to your discussion, do not merely describe them; let them update him on our (but not his!) understanding of modern cosmology and the contents and history of the universe. Because of the word limit, you will have to be judicious in what topics and level of detail you include; think carefully about what content you need to include before you begin writing. Be especially careful not to go off on irrelevant tangents (such as discussions of dust in the interstellar medium, stellar populations, the evolution of stars leading to supernovae, black holes, galaxy collisions, etc); stick to a discussion of what contributes to the matter and energy density of the universe of relevance to its past history and future fate. Be sure to explain not only what we know but how we know it.

For the purpose of this assignment, please attach a citation list of all sources you consult. Also, you need not dwell on the feasibility of time travel as your guest has already promised to explain that to you afterwards.

By establishing the audience as one of the most prominent astronomers of the last century, we allow students to assume some level of astronomical knowledge and to focus on how the astronomical evidence for dark matter and dark energy has revolutionized cosmological understanding. Students have already seen the images in the assignment during earlier in-class group assignments, but the interrelationship of the images has not been directly laid out for them; they must identify the linkage themselves. In fact, a great deal of irrelevant information (as will be recognized by those readers of this essay who are familiar with the images) might be conveyed. Nonetheless, both the specific nature of the assignment and the word limit are intended to keep the essay writer focused.

If students search the Web for Zwicky (which nearly all will do), they will discover that he was quite a character and a proponent of the need for dark matter. But the need to update him on cosmology means they will have to go beyond what they can learn about him. They must summarize for him how cosmological understanding has advanced. Because he has basic knowledge of many concepts (such as the expansion of the universe), they do not have to explain every detail, and the images should lead them to the desired content. The word limit especially constrains students to consider carefully what information is most critical to the essay.

## THE COST OF A WRITING COURSE

The greatest disadvantage to our course most likely is the cost of instruction and grading. We deliberately keep the class size small to encourage in-class discussion, and we have a TA for every thirty to forty students. The TA's responsibilities include reading, commenting on, and grading papers and holding weekly office hours (at least three hours regularly, as well as on the day or two before papers are due and by appointment). The faculty instructor generally reviews the papers and the TA's comments before they are returned to students. The feedback provided to students on their writing efforts is critical; thus, the TA must be committed to the effort required to provide quality feedback. While some graduate students prefer to be a TA in a class where they conduct recitation sections and grade tests, some appreciate the in-depth interaction with students that is expected in Cornell's writing program. These TAs value the chance to see students show real improvement in their ability to communicate scientifically. The requirements for being a TA in a writing course are high, and we choose the most qualified students, generally native English speakers who possess well-developed writing skills and are the most enthusiastic about the experience.

## TEACHING MAJORS THROUGH WRITING

Although the subject is beyond the scope of this essay, I have used a similar approach in teaching a seminar class offered to sophomore astronomy majors and concentrators. Scientists also must know how to write, to communicate their ideas and scientific results, and to develop their appreciation of context and audience.

In some instances, the assignments I have made for the science majors' class and Astro2201 have been similar. Reviewing the two groups' responses to similar assignments has shown me how differently the two groups use language. Even when the scientific concepts are the same, the non-scientist uses more vernacular—simpler, familiar words—whereas the scientist quickly adopts mathematical or technical jargon. The non-scientists are not wrong in their expression, but their language is different. By understanding how the two groups use language in distinct ways, I have been better able to adapt my teaching to each group, which, I believe, has helped me become a better lecturer.

One of the most interesting experiences in the class taught for majors has been a "symposium" that we organize toward the end of the semester. Typically, the symposium focuses on a particular theme, with each student assigned to write a paper and make an oral presentation reviewing an article from the professional literature. The written papers are revised and published electronically in a "symposium proceedings." (A selection of the proceedings can be found at http://www.astro.cornell.edu/academics/courses/astro233.) Orchestrating the symposium and publishing the proceedings creates a fair amount of work for my graduate assistants and me, but seeing the final, impressive product is immensely satisfying for us—not to mention for the students.

## FINAL THOUGHTS

The course format adopted for Astro2201 is unlikely to fit all situations. Because not every fact or important topic is discussed in detail, a student who planned to take a higher-level astronomy course after taking Astro2201 would probably find we had skipped over some concepts that a survey course would have covered. On the other hand, we can claim that our writing assignments require more processing and synthesis of information and that they take students well beyond the memorization of facts or the repetition of concepts that is often expected in a survey course. Writing can be a natural medium for learning about any topic, including science.[3]

3. Over the years, I have often taught Astronomy 2201 in collaboration with Riccardo Giovanelli, whose wit, vast knowledge of everything from Mayan writings to black-and-white movies, and complementary approach to teaching have helped shape the course as it is today. I also greatly appreciate the continuing encouragement and support of Keith Hjortshoj, director of the Knight Institute Writing in the Majors program at Cornell, especially for his nurturing the astronomy graduate teaching assistants. Finally, I send my thanks to the many undergraduate students who over the years have participated in—and seemingly enjoyed—Astronomy 201/2201 and to the graduate teaching assistants whose communication skills and commitment to education have often inspired me.

# CHAPTER 8

# Teaching Science for Understanding: Focusing on Who, What, and Why

Sally G. Hoskins

## THE CHALLENGE

As scientific decision-making is increasingly influenced by the non-scientist voting public, it is essential that all college students be well informed about science. Many are required to study the topic for at least one semester; however the student audience for general education science courses is often the same cohort that lost interest in science well before starting college. Such students may now get much of their science information from television, which alternates between frightening the audience with doomsday scenarios ("Hazards in your breakfast cereal! . . . News at 11") and making heroes out of geeky gurus who solve complex medical mysteries in sixty minutes of prime time. Some students seem unaware of the accomplishments or relevance of twentieth- and twenty-first-century biology research, while others are not science-neutral but actively anti-science. Given that their votes on science-related issues will do much to shape the progress of science and society in the twenty-first century, students who do not choose to major in the sciences nevertheless need to understand *who* does science, *what* scientists do, and *why* anyone would be drawn to a science career.

With these issues in mind, I have shifted my focus in teaching biology for non-science majors from a broad-based yet superficial coverage of many topics to a more focused approach aimed at imparting not just content but also insight into the "who, what, and why" of science. I use scientific literature—whether magazine articles for the general public, research reports in scientific journals, or articles from newspapers or news websites—as a means to reveal how scientists think. I have designed classroom approaches that introduce non-science majors to some of the intellectual activities common to working scientists, including analyzing data, designing experiments, devising models to explain results, and constructively criticizing each other's proposals. My goal is to demystify what scientists do, provide some insight into why someone would choose a science career, and at the same time increase respect for the processes and accomplishments of science research among students who are unlikely to engage directly in such research themselves.

## DEPTH VERSUS BREADTH—THE EVOLUTION OF A TEACHING STYLE

Initially, I taught using traditional textbook-based lectures, drawing from a "biology for the non-major" textbook that used creative graphics and science stories taken from the news as a springboard for explaining basic principles. Despite the topical book, I found myself spending much class time going over pathways and processes that I knew the students had encountered in high school biology, memorized, and quickly forgotten. Rather than conveying an experience of "thinking like a scientist," teaching in this way recapitulated the same approach that students had rejected previously. Many textbooks focus on scientific content in the near-absence of emphasis on scientific thinking, critical analysis, or creativity. They do not give students a real sense of how scientists design studies, interpret the data they gather, or use the findings to determine the next step in a long-term research project. Because the universal languages of study design and data analysis are at the heart of biology and are perhaps the aspects in which science differs most from nonscience fields, these topics deserve more focus, especially for the students least familiar with science.

Cognizant of the challenges of research science, the National Research Council has made specific recommendations on teaching science for understanding:

To develop confidence in an area of inquiry, students must
(a) have a deep foundation of factual knowledge
(b) understand facts and ideas in the context of a conceptual framework
(c) organize knowledge in ways that facilitate retrieval and application.
(National Research Council, 2003a)

Although these suggestions are aimed at "future research biologists," I suggest that the latter two are also important for *all* science-literate citizens. In recent semesters I have altered my teaching approach for general-education science students, now focusing mainly on how scientists frame questions and test hypotheses. Because of the rate at which biology is changing, at least some of today's "deep foundation of factual knowledge" may be tomorrow's historical footnote. In the thirty years since I took introductory biology, entirely new fields (such as proteomics or bioinformatics) have developed, novel organelles (for example, the proteasome) and processes (like RNA interference) have been discovered in the cytoplasm, and recognition of an unanticipated conservation of developmental mechanism across phyla (see, for example, Lall & Patel, 2001) has spurred the emergence of a major field, evolutionary developmental biology. During the same decades, some long-held "facts" (such as the "fact" that no neurons are produced postnatally in the vertebrate nervous system) have been disproven by new findings. Thus, focusing on scientific facts at the expense of process shortchanges students and deprives them of insights into scientific approaches to problems.

For students whose single semester of college biology will be their last formal science course, perhaps what is needed is the development of a toolkit of approaches for use in understanding science as it grows and changes in the coming decades. Students need to be able to integrate new findings into their existing conceptual frameworks and, when necessary, construct novel frameworks. Ultimately, society may be better served if general education students have a foundation of scientific analysis skills, transferable approaches to scientific questions, and an understanding of the types of cognitive activities in which scientists engage on a daily basis, rather than "a deep foundation of facts" derived from what scientists have already done. I have shifted my classroom approach to focus on how to read/analyze science, how scientists approach problems, how to think critically about science, and how to develop, explain, and defend one's own ideas about science.

## ACTIVE LEARNING THROUGH SCIENTIFIC READING—BEHIND THE SCENES OF THE "VIRTUAL LABORATORY"

My current teaching uses active-learning assignments adapted from the C.R.E.A.T.E. method—*consider, read, elucidate* hypotheses, *analyze* data, and *think* of the next *experiment* (Hoskins & Stevens, 2009; Hoskins, Stevens & Nehm, 2007)—an approach that uses close analysis of primary literature (journal articles) to help upper-level biology students get "inside" research projects while simultaneously learning "who does science, and why." The typical C.R.E.A.T.E. class studies a module of four papers published in series from one lab, thus following a research project as it unfolded in real time. The focus on data analysis in virtually every class session makes the C.R.E.A.T.E. classroom resemble a lab meeting, in which results are examined, interpretations are debated, and potential directions for follow-up experiments are considered. Students use novel pedagogical tools and carry out specific assignments at home in preparation for narrowly focused classroom analyses of a paper's findings (see Table 1; Hoskins, Stevens & Nehm, 2007). Late in the semester, students complete email interviews with paper authors for behind-the-scenes insight into these scientists' motivations and lifestyles.

As recommended in numerous science-education reform documents (AAAS, 1989, 1990; Brooks & Brooks, 1993; Glenn Commission, 2000; National Research Council, 1996, 2000, 2003a, 2003b, especially 20–21; Siebert & McIntosh, 2001), C.R.E.A.T.E. is an active-learning approach. It involves close analysis of a single line of scientific research, illustrating "the narrative

**Table 1: C.R.E.A.T.E. Steps and Activities Undertaken by Students in Class**

| The C.R.E.A.T.E. Approach as Applied to Newspaper Science | |
|---|---|
| **C.R.E.A.T.E. Step** | **Student Activity** |
| *Consider* | Construct concept maps, note topics for review, define variables and begin to sort out their relationships. |
| *Read* | Define unfamiliar words and draw cartoons or diagrams to depict studies done or create charts or graphs to represent the data described. |
| *Elucidate hypotheses* | Break down the reporter's summary into individual experiments or studies that each addressed a particular question or tested a specific hypothesis. |
| *Analyze and interpret the data* | Examine the cartoons, diagrams, hypotheses, and graphs to determine what the data mean. Decide whether you have represented data appropriately. |
| *Think of the next Experiment* | What experiment or study should be done next? Outline our follow-up study on a transparency for in-class discussion. |

Source: Adapted from Hoskins, S. G. 2010. "But if it's in the newspaper, doesn't that mean it's true?" Developing critical reading and analysis skills by analyzing newspaper science with C.R.E.A.T.E. *American Biology Teacher* 72(7):415–420.

nature of science" (Kitchen et al., 2003; Muench, 2000) and putting students into a "virtual laboratory," where they interpret the papers' findings and data as if they had made these discoveries themselves. This method aligns well with long-held views of educational psychologists regarding the mental activities that facilitate learning. In the mid-twentieth century, psychologist Benjamin Bloom determined that many exams tested primarily students' ability to "recall," "name," or "classify," yet many teachers would agree that real learning requires more complex cognitive activities, such as the ability to defend ideas, frame arguments, or design studies (Bloom et al., 1956). The Bloom scale is a six-point classification system for levels of mental involvement considered essential to learning (see Figure 1). Figure 1 can serve as a useful guideline for classroom activities that facilitate students' ability to "think like scientists." The C.R.E.A.T.E. method and the adapted outline in this paper aim to engage students in activities at the upper end of the scale—where research scientists spend a good deal of mental time—with the understanding that the ability to analyze, synthesize, and evaluate builds upon the foundation of facts and simpler concepts at the broad base of the pyramid.

Although wet-lab work is not a part of the C.R.E.A.T.E. model, intense focus on the data of each paper through independent evaluation of every figure and table casts students as scientists working in a virtual laboratory. By concluding their analysis of each paper with a design for "the experiment I would do next," students see that research does not follow a preset path; instead,

**Figure 1: The Bloom Scale**

6. **Evaluation:** appraise, argue, assess, attach, choose, compare, defend, estimate, judge, predict, rate, core, select, support, value, evaluate.

5. **Synthesis:** arrange, assemble, collect, compose, construct, create, design, develop, formulate, manage, organize, plan, prepare, propose, set up, write.

4. **Analysis:** analyze, appraise, calculate, categorize, compare, contrast, test, criticize, differentiate, discriminate, distinguish, examine, experiment, question.

The Bloom scale, formulated by a group of educational psychologists, is a classification system for mental activities thought to facilitate learning. Source: Modified from http://www.officeport.com/edu/blooms.htm; Bloom, B., M. Englehart, E. Furst, W. Hill, and D. Krathwohl. 1956. *A Taxonomy of Educational Objectives: Handbook 1: Cognitive Domain.* New York: McKay.

3. **Application:** apply, choose, demonstrate, dramatize, employ, illustrate, interpret, operate, practice, schedule, sketch, solve, use, write.

2. **Understanding:** classify, describe, discuss, explain, express, identify, indicate, locate, recognize, report, restate, review, select, translate.

1. **Knowledge:** arrange, define, duplicate, label, list, memorize, name, order, recognize, relate, recall, repeat, reproduce, state.

multiple directions are possible. Vetting one another's experiments in class builds students' critical abilities while broadening their understanding of how science is funded. The author interviews humanize the research process by providing unique insights into the people behind the papers. For biology majors, this approach improves critical thinking and content integration skills and stimulates enthusiasm for science; it also enhances understanding of "who does research, and why" (Hoskins, Stevens & Nehm, 2007). Challenging general education students in similar ways should prepare these individuals to articulate their thoughts on science, explain the nature of science to their friends and families, and encourage understanding of and better attitudes toward science in the general public.

## ACTIVE LEARNING FOR NON-SCIENCE MAJORS

I summarize below three active-learning approaches that I have developed for biology classes aimed at students who do not plan to major in science: (1) *Science, Interpreted*—a close reading of an article written for the general public with subsequent reference to the published article from which the lay account was derived; (2) *Rewrite the Textbook*—an illustration of how "established" science changes, through a classroom experience focused on a recent paradigm shift in developmental biology; and (3) *It's Published, But Should You Believe It?*—an activity centered on newspaper/Internet science, perhaps the most likely source of post-college science information for the general education student. Each activity is designed for groups of twenty to twenty-five students and can be taught in elective classes or in laboratory sections of larger lecture classes. Alternatively, with enough small-group work and instructor energy, these approaches could be scaled to the large lecture hall.

My impression from the general education students I have taught is that many found high school science to be overwhelmingly detailed. Such students may approach college science with low expectations, assuming that memorization will be their main approach to the material. To jolt students out of a passive approach to biology, I introduce novel pedagogical tools such as concept mapping, cartooning, and figure annotation to help them actively engage with material they read in preparation for class (see Tables 1 and 2). Homework assignments call on students to (1) create concept maps (Allen & Tanner, 2003; Novak, 1990, 1998; Novak & Gowin, 1984) of introductory paragraphs to extract key ideas, ground themselves in the topic under analysis, and define areas for review; (2) draw visual representations (cartoons) of experiments

**Table 2: Novel Classroom Activities Challenge Students to Think Deeply about Science**

| C.R.E.A.T.E. Classroom Tool | Using the Tool Encourages Students to: |
|---|---|
| Concept mapping | Relate old and new knowledge<br>Define what they do and do not know about a topic<br>Review to fill in gaps in knowledge |
| Cartooning | Visualize the experiments<br>Link specific methods to specific data<br>Triangulate information in methods, captions and narrative<br>Construct a context for the data |
| Annotating figures | Actively engage with data<br>Closely read figure legends and narratives<br>Determine the significance of each figure<br>Prepare for in-class analysis of the data's significance |
| Elucidating hypotheses | Define the question being asked or hypothesis being tested |
| Designing a follow-up experiment | Recognize research as a never-ending process<br>Exercise creativity in experimental design<br>Note that multiple options exist |
| Judging experiments in grant panels | Consider how research funding decisions are made<br>Use critical analysis to rank student-designed experiments<br>Improve verbal communication skills<br>Learn to work in small groups to reach consensus |
| Interviewing authors by email | See scientists as individuals much like themselves<br>Make personal connections to research/researchers<br>Get their own questions answered<br>Recognize that the term "scientist" encompasses diverse personalities |

C.R.E.A.T.E. tools help address scientific issues often omitted from textbooks. Source: Hoskins, S. G., and L. S. Stevens. 2009. Learning our L.I.M.I.T.S.: Less is more in teaching science. *Advances in Physiology Education* 33:17–20.

described, thus creating a context that will aid their understanding of the reported results (Mathewson, 1999; Schnotz, Picard & Hron, 1993); (3) annotate all figures by relabeling them based on information in the narrative, methods (if present), and figure captions to ensure that they fully understand what is being represented; and (4) triangulate among figures, captions, and the paper narrative to define the broad question being addressed by the data in each figure or table. In sum, I challenge students to reconstruct the study; they review the methods, outline the experimental design, and interpret the data as if they had made the findings themselves. This level of at-home student preparation allows class time to be spent in discussion alternating with large- and small-group work in which the faculty member acts as a facilitator of active discussion rather than the sole source of information. Students spend the majority of class time engaged in higher-level cognitive activities thought to facilitate understanding (See Figure 1 and Tables 1 and 2; Bloom et al., 1956). This teaching style aligns well with twenty-first-century "active classroom" teaching practices (Bransford, Brown & Cocking, 2000; Knight & Wood, 2005) as well as with recommendations that the way science is taught should reflect the way science is actually done (Alberts, 2005; Handlesman et al., 2004; Steitz, 2003).

*Science, Interpreted*

The general public gets much of its science not from primary sources but from digests of journal articles, that is, peer-reviewed work that has been summarized and condensed by a reporter and then edited for publication in a newspaper or general-interest periodical. To begin sharpening students' critical reading skills, I assign one such article, "Babies Recognize Faces Better than Adults, Study Says," published in *National Geographic News* (Mayell, 2005). This brief piece distills for the general reader a paper from *Proceedings of the National Academy of Sciences (PNAS)* titled "Plasticity of Face Processing in Infancy" (Pascalis et al., 2005).

After teaching concept mapping in an introductory class (Novak, 1990; Novak & Gowin, 1984), I provide students with the two-paragraph introduction to journalist Hillary Mayell's article and ask them to map by defining key terms, creating diagrammatic linkages among them, and appropriately labeling the links. Students work in groups of three or four to quickly orient themselves in the topic area and sketch maps to review central issues. In this case, the article recaps a study that examined whether six-month-old babies could distinguish facial features of primates and recall them well enough three months later so as to know when a face not previously seen was added to the mix. Considering the research objective, students review what they know about the visual system, brain memory centers, and human development and raise questions—for example, how, in principle, could we measure whether a preverbal baby "recognizes" or "remembers" something?

We then read the rest of Mayell's piece, and students return to groups to make visual representations, sketched on transparencies, of how the study was done. Mayell's article does not provide any diagrams, so this "cartooning" step clarifies experimental methodology while raising questions that set the stage for later critical analysis of the method and findings. During this phase, students begin to realize they need more information about methods than is provided in the Mayell version. In response to specific questions, I supply additional information from the PNAS paper. We compare the groups' cartoons and come to a consensus on how the experiment was performed: After an initial training session in which all participant babies viewed photos of monkey faces, the babies were split into experimental and control groups. "Experimental" babies were trained at home on similar photos over a period of months, control babies were not. All babies were subsequently tested at the lab, where they were videotaped while being presented photos of monkey faces, in pairs. Some pairs were composed of two faces that had been used previously, during initial (and for experimental babies, continued) training. Other pairings combined a photo that the babies had seen previously with a new monkey photo. Using a method developed in previous work, the experimenters measured "looking time," or how long the infants gazed at particular pairs of photos, from the videotapes. "Longer looking time" for the pairings that included new monkey faces was considered evidence of recognition of novelty (Pascalis et al., 2005). Ultimately, if the experimental group looked longer at novel pairings than did the control group, the finding suggested that the former set of infants was better able to detect novelty. This in turn suggested that the trained babies remembered the faces on which they had trained, while the control babies were less able to recall the faces they had seen during only the initial session.

Students raise numerous questions about the study design and interpretation: Are the cognitive processes involved in "detecting novelty" the same ones involved in "recognizing" a familiar face? Do adults, when "recognizing faces," stare longer at novel than familiar ones? What would "looking time" measurements be for a hypothetical additional control group, composed of babies that were never shown monkey faces? Is it okay that the control babies in the study experienced zero visual training during the months between the start of the experiment and the final testing, given that training for experimental babies involved periodically sitting on a parent's lap and being shown a series of photos? As they delve more deeply into methodology, students begin to raise additional questions about aspects of the experimental design that are not included in the lay summary: how many babies were studied, what was the proportion of girls versus boys, and was the training standardized for the experimental group? Such concerns link to broad issues that must be considered in any experimental study.

Some students raise questions about possible differences in rate of cognitive development of girls and boys. As the more critical students explain their concerns (if girl babies talk earlier on average, might they also "recognize" earlier?), they gain experience at framing a scientific argument and backing up their opinions with additional facts (such as, *do* girl babies, on average, talk sooner, or is this hearsay?). Students research supporting evidence during class, providing an opportunity to address the validity of different sources of information available online. We turn again to the *PNAS* paper (Pascalis et al., 2005) for clarification on the demographics of experimental subjects. To practice representing data quantitatively, students convert the actual numbers of girls and boys in the study to percentages and draw a histogram. These data typically heighten student concerns. If girls are faster at developing the skills under study, students point out, then the fact that the experimental group was majority female and the control group was majority male is potentially problematic.

We consider what a reasonable sample size would be. Would an *N* of four be large enough? Do you need twenty thousand babies? Why or why not? We discuss the challenges of working with human subjects and whether an investigator can or should still carry out a study if conditions are less than "perfect." This discussion can extend into a consideration of how statistical techniques can be used to aid in data analysis. The important issues raised in these discussions are not covered in depth in any of the "science for the non-scientist" textbooks I have investigated, but they are central to study design. As additional questions are raised, students who might have been intimidated if initially challenged to read a *PNAS* paper now look closely at the methods section for answers.

Many questions focus on the training/testing setup. All babies saw "training pictures" when they were six months old, after which the experimental group's parents repeated the training task at home over a period of months, while control babies were not trained further. During both training and testing, babies were held on their mothers' laps while viewing the pictures. Students point out that the control and experimental babies thus differed slightly in terms of experience with the mother, and suggest that less familiarity with the training/testing setup might have influenced the performance of controls during testing sessions. Other concerns include whether babies were all trained and/or tested at equivalent times of day (just before eating? just after a nap?) and whether any babies had "previous monkey experience" that could have been influential—that is, should the babies have been matched with regard to which ones had gone to the zoo, seen more primates in picture books, and so on? Even criticisms that seem far-fetched can stimulate useful discussion. Finally, some students raise the issue of a possible "Clever Hans" effect: if the mothers learned the discrimination task during the training sessions, which seems likely, might they have cued their babies during testing? The concerns raised link to general issues for experimental design: Has a potentially confounding variable been overlooked? Are additional controls needed? Can the method be improved? With a bare minimum of facts, students with little or no background in biology can critically analyze study design and begin to "think like scientists."

Students are then challenged to design their own experiments centered on questions of facial recognition and/or visual memory in infants. Students initially work in groups of four to frame a hypothesis and create a group-consensus experiment, then sketch it on a transparency for evaluation by the entire class. (See Figure 2 for an example.) For homework, students design additional studies independently.

Challenging students to diagram their experiment on a transparency, rather than just describe it verbally, helps them to commit to an idea and hone visualization skills. Providing a limited time frame in class for designing the experiments demystifies the process of experimental design and indicates that it is not an esoteric activity open only to "trained professionals." Showing transparencies on an overhead projector facilitates in-class discussion. Teamwork on the early designs provides a nonthreatening forum in which shy students can express their ideas without fear of "sounding dumb" in front of the entire class, while the homework assignment stimulates independent thinking. Together, the range of ideas that emerge from the group and individual experimental design assignments underscore the wide variety of new studies that could, in principle, be performed. This approach helps alter preconceptions of science as a predetermined series of steps that lead to a known outcome (Ryder, Leach & Driver, 1999).

**Figure 2: Modification of "Training" Phase of the Experiment, Designed in Class by a Group of Four Students Working on a Consensus Experimental Design**

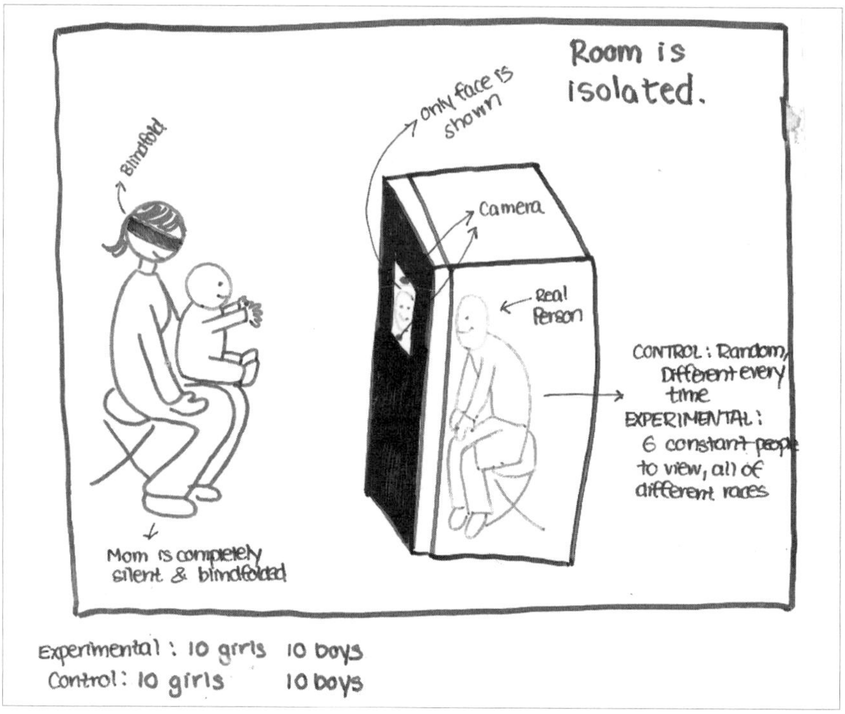

Here, the mother has been blindfolded to ensure that she does not learn the visual discrimination task.

Student-designed experiments are vetted in a "grant panel exercise" (for details, see Hoskins, Stevens & Nehm, 2007), which is preceded by an activity aimed at illuminating the nature of science. Prior to evaluating proposed experiments, students are grouped into "grant panels" and charged with enumerating criteria that scientific panels "should" use in deciding how to allocate taxpayer dollars for science research. Each group lists bullet points for discussion. For almost all students, this experience is the first time they have considered how science research is funded, who makes funding decisions, or how competitive the process might be.

Typically, some groups suggest reserving funds for "established" scientists, leading other students to defend newcomers who might bring novel perspectives. Multiple groups propose that "the work must be relevant to human beings." This statement provides a useful springboard for discussing model systems—that is, does the statement imply that for maximum "human relevance" all researchers should work on human beings? Barring that possibility, should everyone work on primates? Usually some students are cognizant of the fruit fly's relevance to genetics, but few have thought closely about why studies using the fruit fly (*Drosophila melanogaster*), nematode (*Caenorhabditis elegans*), or the zebrafish (*Danio rerio*) might in fact prove "relevant to human beings." In turn, considering why "model systems" are often funded provides an opportunity to review evolutionary concepts that students may have been exposed to previously but dismissed. The genetic code table, for example, was likely covered in high school biology but may not have been presented in an evolutionary context. Students begin to see that if human beings and simpler organisms all "spell" proteins using the same genetic alphabet, studying organisms with more accessible genetics could provide insights relevant to humans. Discussions of this sort are particularly interesting in classes with students who started the semester skeptical about the theory of evolution.

After the grant-panel criteria have been discussed, all student-designed experiments are viewed. The designs generally reflect a wide variety of approaches. (See Figures 3 through 5, for example.) Some students concentrate on making the control group more parallel to the experimental by, for example, instituting "control group sham training" in which control babies spend an equal amount of time in a training situation, but look at pictures of landscapes or nonprimate animals rather than monkey faces. Other students decide to use only girls or only boys in their study. Some alter the testing conditions so that the mother is blindfolded or the training and testing use pictures projected on the bedroom ceiling and viewed by the baby lying in a crib, thus eliminating possible parental cueing. Students see that experimental design requires careful thought and attention to controls but is not beyond the capacity of the average thinking person.

Student grant panels reconvene to discuss and debate the merits of the proposed experiments and select one for "funding." This exercise links science research with broader societal concerns: what experiment has the greatest po-

**Figure 3: Sample Student-Designed Improved Experiment, Done as Homework**

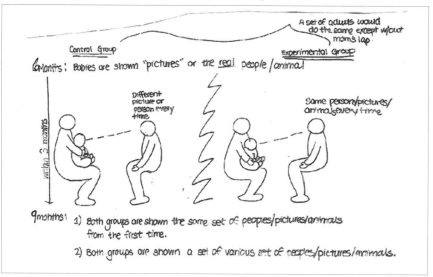

A set of adults would do the same except w/out moms lap.

Control Group  Experimental Group

6 Months: Babies are shown "pictures" or the real people/animal

Different picture or person every time.

Same person/pictures/animals every time

within 3 months

9 months:
1) Both groups are shown the same set of peoples/pictures/animals from the first time.

2) Both groups are shown a set of various set of peoples/pictures/animals.

**Figure 4: Sample Student-Designed Improved Experiment, Done as Homework**

Diagram to improve the babies experiment
Since the experiment "reads emotions" I would organize it in different conditions to understand how emotions are read culturally

• Test the universality of this assumption

• Test the infant's environment during the tests

    1) Seated on Mom's lap

    2) Seated on the scientist's lap

    3) Decoration of the room

        a. White room
        b. Wall paper—distracting room

• Test the experiment with other images—[see] how far recognition goes?

    1) Landscape recognition

• Narrow the control of "the control group"

    1) To how many visual stimuli?

    2) How different is their family status from that of the tested infants?

• Emphasize the equal nature of the kids studied

    1) Both control and tested infants should come from similar environments

International panel to discuss the findings: Asia/America/Europe/Australia

This student has considered multiple variables that could affect "recognition" and also has raised the issue of whether experimenters' interpretation of babies' emotional reactions to particular stimuli could be affected by differing cultural interpretations of emotion, based on country of origin. Whether all the variables raised could be addressed in a single study, or whether it would instead be wise to devise individual studies on particular sub-issues, can become a focus of further class discussion.

Figure 5: Sample Student-Designed Improved Experiment, Done as Homework

This student's improved experiment focuses on a question raised in class: whether "experimental" babies in the original study performed better during testing simply because they had been trained, not because they had been trained specifically on faces.

tential payoff, for instance, and can we necessarily tell in advance? The exercise also reveals some of the challenges professional scientists face on genuine grant panels: reaching consensus, the likelihood that the number of fundable experiments exceeds the funds available, and the fact that different panel members may have specific and strongly held agendas. The act of considering such issues helps humanize science and shows how personal and societal concerns intersect with basic research.

In a class with six grant panels five or more *different* experiments might be chosen as "the one to fund." This outcome underscores the fact that neither scientists nor general education students playing the roles of scientists are a uniform population in which everyone thinks the same way. Overall, the grant panel exercise builds students' skill at designing, defending, and debating experiments, while also humanizing scientists and providing insight into how science-funding decisions are made.

To conclude the babies/faces activity, I ask students for a one-sentence summary of the study. Many return to some version of the *National Geographic News* title, "Babies Recognize Faces Better than Adults, Study Says," only to realize for the first time that *no* evidence in the article supports this claim. There is no direct comparison of babies' and adults' ability to recognize faces, nor a conclusion that babies are "better" at this task. The article's main reference to adults is a casual claim regarding zookeepers and primates.

Students are startled to realize that even after closely reading the article, they accepted the title's claim that "babies recognize faces better than adults" in the absence of supporting data. One student attributed this reaction to "the font effect," writing: "We believe what we read. If the title is printed in a 72 point bold typeface crowning a two-column article it must be true, no questions about it; and more often than not, no further reading is necessary." The *PNAS* title, "Plasticity of Face Processing in Infancy," makes no claims about the recognition capabilities of babies versus that of adults. The class considers whether the magazine article was titled by the reporter or an editor and whether the desire for a catchy headline might have precluded accuracy. Students note that some key features of the *PNAS* study were absent from the version summarized for the general public even as a new "fact" about adults was added. This dialogue underscores for the non-scientist student both the need to read "digested" information about science with a critical eye, and the value of referring to primary sources when clarification is needed. Overall, active-learning tools and activities (see Table 2) applied to "simple" popularized science can help students learn to read critically, to visualize the experiments behind the summaries, to gain experimental design and evaluation skills, and to realize that in science writing for the general public something important may have been lost in translation.

*Rewrite the Textbook: Paradigm Shifts and the Nature of Science*

General education students often hold strong opinions about biological science that do not align with the reality of the field. Few seem cognizant of controversies in science, of sometimes nonlinear paths to discoveries, or of the evolutionary links among all forms of life. In addition to omitting consideration of the grant process, scientific textbooks tend to ignore the controversies, conflicting data, and failed hypotheses that are part of much scientific investigation and that, when analyzed, can stimulate understanding (Seethaler, 2005; Oulton & Grace, 2004; Mead & Scharmann, 1994). Non-scientist students who participate in the cognitive activities typical of science research labs—interpreting data, resolving controversies, creating models to represent and explain biological phenomena, and designing experiments—can gain appreciation for what scientists do, including the fact that sometimes scientists' findings refute previously well-established "truths." To help students discover that published textbook science may need periodic revision, and that even well-established scientific models may not hold up in the face of unexpected new data, I introduce a recent paradigm shift in developmental biology (for details, see Hoskins, 2008).

Paradigm shifts occur when well-established, widely accepted models are overturned by new data that cannot be made to fit (Kuhn, 1970). Most general education students have heard of the Copernican revolution, arguably the best-known example, but smaller-scale paradigm shifts can also be instructive. The history of developmental neurobiology includes a paradigm shift regarding early events in the formation of the vertebrate nervous system. With a brief introduction to the basics of embryogenesis—a minimal set of facts—general education students work through the logic of an experimental story as it progressed over seven decades, gaining insight into how scientific models develop and change.

Studying this issue also provides an opportunity for students to create explanatory models. While designing models based on experimental data is an important activity for scientists—the double helix probably the best-known example—modeling is not typically taught in the science classroom. As a consequence, students may be largely unaware of scientists' use of visual representations to stimulate thinking and suggest new experiments.

I begin with embryonic development, reminding students that all the cells of their bodies can be traced back to the fertilized egg. First, focusing on the amphibian embryo, we review gamete formation, fertilization, and the cleavage divisions that rapidly produce in a three-layered embryo whose outermost layer, ectoderm, will eventually form both skin and nervous system. Second, I present key grafting studies carried out by embryologist Hilde Mangold in the early twentieth century (Spemann & Mangold, 1924); the studies show that embryonic pattern formation involves cell-to-cell interactions and some form of signaling. Given Mangold's results, student working groups are challenged to derive a consensus interpretation of the cellular interactions that give rise to the embryonic nervous system and illustrate those interactions with a diagrammatic model. Third, I describe additional studies of the system whose results are consistent with Mangold's findings (Holtfreter, 1933; Nieuwkoop, 1969). Students integrate the new findings into their existing models and typically emerge with a diagrammatic explanation built on two postulates: 1) that embryonic cells are "preprogrammed" to form skin as "baseline fate"; and 2) that nervous system tissue forms when the preprogramming is overridden by an external chemical signal, such as that which hypothetically emanates from Mangold's graft. (See Hoskins, 2008 for examples of models devised by student groups.) If prompted for a molecular mechanism, students propose that the graft caused the "turning on" of neuronal genes in nearby cells, overriding these cells' inherent tendency to differentiate as skin. This interpretation parallels the historic idea that ectoderm could only produce neurons if induced by an external signal, a view that persisted in textbooks for more than a half-century.

At this point, I provide information from a later experiment (Hemmati-Brivanlou & Melton, 1992, 1994), with some surprising results—namely that ectodermal cells isolated from any "signal" differentiate as neurons, not skin. When asked to integrate the additional findings into their existing models, students soon discover that the modification is not possible, and frustration leads some to assume that at least one of the previous experiments is "wrong." (In fact, the experiments and their outcomes have all been described accurately; the interpretation of the initial findings was inaccurate.) Without confirming or denying this possibility, I challenge students to design a new model that makes sense of *all* the results. Working in groups, students discover that this requirement can be met only if they are willing to abandon *both* of their initial postulates: that the baseline, preprogrammed fate of embryonic ectoderm cells is epidermal (skin), and that ectoderm cells become neurons only if they receive an external "instructive" chemical signal. Rather, according to students' new models, the baseline, preprogrammed fate of embryonic ectoderm cells is *neuronal*. These cells become skin only if a *signal they are already receiving from their neighboring cells*, which is promoting their differentiation into skin, is turned *off* by the action of an external, overriding signal. To reach this conclusion, students must note that when cells communicate through chemical signals, the chemical communication might turn *off* an existing process, rather than simply activate a new process, as they had assumed initially. As pointed out by embryologists Ali Hemmati-Brivanlou and Douglas Melton (1997), this reinterpretation represented a fundamental paradigm shift in vertebrate embryology. As students grapple with conflicting data and the need to jettison their no-longer-useful original models, they experience many of the cognitive activities that characterize authentic science, where interpretations are not just matters of opinion but are data driven and where, if solid new data do not fit the prevailing model, the model, no matter how entrenched, must be reconsidered. The paradigm-shift story thus allows general education students to experience science both as a logical pursuit of explanations and an evolving set of interpretations.

An additional insight into the nature of science comes from Hemmati-Brivanlou and Melton's observation that their paradigm-shifting data were not the first to conflict with the established model for neural/epidermal fate choice (Hemmati-Brivanlou & Melton, 1997). Nearly a decade earlier, two groups of researchers (Grunz & Tacke, 1989; Godsave & Slack, 1989) working on slightly different questions had also observed isolated ectodermal cells unexpectedly differentiating as neurons, even though the cells had not received any theoretically required "external signal" (see also Figure 6). Neither previous team, however, used its novel results as a basis for challenging the prevailing "skin is the default fate" model. Students closely read the discussion sec-

**Figure 6: Using a Paradigm Shift to Illuminate the Self-Correcting Nature of Science**

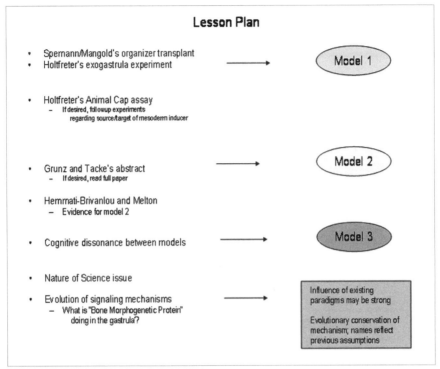

Depending on the instructor's goals, some steps could be assigned as homework rather than being carried out in class. Source: Adapted from Hoskins, S. G. 2008. Using a paradigm shift to teach neurobiology and the nature of science: A C.R.E.A.T.E.-based approach. *Journal of Undergraduate Neuroscience Education* 6(2):A40–A52.

tions of each paper to determine how the unexpected results were explained, and note that each group found a way to interpret what had happened *without* drawing the conclusion that the new findings overturned a well-established model, suggesting that the influence of existing paradigms can be strong.

The paradigm-shift story also offers an opportunity to address student understanding of evolution, in this case in the context of "recycling" biological signaling mechanisms. Bone morphogenetic protein (BMP) (Kudoh et al., 2004; Zimmerman, De Jesus-Escobar & Harland, 1996) is a key player in the "decision" of embryonic cells to become skin or neuron, and is involved in active signaling among ectodermal cells at a stage when earlier researchers assumed no outside signals were being exchanged. When students consider that "bone protein" plays a role during normal development of the embryonic nervous system, they are initially mystified, often incorrectly proposing that mature bone cells are present in the embryo, or that the ectodermal cells that release BMP are bone precursors. Discussion of the history of BMP sheds light on the issue: the molecule was discovered in a bone cell growth assay and named at that time based on its presumed bone specificity. Unexpectedly, in a different scenario, studied by different researchers, the same factor plays a role. As one student pointed out, if this morphogen had first been discovered in the embryo, it might have been named "SIP—Skin Induction Protein," in which case later investigators might have been surprised to discover a role for "skin inducer" SIP in developing bone. Students perceive that signaling molecules and mechanisms can be "recycled" in a variety of species and situations (Salie, Nierderofler & Arber, 2005) in unanticipated ways. Linking this discussion with the "model systems" issue outlined above illustrates why learning the molecular basis for pattern formation in such disparate organisms as fruit flies and frogs can be expected to provide results that will indeed be relevant to human beings.

Focusing on paradigm shifts helps dispel student preconceptions that science doesn't change. A second example in the nervous system is the unexpected and dogma-contradicting discovery that the vertebrate brain is not "complete" at birth but in fact adds new cells postnatally. The finding that new neurons arise in adult canary brains (Goldman & Nottebohm, 1983) was followed by proof, in the face of some initial skepticism from the scientific community, that the new cells were genuine neurons (Paton & Nottebohm, 1984). The new cells were subsequently characterized anatomically, though the initial determination that nearly all were local interneurons (Paton, O'Loughlin & Nottebohm, 1985) was later supplanted by the finding that many are actually projection neurons (Alvarez-Buylla, Theelen & Nottebohm, 1988).

These papers form a useful module that, once the relevant techniques are clarified, is not beyond the grasp of general education students. The story is particularly interesting in that it includes both a major paradigm shift—the surprising discovery of newly formed neurons in adult vertebrates—and a follow-up study that missed a class of newborn projection neurons due to limitations in the then-available tracing techniques. The fact that all four publications are from the same lab is notable, and the story can be complemented by an interesting essay (Kaplan, 2001) from a researcher who was ahead of his time in the 1970s. He hypothesized that new neurons were born in postnatal mammalian brains, leading him to a career-threatening conflict with existing dogma. Examples such as these reflect the reality that new data may compel reevaluation of old interpretations.

*It's Published, But Should You Believe It?*

Once general education students complete their college science requirement, many will not take another biology class. My overarching goal is to develop new habits of scientific thinking in such students before they return to a focus on history, architecture, philosophy, or literature. Ideally, attention to experimental design, the use of diagrams to aid understanding, the ability to construct models that organize data and suggest mechanisms, and the development of critical analysis skills will inform students' approach to whatever scientific in-

**Table 3: Newspaper Science as a Springboard for Discussion of Key Aspects of Science that are Underemphasized in Textbooks**

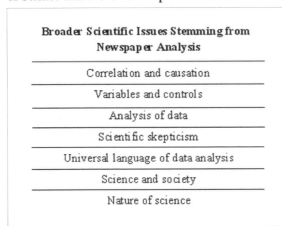

| Broader Scientific Issues Stemming from Newspaper Analysis |
| --- |
| Correlation and causation |
| Variables and controls |
| Analysis of data |
| Scientific skepticism |
| Universal language of data analysis |
| Science and society |
| Nature of science |

Source: Adapted from Hoskins, S. G. 2010. "But if it's in the newspaper, doesn't that mean it's true?" Developing critical reading and analysis skills by analyzing newspaper science with C.R.E.A.T.E. *American Biology Teacher* 72(7):415–420.

formation they encounter in the future. A great deal of this information will likely come from the newspaper, online sources, or television (Gudrais, 2007; Knight Foundation, 2007). I thus developed a literature analysis activity focused on "newspaper science" (see Table 3; Hoskins, 2010).

Science articles found in newspapers and on the Internet often refer to data but do not include illustrations, making it easy for casual readers to ignore the actual findings that (theoretically) underlie the headlines. Reporters may give the briefest of overviews or only superficially summarize information from studies published in scholarly journals. Information lost in the editing process may make the scientific basis of the newspaper claim difficult to understand or even inaccurate. Newspaper science is thus an excellent venue for training students to read critically and skeptically, enhancing the skills that support development of scientific literacy (Elliott, 2006; Strauss, 2005).

One example of newspaper science that I have used in teaching general education students is an article titled "Study Links Produce Prices to Obesity" (Rundle, 2005). (For details, see Hoskins, 2010.) The article reports on a study funded by the Rand Corporation and published in the journal *Public Health* (Sturm & Datar, 2005). Per the newspaper version, the study examined children's weight gain over a three-year span—kindergarten to third grade—in a range of cities in the United States. Prices of fruits and vegetables in those communities were also monitored. The article gives the casual reader the impression that when produce prices rise, parents buy less produce and, as a consequence, children eat less produce, consume fast food instead, and gain excess weight. No data are presented supporting any of these implied causal relationships, however. The article provides some information on produce prices and children's average weight gain over the three-year span in two towns, one in California and one in Alabama. Part of the challenge for students reading this article is to determine whether the study described indeed "links" obesity

**Figure 7: Group Concept Maps Done Quickly in Class as a First Step in Analyzing the "Produce Prices" Article**

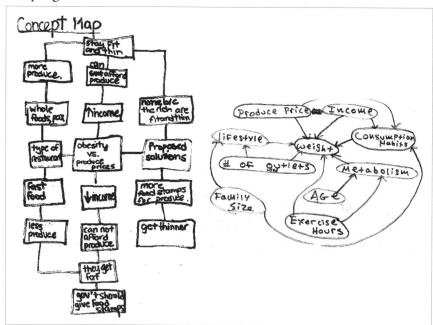

Links are unlabeled. Note that different groups emphasize different ideas, with one map (left) focusing on income as a central factor, and the other noting income as one factor along with metabolism, exercise, and consumption of produce. Comparing maps in class prepares students to discuss the scientific issues that underlie the article, while underscoring the fact that different individuals (and by extension, scientists) can view the "same" data differently.

to produce prices. As students work through this issue, they also consider the broader question of correlation and causation, a fundamental distinction often overlooked in science-based arguments made to the general public (see Table 3).

Students orient themselves in the subject area by concept-mapping the topics of food, weight, and produce prices and considering multiple variables that relate to each (see Figure 7). They next hone visualization skills by asking themselves how the study must have been done, that is, what sort(s) of data would compel the conclusion that there are "strong links" between produce prices and obesity, and how might such data be gathered? Students make their own decisions about what hypothetical data to represent and how to represent it. This is the first time many students have been challenged to represent data without being told how or being provided prelabeled axes. As charts from different groups are compared, common graphing errors can be addressed; for example, some students connect points that represent different cities with a (meaningless) continuous line because "it's a graph; you always connect the dots" (See Figure 8; Clement, 1989; Berg & Philips, 1994; Foertsch, 2000).

Students are initially unconcerned about the scope of the study, which encompassed around 6,900 children in 59 towns. Plotting graphs and thinking about how the study might have been done raises questions of sample size,

**Figure 8: Sample Data Produced by Students Working in a Small Group During Class**

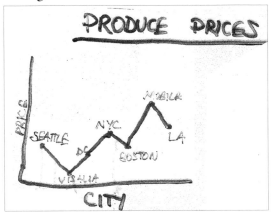

This figure reveals misconceptions about graphing that are addressed later with the entire class.

and in turn, the question of whether studying some 117 children per community is a sufficiently large sample, especially in large cities with diverse neighborhoods. This concern bridges to a discussion of a fundamental issue: to what extent does one's confidence in conclusions reached depend on the size of the population studied, whether that cohort is populated with children in a obesity study or by citizens polled on a political issue?

Students initially accept the article at face value, but after concept-mapping it, carefully examining the data, and thinking about how they would study the obesity question, they are startled to note in the final paragraph that "the Rand study didn't measure actual consumption of fruits and vegetables anywhere in the country" (Rundle, 2005). Given that the title claims "links" between produce prices and obesity, the lack of data on what was eaten by the children whose weight was monitored raises concerns and provides many ideas for student-designed improved studies.

Challenged to design a study or experiment that checks for actual causal relationships, some students propose overseeing the diets of selected subsets of children, carefully matching control and experimental populations. Some design broad surveys to examine whether parents in fact buy less produce when it is expensive. Others plan experiments in animal model systems, in which the food intake weight of one cohort of laboratory mice eating fruits and vegetables and another eating the rodent equivalent of a fast-food diet can be closely monitored. Student grant panels evaluate proposed studies and discuss how their findings could potentially be applied to improve human health. In this context, a sidebar discussion of the U.S. Department of Agriculture's changing food pyramid (that is, comparing the 1994 and 2005 versions) provides additional insight into the nature of science. In this case the focus is on the issue of whether nutritional recommendations from the U.S. government are made or revised based exclusively on nutritional research, or whether food lobbies also play a role.

Applying new analytical tools (Table 1) to newspaper science allows students to experience, after reading fewer than 750 words, critical analysis, data representation, interpretation of charted findings, design and vetting of studies, and consideration of how science research is funded. Ideally, students gain fluency in the language of scientific analysis and master skills that they can apply to any scientific reading, however casual, that they do in the future.

## PERSPECTIVE AND PROSPECTS FOR CHANGE

Taken together, the active-learning approaches I have adapted for the general education classroom complement approaches typical of textbooks by providing opportunities for students to think independently as they design experiments or criticize methods (see Table 4). Students working with other student-scientists to reach consensus in group experimental design challenges or grant-panel debates may begin to view science as a social activity rather than one open only to antisocial geek-geniuses of popular culture's stereotypes.

To get a sense of whether student attitudes about science shift over the course of the semester in classes using such approaches, I probed opinions in an anonymous pre/post survey. Students responded to a series of statements about science, biology, and science/society issues by indicating the degree to which they agreed or disagreed with each proposition (for example, "Experiments in model organisms like the fruit fly have led to important advances in understanding human biology"). In two general education cohorts (2006, 2007), I administered the survey during the first and final classes of a fourteen-week semester, in a biology course focused on genetics, development, and evolution. Surveys were coded with numbers known only to the students themselves, to allow statistical comparisons between individuals as well as groups. In each cohort, students underwent significant shifts on measures of self-rated understanding of content (Figure 9a), understanding of applicability of research on model organisms (Figure 9b), self-rated ability to visualize experimental scenarios (Figure 9c), and self-assessed critical reading skills (Figure 9d). While these shifts must be interpreted with caution because of the small sample sizes, they suggest that active-learning approaches can help students gain deeper insight into science.

Faculty tend to teach as they were taught, and most college science teachers are trained by lecturers. Unlike K–12 teachers, college faculty are largely untrained in theories of teaching and learning. This situation, coupled with the multiple demands on faculty time, can make it difficult for professors to shift their teaching style away from the lecture format (see Hoskins & Stevens, 2009). The active-learning classroom activities with which I have experimented are designed to facilitate change by decreasing preparation time and capitalizing on faculty members' deep understanding of scientific process. Working

**Table 4: Complementing Textbook Teaching with Literature-Based Approaches Provides Insight into Scientific Thinking and Science Process**

| ISSUE | Textbooks Aimed at General Education Students | Science Articles Scaffolded to Original Papers | Focus on Paradigm Shifts | Close Analysis of Newspaper Science |
|---|---|---|---|---|
| Focus mainly on content | X | | | |
| Focus mainly on scientific process | | X | X | X |
| Use creative graphics to clarify content | X | | | |
| Create your own graphics to clarify content | | X | X | X |
| Read with a critical eye | | X | X | X |
| Learn that "established" science can change | | | X | X |
| Move from verbal description to data representation | | X | X | X |
| Learn to evaluate scientific proposals in grant panels | | X | | X |
| Find more than one way to answer a scientific question | | X | X | X |
| Learn to design a good experiment | | X | | X |
| View science as creative | | X | X | X |
| Learn to intelligently criticize research findings or proposed experiments | | X | X | X |
| Focus on the universal logic of data analysis | | X | X | X |

C.R.E.A.T.E.-based activities complement the content coverage typical of textbooks in order to actively involve students in key aspects of scientific thinking.

Figures 9a–9d: Contributions of C.R.E.A.T.E. Methods to Student Gains in Insight into the Nature of Science

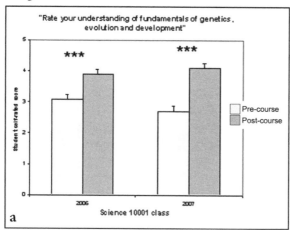

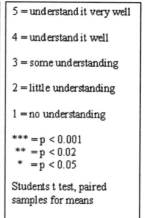

a

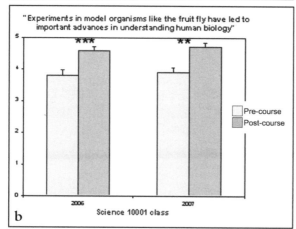

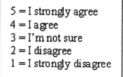

b

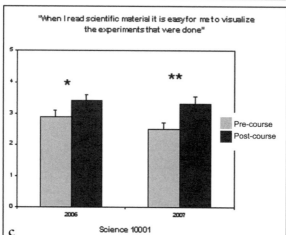

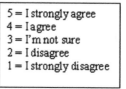

c

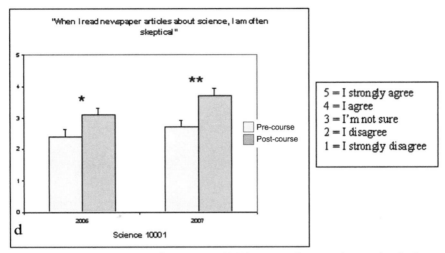

Students in "Man and Nature; Life" (Science 10001), a course for non-science majors in the City College of New York Honors College, took an anonymous survey pre- and post-course, responding on a five-point scale to statements about science or to the request to rate their understanding of science (Figure 9a). The surveys were coded using numbers known only to participants (see Hoskins, Stevens & Nehm, 2007). Average score pre and post; error bar = standard error. N = 16 (2006); N = 15 (2007).

scientists constantly evaluate data, design studies, and vet proposals. Faculty who bring these authentic (and high-Bloom scale; see Figure 1) activities into the classroom can thus play to their strengths, while also benefiting general education students by revealing *who* does science, *what* scientists do, and *why* they do it. Rather than delivering a detailed lecture, a teacher using approaches of the sort outlined above will coach students in developing scientific reasoning skills in a class session that resembles a lab meeting. Ideally, providing students a new toolkit of approaches for understanding biology and helping them use the tools to analyze and intelligently criticize data, to design models, and to outline novel experiments will help develop a cadre of science-aware citizens who appreciate science as a way of knowing, understand what drives scientists, and respect the goals of research science.[1]

1. I thank Leslie Stevens for ongoing discussion and advice on implementing C.R.E.A.T.E. methods for general education students, and Cheryl Harding for compiling the "postnatal neurogenesis" module. I am gratefully indebted to John Hildebrand and Jerrold Meinwald for focusing attention on the critical issue of general education science and inviting me to participate in their project. I also greatly appreciate their editing of an earlier draft of this chapter. I also thank students of Science 10001 and the National Science Foundation for support of the C.R.E.A.T.E. project. (This material is based on work supported by the National Science Foundation under Grant No. 0618536. Any opinions, findings, and conclusions or recommendations expressed in this material are those of the author(s) and do not necessarily reflect the views of the National Science Foundation.)

REFERENCES

Alberts, B. 2005. A wakeup call for science faculty. *Cell* 123:739–741.

Allen, D., and K. Tanner. 2003. Approaches to cell biology teaching: Mapping the journey—Concept maps as signposts of developing knowledge structures. *Cell Biology Education* 2(3):133–136.

Alvarez-Buylla, A., M. Theelen, and F. Nottebohm. 1988. Birth of projection neurons in the higher vocal center of the canary forebrain before, during, and after song learning. *Proceedings of the National Academy of Sciences of the United States of America* 85:8722–8726.

American Association for the Advancement of Science (AAAS). 1989. *Science for All Americans: A Project 2061 Report on Literacy Goals in Science, Mathematics, and Technology.* Washington, D.C.: AAAS.

———. 1990. *Science for All Americans.* New York: Oxford University Press.

Berg, C. A., and D. G. Philips. 1994. An investigation of the relationship between logical thinking structures and the ability to construct and interpret line graphs. *Journal of Research in Science Teaching* 31:323–344.

Bloom, B., M. Englehart, E. Furst, W. Hill, and D. Krathwohl. 1956. *A Taxonomy of Educational Objectives: Handbook 1: Cognitive Domain.* New York: McKay.

Bransford, J., A. Brown, and R. R. Cocking. 2000. *How People Learn: Brain, Mind, Experience, and School.* Expanded Ed. Washington, D.C.: National Academies Press.

Brooks, J. G., and M. G. Brooks. 1993. *The Case for Constructivist Classrooms.* Alexandria, Va.: Association for Supervision and Curriculum Development.

Clement, J. 1989. The concept of variation and misconceptions in Cartesian graphing. *Focus on Learning Problems in Mathematics* 11:77–87.

Elliott, P. 2006. Reviewing newspaper articles as a technique for enhancing the scientific literacy of student-teachers. *International Journal of Science Education* 28(11):1245–1265.

Foertsch, J. 2000. Models for undergraduate instruction: The potential of modeling and visualization technology in science and math education. In *Targeting Curricular Change: Reform in Undergraduate Education in Science, Math, Engineering, and Technology*, 37–40. Washington, D.C.: American Association for Higher Education.

Glenn Commission. 2000. *Before It's Too Late: A Report to the Nation from The National Commission on Mathematics and Science Teaching for the 21st Century.* Washington, D.C.: U.S. Department of Education.

Godsave, S. F., and J. M. Slack. 1989. Clonal analysis of mesoderm induction in *Xenopus laevis. Developmental Biology* 134:486–490.

Goldman, S. A., and F. Nottebohm. 1983. Neuronal production, migration, and differentiation in a vocal control nucleus of the adult female canary brain. *Proceedings of the National Academy of Sciences of the United States of America* 80(8):2390–2394.

Grunz, H., and H. Tacke. 1989. Neural differentiation of *Xenopus laevis* ectoderm takes place after disaggregation and delayed reaggregation without inducer. *Cell Differentiation and Development* 28:211–218.

Gudrais, E. 2007. Teen tune-out nixing the news. *Harvard Magazine* 110(2). http://harvardmagazine.com/2007/11/nixing-the-news.html.

Handlesman, J., D. Ebert-May, R. Beichner, P. Bruns, A. Chang, R. DeHaan, J. Gentile, S. Laufer, S. Tighlman, and W. Wood. 2004. Scientific teaching. *Science* 304:521–522.

Hemmati-Brivanlou, A., and D. Melton. 1992. A truncated activin receptor inhibits mesoderm induction and formation of axial structures in Xenopus embryos. *Nature* 359:609–614.

———. 1994. Inhibition of activin receptor signaling promotes neuralization in Xenopus. *Cell* 77:273–281.

———. 1997. Vertebrate embryonic cells will become nerve cells unless told otherwise. *Cell* 88:13–17.

Holtfreter, J. 1933. Die totale Exogastrulation, eine Selbstablösung des Ektoderms vom Endomesoderm. *Wilhelm Roux' Archiv für Entwicklungsmechanik der Organismen* 129:669–793.

Hoskins, S. G. 2008. Using a paradigm shift to teach neurobiology and the nature of science: A C.R.E.A.T.E.-based approach. *Journal of Undergraduate Neuroscience Education* 6(2):A40–A52.

———. 2010. "But if it's in the newspaper, doesn't that mean it's true?" Developing critical reading and analysis skills by analyzing newspaper science with C.R.E.A.T.E. *American Biology Teacher* 72(7):415–420.

———, and L. S. Stevens. 2009. Learning our L.I.M.I.T.S.: Less is more in teaching science. *Advances in Physiology Education* 33:17–20.

———, L. S. Stevens, and R. H. Nehm. 2007. Selective use of primary literature transforms the classroom into a virtual laboratory. *Genetics* 176:1381–1389.

Kaplan, M. S. 2001. Environmental complexity stimulates visual cortex neurogenesis: Death of a dogma and a research career. *Trends in Neuroscience* 24(10):617–620.

Kitchen, E., J. D. Bell, S. Reeve, R. Sudweeks, and W. Bradshaw. 2003. Teaching cell biology in the large-enrollment classroom: Methods to promote analytic thinking and assessment of their effectiveness. *Cell Biology Education* 2(3):180–194.

Knight, J. K., and W. B. Wood. 2005. Teaching more by lecturing less. *Cell Biology Education* 4(4):298–310.

Knight Foundation. 2007. Survey finds young Americans' news use is half that of older adults: Teens' daily news use is even lower than that of young adults. Press release, http://www.knightfoundation.org/news/press_room/knight_press_releases/detail.dot?id=13032.

Kudoh, T., M. L. Concha, C. Hourat, I. B. Dawid, and S. W. Wilson. 2004. Combinatorial Fgf and Bmp signaling patterns the gastrula ectoderm into prospective neural and epidermal domains. *Development* 131:3581–3592.

Kuhn, T. S. 1970. *The structure of scientific revolutions.* 2nd Ed. Chicago: University of Chicago Press.

Lall, S., and N. H. Patel. 2001. Conservation and divergence in molecular mechanisms of axis formation. *Annual Review of Genetics* 35:407–437.

Mathewson, J. H. 1999. Visual-spatial thinking: An aspect of science overlooked by educators. *Science Education* 83:33–35.

Mayell, H. 2005. Babies recognize faces better than adults, study says. *National Geographic News,* May 22. http://news.nationalgeographic.com/news/2005/03/0321_050321_babies.html.

Mead, J., and L. Scharmann. 1994. Enhancing critical thinking through structured academic controversy. *American Biology Teacher* 56:416–419.

Muench, S. 2000. Choosing primary literature in biology to achieve specific educational goals. *Journal of College Science Teaching* 29:255–260.

National Research Council. 1996. *National Science Education Standards.* Washington, D.C.: National Academies Press.

———. 2000. *Inquiry and the National Science Education Standards: A Guide for Teaching and Learning.* Washington, D.C.: National Academies Press.

———. 2003a. *Bio 2010: Transforming Undergraduate Education for Future Research Biologists.* Washington, D.C.: National Academies Press.

———. 2003b. *Evaluating and Improving Undergraduate Teaching in Science, Technology, Engineering and Mathematics.* Washington, D.C.: National Academies Press.

Nieuwkoop, P. D. 1969. The formation of mesoderm in urodelan amphibians. Paper I. Induction by the endoderm. *Roux's Archives of Developmental Biology* 162:341–373.

Novak, J. D. 1990. Concept mapping: A useful tool for science education. *Journal of Research in Science Teaching* 27:937–949.

———. 1998. *Learning, Creating and Using Knowledge: Concept Maps^TM as Facilitative Tools in Schools and Corporations.* Mahwah, N.J.: Lawrence Erlbaum Association.

————, and G. B. Gowin. 1984. Concept mapping for meaningful learning. In *Learning How to Learn*, 15–54. New York: Cambridge University Press.

Oulton, C., and M. M. Grace. 2004. Reconceptualizing the teaching of controversial issues. *International Journal of Science Education* 26:411–423.

Pascalis, O., L. Scott, D. Kelly, R. Shannon, E. Nicholson, W. Coleman, and C. Nelson. 2005. Plasticity of face processing in infancy. *Proceedings of the National Academy of Sciences of the United States of America* 102:5297–5300.

Paton, J. A., and F. N. Nottebohm. 1984. Neurons generated in the adult brain are recruited into functional circuits. *Science* 225:1046–1048.

————, B. E. O'Loughlin, and F. Nottebohm. 1985. Cells born in adult canary forebrain are local interneurons. *Journal of Neuroscience* 5(11):3088–3093.

Rundle, R. 2005. Study links produce prices to obesity. *The Wall Street Journal*, October 6.

Ryder, J., J. Leach, and R. Driver. 1999. Undergraduate students' images of science. *Journal of Research in Science Teaching* 36(2):201–209.

Salie, R., V. Nierderofler, and S. Arber. 2005. Patterning molecules: Multitasking in the nervous system. *Neuron* 45:189–192.

Schnotz, W., E. Picard, and A. Hron. 1993. How do successful and unsuccessful learners use texts and graphics? *Learning and Instruction* 3:181–199.

Seethaler, S. 2005. Helping students make links through science controversy. *American Biology Teacher* 67:265–274.

Siebert, E. D., and W. J. McIntosh. 2001. *College Pathways to the Science Education Standards*. Arlington, Va.: National Science Teachers Association.

Spemann, H., and H. Mangold. 1924. Über induktion von Embryonalagen durch Implantation Artfremder Organisatoren. *Wilhelm Roux' Archiv für Entwicklungsmechanik der Organismen* 100:599–638.

Steitz, J. 2003. Commentary: *Bio 2010*—New challenges for science educators. *Cell Biology Education* 2(2):87–91.

Strauss, B. 2005. Pub Med, *The New York Times*, and *The Chicago Tribune* as tools for teaching genetics. *Genetics* 171:1449–1454.

Sturm, R., and A. Datar. 2005. Body mass index in elementary school children, metropolitan area food prices and food outlet density. *Public Health* 119(12): 1059–1068.

Zimmerman, L., J. De Jesus-Escobar, and R. Harland. 1996. The Spemann organizer signal noggin binds and inactivates bone morphogenetic protein 4. *Cell* 86:599–606.

# CHAPTER 9

# Molecules of Life: A General Education Approach to the Science of Living Systems

Brian N. Tse, Jon Clardy, and David R. Liu

The life sciences are devoted to the origins, interrelations, functions, and manipulation of living systems. Over the past several decades, life sciences research has made tremendous gains in scope and depth. The widespread application of this knowledge has led to dramatic changes in the way ordinary people live. We eat foods derived from genetically modified organisms, rely on biotechnology for life-saving diagnostics and medicines, and look to biofuels to sustainably power our automobiles. More advanced applications such as personalized medicine and stem cell therapies were once thought to be futuristic, long-term goals, but have recently begun to be realized.

The expanding role of science in society raises many ethical questions. Topics such as stem cell research, the theory of adaptive evolution, human reproductive cloning, genetic manipulation, and the patenting of living systems are hotly debated in public circles. Advancing technology has unprecedented potential to change our lifestyles, with intensifying social controversy. How we will respond to these transformations in many cases remains unclear.

The profound impact of recent scientific advances on society warrants a reevaluation of our educational programs. As part of a liberal education, students should be prepared for meaningful civic participation and taught to think critically about the broader consequences of their lifestyle choices (*Report of the Task Force on General Education*, 2007). The curriculum should expand students' perspectives on the modern world and encourage them to reexamine their place within it. The curriculum should also prepare students to respond constructively to the societal changes they are likely to experience in their lifetime. The dynamic nature of these goals requires the regular revision of courses, to reflect modern perspectives and practices.

The ubiquity of science in modern society necessitates stronger basic science requirements for liberal arts curricula. Individuals (acting as voters, consumers, or parents) are faced daily with choices that require a functional level of scientific knowledge. If we wish to empower students to make sound choices (lifestyle and civic), we need to ensure that they have the intellectual wherewithal to think critically about scientific matters. A relevant knowledge set should include a basic scientific vocabulary, a clear understanding of fundamental scientific concepts, and an adequate grasp of the scientific process itself.

Establishing science courses for a broad audience requires careful consideration on the part of educators. The goals of general education are unlike those of departmental programs geared toward science and engineering majors; they do not seek to provide a specific knowledge set with vocational relevance and typically do not serve as prerequisites for more advanced technical courses. Rather, general education courses seek to impart a broad understanding of key concepts, facts, and theories while providing a clearer picture of how these ideas relate to real-world problems of wide concern.

Because most science-affiliated faculty were themselves educated through specialized programs of study, science departments are inclined—perhaps through some combination of familiarity, habit, and convenience—to use existing specialist classes as content sources for general education. The distinctly different goals of general education, however, warrant de novo design of these courses. This approach ensures a fresh perspective on scientific theories, a coherent course syllabus, a uniform difficulty level, and greater relevance to current events. A fresh start also provides the opportunity to apply new pedagogical approaches.

Designing a new general education science course involves meeting several distinct challenges. First, the course must be taught at a level that assumes minimal prior scientific knowledge: the material must be accessible to students of all backgrounds. Though educators might be tempted to include intricate detail, such intensity can overwhelm students and prevent them from assimilating the most salient points. If a class establishes itself as unduly work intensive, it will also discourage many students (particularly those who might stand to benefit most) from taking future iterations of the course.

Second, the syllabus must be designed for an audience that has only a casual interest in scientific matters. Most of the targeted students are non-science majors pursuing careers unrelated to scientific research. In light of this fact, the course should emphasize connections to everyday life by relating the lessons to current events, common experiences, or subjects they are likely to encounter post-college. Relevant topics include (but are not limited to) human behavior, disease, medicine, nutrition, and conflicts relating to education, law, and public policy. Adequate time should be spent on the social consequences and ethical dimensions of developing technologies. Emphasis should also be placed on providing an overall positive science experience, so as to encourage a lifelong interest in scientific issues and technological developments. Because these courses do not serve as prerequisites for more advanced classes, few restrictions need be placed on what can (and cannot) be included in the syllabi.

From a pedagogical standpoint, courses directed at a broader audience will benefit from the abundant use of activity-based learning (*Report of the Task Force on General Education*, 2007). Hands-on activities (such as debating controversial social issues, manipulating unfamiliar objects, or experiencing phenomena through direct sensory exposure) connect abstract concepts to personal experience, thereby demonstrating scientific principles powerfully and intuitively. Interactivity also increases student engagement, facilitates deeper examination of philosophical and ethical implications, and fosters a more productive relationship between the teaching staff and students. Activities that directly complement and build on concepts presented in the lectures help link ideas to life outside the classroom.

The hands-on exercises should require minimal technical proficiency, and must present no significant risk to students (no dangerous chemicals, for instance). Because many institutions have limited classroom infrastructure devoted to science experiments, the activities should also require minimal advanced equipment or laboratory space. If the class format does not provide for extra laboratory time, the activities should be executable within the span of a single section meeting. Additionally, the corresponding activity handouts should focus on ease of use and refrain from dense, abstract language. Tedious write-ups (pre- and post-lab) should be avoided when possible.

Molecules of Life is a novel science-oriented general education course taught at Harvard University. The course uses the dynamic interplay of small molecules and macromolecules as a theme for explaining the scientific principles underlying life. The lectures connect these principles to concrete problems of wide concern, often framing the scientific concepts within a historical, social, economic, or ethical context.

Molecules of Life was designed to meet the requirements of Harvard's new general education curriculum; its intended audience is a diverse body of non-science majors from all backgrounds and collegiate years. In this sense, the course is not intended to prepare students for more advanced science courses or to provide them with a specific vocational knowledge set. Rather, its central goal is to teach undergraduates the key concepts, facts, and theories associated with living systems. Through its connections to other disciplines, the course also seeks (in some instances by means of disorientation) to provide students with new perspectives on familiar issues and to prepare them to react constructively to the societal change wrought by science and technology. Lastly, the course seeks to provide students with a positive science-oriented experience. In doing so, it hopes to kindle a lifelong interest in scientific matters.

The syllabus is divided into four major parts, to be taught in sequence: Molecules and the Flow of Information, Molecular Messengers in Humans, Molecular Medicines and Human Diseases, and Molecules in Our Future. These units cover a wide variety of topics, such as heredity, evolution, human disease, sexual development, and aging. The lectures make abundant use of case studies and draw upon recognizable stories or trends. Current events (as highlighted by articles from the popular media) are frequently integrated into the discussions.

The course incorporates a unique section format: section time is divided between a weekly review and an interactive activity. Each activity is specifically designed to illustrate and punctuate the material covered in that week's lectures. The activity syllabus includes (among other tasks) the hands-on extraction of DNA from strawberries, the phenotyping and genotyping of students' bitter taster genes (*TAS2R38*), a debate on the legalization of marijuana, a game theory competition between students, and a demonstration of pheromones using live silkworm moths. These activities underscore the fundamental concepts in a memorable fashion, better engage students in the course material, and encourage deeper ethical contemplation. Consequently, the sections play an indispensable role in the course.

## COURSE STRUCTURE

In Fall 2008, Molecules of Life (formally listed as Science of Living Systems 11: Molecules of Life) was taught by two professors who each wrote and delivered half of the lectures. The course also employed a non-tenure-track faculty member known as a course preceptor. The preceptor's primary responsibilities were to design and facilitate the weekly section activities and to assist the professors in the creation of new lectures. The preceptor also oversaw the daily course logistics, including organizing and instructing the teaching staff, maintaining the course website, creating homework problem sets and keys, and holding review sessions. The teaching staff, comprising the above individuals and six graduate students, met weekly to review the progress of the course, listen to student feedback, and discuss upcoming topics. This meeting typically included training for the weekly section activity.

A total of eighty students enrolled in the course for the Fall 2008 semester: thirty-three seniors, twenty juniors, twenty-five sophomores, and two freshmen. By concentration, fourteen majored in economics, seven in government, six each in history and social studies, five in history & literature, three each in history of science and mathematics, two each in philosophy and sociology, and one each in computer science, East Asian studies, English, environmental science & public policy, music, and psychology. Twenty-six students were listed as "undecided" for their concentration.

Molecules of Life followed a standard liberal arts class configuration: lectures were given twice weekly (Tuesday and Thursday) and lasted ninety minutes. The lectures made use of PowerPoint slides and, on occasion, a blackboard. Sufficient time was set aside from each lecture to answer questions from the audience, as questions were strongly encouraged.

Each student was assigned to a one-hour section group that met weekly. Sections, led by a graduate-level teaching fellow, were designed to supplement the course by providing a more intimate atmosphere for discussions. These groups were capped at a maximum of fifteen students. Section time was generally divided between a weekly lecture review and a complementary interactive activity (except in the weeks preceding an exam, when section time was devoted exclusively to review).

Because the course draws heavily from current events, students were not assigned a textbook. Rather, weekly readings were posted on the class website and were drawn from popular media sources (such as *The New York Times* or *The Boston Globe*) or from the news sections of scientific journals. Scholarly articles were often posted as optional reading for advanced students seeking enrichment. To serve as a primary resource, the lecture slides were posted online with the professor's notes, written in descriptive prose. Digital video recordings of each lecture were also linked to the website, enabling online review of the lectures at a later time. Three-dimensional computer renderings of important molecules were provided, along with a glossary of scientific terms, as educational supplements.

The class was graded on the basis of exams (50 percent), a final project (25 percent), homework scores (12.5 percent), and participation in section (12.5 percent). Two in-class exams and one final exam were given; the lower of the two in-class examination scores was dropped. Students were also given a weekly homework assignment based on the current week's lectures. As a final project, students were assigned a ten-page *Scientific American*–style term paper on an approved topic of their choosing. Suggested topics were posted on the course website throughout the semester. Students also had the option of submitting their project in an alternative format (this was encouraged for students with artistic backgrounds), so long as it accurately represented the scientific concepts. Some submitted musical scores, science-themed children's books, and creative writing projects in verse.

## SYLLABUS OVERVIEW

The course is divided into four interrelated parts: Molecules and the Flow of Information, Molecular Messengers in Humans, Molecular Medicines and Human Disease, and Molecules in Our Future. The units are designed to be taught in sequence because each unit cumulatively builds on the preceding units.

### Part 1: Molecules and the Flow of Information (Lectures 1–8)

**L1**: Introduction
**L2**: Structures of small molecules
**L3**: Shapes of small molecules
**L4**: The macromolecules of life and the central dogma
**L5**: The central dogma and its impact on your life

**L6**: Evolution as a molecular and human phenomenon

**L7**: Steroids and sexual development

**L8**: Steroids, birth control, breast cancer, and sexual behavior

### Part 2: Molecular Messengers in Humans (Lectures 9–14)

**L9**: Thyroid hormones

**L10**: Oxytocin and vasopressin

**L11**: Adrenaline and its relatives

**L12**: Serotonin and SSRIs

**L13**: Cannabinoids and endocannabinoids

**L14**: Opioids and endorphins

### Hour Exam I

### Part 3: Molecular Medicines and Human Diseases (Lectures 15–19)

**L15**: Diabetes and diabetes therapies

**L16**: Cellular and molecular origins of cancer

**L17**: The past, present, and future of cancer therapies

**L18**: Infectious diseases and their molecular basis

**L19**: Molecules that fight infectious disease

### Part 4: Molecules in Our Future (Lectures 20–23)

**L20**: Pheromones

**L21**: Drug discovery and personalized medicine

**L22**: Stem cells

**L23**: Aging

### Hour Exam II

The first unit, Molecules and the Flow of Information, introduces the basic properties of small molecules and macromolecules. An intriguing case study of abnormal sexual development (pseudohermaphroditism) provides a striking theme. The section emphasizes the interrelatedness of molecular structure, shape, and function. Steroids (testosterone, estradiol, and so on) serve as models to introduce the basic concepts behind atomic and molecular theory. The biological flow of information from DNA sequence to protein structure (the central dogma) is introduced within the context of heredity, sexual development, and sexual behavior. A lecture detailing evolution at the molecular level provides a historical framework for living systems. The latter lectures of the unit describe how knowledge of the central dogma has significantly impacted modern life, including personalized diagnostics, genetically modified organisms, and the sequencing of the human genome.

The second unit, Molecular Messengers in Humans, focuses on small molecules as dynamic information carriers within the body, specifically as hormones and neurotransmitters. Lectures are taught using small molecule-specific case studies involving thyroid hormones, oxytocin, vasopressin, adrenaline, cannabinoids, and opioids. Emphasis is placed on small molecule-protein interplay, and how this dynamic relationship modulates cellular function. This section also highlights the link between endogenous small molecule messengers and their exogenous analogs (both natural and manmade). For example, students are taught how the identification of the active ingredient in marijuana, tetra-hydrocannabinol, led to the discovery of the endogenous neurotransmitter anandamide, as well as to the development of the cannabinoid receptor antag-onist rimonabant.

The third unit, Molecular Medicines and Human Diseases, focuses on a select group of diseases that have significantly impacted the history of mankind. Diseases are chosen to showcase three different molecular mechanisms of ill-ness: parasitic infection (viral and bacterial), regulatory imbalance at the body level (type I and type II diabetes), and uncontrolled proliferation of specific tissues (cancer). The lectures also provide historical and scientific perspectives of the drug development process. Key discussions include the relative impor-tance of lifestyle versus genetics, the emergence of drug resistance, and the controversies surrounding the U.S. Food and Drug Administration's (FDA) approval of new drugs and therapies.

The fourth and final unit, Molecules in Our Future, addresses the rising importance of biotechnology and molecular medicine in society. The lectures discuss the latest advances in stem cells, aging, pheromones, and personalized medicine by introducing the basic scientific principles behind them. Articles from the popular media are frequently cited to establish a real-world connec-tion. The instructors then extrapolate powerful predictions and possibilities regarding their potential social impact. The ethical quandaries that these emerg-ing fields present to society are discussed at length.


SECTION ACTIVITIES OVERVIEW

An essential component of Harvard's new general education program is its commitment to improved pedagogy (*Report of the Task Force on General Edu-cation*, 2007). Instructors are strongly encouraged to explore formats that will foster faculty-student interactivity and maximize student engagement.

With this directive in mind, Molecules of Life was designed with a unique vision for its sections. A new section syllabus of hands-on activities and topical debates was designed with the specific intent of capturing the students' atten-tion. Both formats serve as intuitive learning aids; the hands-on activities pro-vide vivid, interactive demonstrations of lecture topics, while the debates allow students to formulate their own opinions on controversial topics of wide pub-lic interest. Notably, each section is specifically designed to complement the corresponding week's lectures.

Although the hands-on activities are reminiscent of more conventional laboratory exercises used in specialized departmental courses, the practical restraints and distinct intentions produce a very different student experience. Each activity requires almost no procedural expertise, assumes minimal scientific knowledge, and utilizes only safe materials and equipment (no fume hoods, gloves, or goggles are needed). The exercises are easily completed in the allotted section time of one hour. To maximize efficiency and minimize tedium, no lengthy pre-laboratory or post-laboratory write-up is required. Background information is provided in a user-friendly "frequently asked questions" format. The teaching fellows are trained to oversee all procedures and to lead all section discussions as necessary.

The section syllabus consists of twelve total section meetings (roughly one section for every two lectures):

**Part 1: Molecules and the Flow of Information (Lectures 1–8)**
> **Wk 1:** Debate: Genetic research & proprietary information
> **Wk 2:** Activity: Extraction of DNA from strawberries
> **Wk 3:** Activity: Demonstrating the Central Dogma using PTC taste testing and genotyping
> **Wk 4:** Activity: The tricky task of gender determination

**Part 2: Molecular Messengers in Humans (Lectures 9–14)**
> **Wk 5:** Activity: The oxytocin trust game: a competition for bonus points
> **Wk 6:** Review: Exam I
> **Wk 7:** Debate: The legalization of marijuana

**Part 3: Molecular Medicines and Human Diseases (Lectures 15–19)**
> **Wk 8:** Activity: Monitoring blood glucose levels in real time
> **Wk 9:** Debate: The benefits & costs of new cancer therapies
> **Wk 10:** Activity: Visualizing the bacterial menace at hand

**Part 4: Molecules in Our Future (Lectures 20–23)**
> **Wk 11:** Activity: Pheromone demonstration with live silkworm moths
> **Wk 12:** Review: Exam II

SYLLABUS WALKTHROUGH

*Part 1: Molecules and the Flow of Information*

The course begins with a brief discussion of the fundamental attributes of small molecules and macromolecules (L1). This introductory approach familiarizes students with life's molecular participants and establishes a basic vocabulary. Students are given a course overview and are introduced to the concept of heritable versus dynamic information flow in living systems. The lecture then introduces an extraordinary case study based on a 1974 *Science* article, "Steroid-5-Alpha-Reductase Deficiency in Man: An Inherited Form of Pseudohermaphroditism" (Imperato-McGinley et al., 1974). This report details the unique emergence of pseudohermaphroditism in a rural village of the Dominican Republic where the male carriers of a certain genetic trait are born with am-

Figure 1: The Emergence of Pseudohermaphroditism in a Rural Village of the Dominican Republic

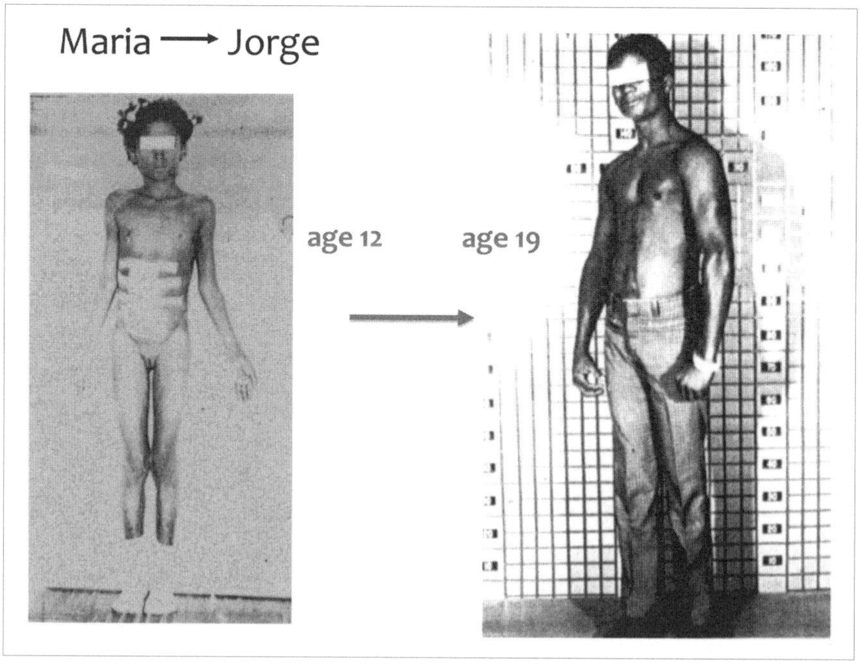

The male carriers of a certain genetic trait are born with ambiguous external genitalia and are consequently raised as females in childhood. Once puberty is reached, the subjects quickly develop into the full male phenotype. This unusual phenomenon serves as a striking theme for the introduction of basic chemical and biological concepts. Source: Peterson, R. E., J. Imperato-McGinley, L. Guerrero, T. Gautier, and E. Sturla. 1977. Male pseudohermaphroditism due to steroid 5-alpha-reductase deficiency. *The American Journal of Medicine* 62:170–191.

biguous external genitalia and consequently are raised as females through childhood (see Figure 1). Once puberty is reached, the subjects develop fully into the male phenotype, which includes the appearance of a fully functional penis. The physiological change is so remarkable that the townspeople have labeled the subjects *guevedoces*—literally, "penis [or testicles] at twelve." To provide a more personal perspective, a brief excerpt from Jeffrey Eugenides' *Middlesex* (2002), a Pulitzer-winning novel that recounts the fictional life of one such affected person, is assigned as a reading.

The Dominican Republic case study provides a striking introductory example of the link between small molecules, macromolecules, and biology. Understanding the morphological phenomenon of pseudohermaphroditism requires basic knowledge of molecular structure, heredity, and sexual development in human beings. Using this anatomical abnormality as the context, the course transitions to the next two lectures on small-molecule structure (L2) and three-dimensional shape (L3). Lecture L2 focuses on atomic theory and connectivity. Students are introduced to the basic attributes of physical and biological systems. The lecture traces molecular theory from Berzelius to Dalton, for historical perspective. To maximize accessibility, bonding is simplified

**Figure 2: Comparing the Evolution of the Kanji Symbol for "Horse" to the Evolution of Chemical Notation**

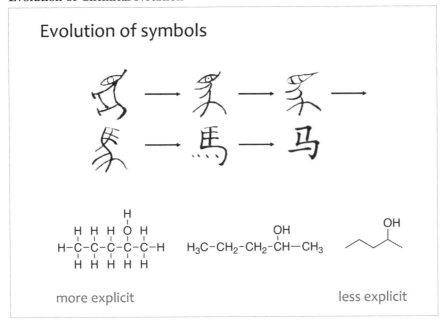

to a series of rules for each element (carbon forms four bonds, nitrogen forms three, oxygen forms two, and hydrogen forms one). The lecture emphasizes the idea that a molecule's "information" is stored within its shape and concludes with a lesson on drawing two-dimensional representations of atoms. An analogy is drawn between the evolution of kanji from pictographs and the evolution of two-dimensional molecular notation from early structural depictions of chemicals (see Figure 2).[1]

The third lecture (L3) transitions from drawing two-dimensional representations to visualizing three-dimensional molecules. Students are taught the basic concepts behind isomerism and how ambiguous two-dimensional representations can symbolize multiple three-dimensional shapes. Empirically proving that methane is shaped like a tetrahedron (rather than a square) exemplifies how carefully designed experiments can resolve mysteries. The 3-D shape of molecules is shown to be the consequence of atomic repulsion, as demonstrated with a tied bundle of balloons. The lecture emphasizes the three-dimensional shapes of different bond types (single versus double) and concludes with a discussion of atomic complementarity in the context of ligands. Students are briefly introduced to the concepts of hydrophobicity and hydrogen bonding.

Keeping with the theme of pseudohermaphroditism for lectures L2 and L3, steroids are used as the molecular focal points. Students are taught how

---

1. Figure 2 and all subsequent figures were created by faculty or graduate teaching assistants for use in the Molecules of Life course. Any further sources or permissions are noted as appropriate.

small changes in molecular connectivity (such as the preservation of a double bond in the failed synthesis of 5 alpha-dihydrotestosterone from testosterone) can produce significant changes in three-dimensional shape and, by extension, profound changes in cellular function (Imperato-McGinley et al., 1974).

The pseudohermaphrodite case study also introduces students to the theme of ethical conflict in science. In the original study, the scientists observed that the causative steroid deficiency also reduces prostate growth and delays the emergence of male pattern baldness. Their observations ultimately led to the development of profitable drugs for the treatment of enlarged prostates and baldness. However, the impoverished subjects of the original study likely did not benefit financially from this commercial application.

In situations such as this, whether or not pharmaceutical companies have a moral obligation to share their profits with their research subjects is debatable. To allow students to engage in meaningful dialogue, the first week's section activity (Wk 1) is designed as a debate on proprietary genetic information. In this exercise, students are presented with a series of hypothetical health conditions, each comparable to those seen in the pseudohermaphrodite case study. Students are then presented with a series of offers to participate as research subjects in a genetic study and must decide whether they would be comfortable participating given the benefits and drawbacks of each offer. As a whole, this exercise demonstrates to students the difficult ethical situations that can emerge as a consequence of advancing science.

Once the basics of molecular structure have been established, the course introduces the flow of heritable information through the central dogma. The specific goal is to teach students how genetic mutations can dramatically change a person's physiology, as illustrated by the pseudohermaphrodite case study. Lecture 4 (L4) introduces two key macromolecule families, nucleic acids and proteins, and emphasizes how the order of building blocks dictates a macromolecule's properties. Students are taught that a protein's amino acid sequence determines its shape, which in turn determines its function (see Figure 3). As a striking example, test tube samples of jellyfish green fluorescent protein (Tsien, 1998) are distributed in class under fluorescent lighting. A survey of the early experiments in genetics provides excellent examples of scientific reasoning and introduces students to Mendelian inheritance.

For individuals who have had limited exposure to laboratory work, the concept of DNA is often abstract. Though most people are aware of its central importance to genetics, few recognize that it is a tangible chemical that can be seen, touched, and even physically manipulated given adequate quantities. Hence, to "demystify" DNA, students are given the opportunity to extract the DNA from a strawberry (Wk 2). The extraction itself requires no harmful chemicals (it uses only rubbing alcohol, soap, salt, and water) and allows students to collect visible quantities of DNA from a familiar food item. Students are then able to manipulate the DNA with their bare hands, which allows them to make the connection that DNA is, after all, a physical reality contained in all cells.

**Figure 3: Introducing Students to the Relationship between Structure and Function in Proteins**

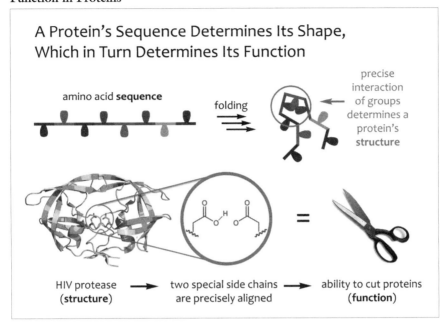

## A Protein's Sequence Determines Its Shape, Which in Turn Determines Its Function

amino acid **sequence**

folding

precise interaction of groups determines a protein's **structure**

HIV protease **(structure)** → two special side chains are precisely aligned → ability to cut proteins **(function)**

The next lecture (L5) connects structure to information flow by detailing how nucleic acids physically encode heritable information, culminating in translation via the genetic code. A survey of the key experiments leading up to the central dogma is given, including simplified descriptions of the seminal work performed by Avery, MacLoed, and McCarthy (identification of the transforming principle), Chargaff, Franklin, Watson, and Crick (the structure of DNA), Brenner (RNA as an information intermediary), and Nirenberg and Khorana (decoding the genetic code itself). To establish everyday relevance, the lecture also details how this knowledge has significantly impacted modern life, particularly through the Human Genome Project. Students are introduced to technologies such as personalized diagnostics and genetically modified organisms. Finally, the mutation behind pseudohermaphroditism is revealed, completing the conceptual link from genetic mutation to steroid deficiency (see Figure 4).

Having introduced the flow of heritable information, the course then provides a historical perspective by framing the central dogma within evolution (L6). Adaptive evolution is taught at the molecular level and is shown as the natural consequence of any system exhibiting translation, selection, and amplification with diversification. To overcome any lingering skepticism, an overview of evolution's supporting evidence is presented (that is, anatomy, the fossil record, and DNA sequencing, all of which support a consistent "tree of life"). Recent examples of "artificial" evolution (the emergence of pathogenic drug resistance and the selection of desired traits in domesticated animals) are

**Figure 4: Revealing the Origin of Pseudohermaphroditism through the Central Dogma**

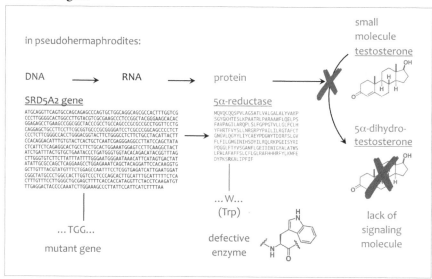

also provided. The lecture then describes surprising research that suggests the human race has evolved significantly within the past ten thousand years, citing such examples as the emergence of lactose tolerance in Africa (Tishkoff et al., 2007) and the appearance of different forms of malarial resistance (sickle-cell anemia, thalassemia, and hemoglobin c; Carter & Mendis, 2002).

The third week's activity (Wk 3) provides a more personal demonstration of the central dogma by showing students the link between their phenotype and genotype. The phenotype utilized is taste sensitivity, a sensory perception. Students are invited (but not required) to test their taste sensitivity for a specific chemical, phenylthiocarbamide (PTC). A person's capacity to taste PTC at low concentrations is dictated by a certain taster gene, called *TAS2R38* (Kim et al., 2005). Two forms of the gene are most prevalent: one is sensitive to PTC; the other is insensitive. Depending on their genetics, most individuals either taste PTC as intensely bitter (a "taster") or not at all (a "non-taster"). Paper strips containing trace amounts of the compound are commercially available, providing a simple oral assay of phenotype.

To establish genotype, a straightforward PCR/endonuclease digestion assay can be performed (as elegantly described by Merritt et al., 2008) using cell samples taken from students. During the section meeting, students transfer cheek cells to a test tube using a sterile inoculation loop. The section leader collects samples and performs the assays in parallel at a later time. Minimal expertise is needed; the only equipment required is a water bath, a PCR block, and a gel electrophoresis box, all of which are routine equipment for a biology lab. The DNA is extracted from the sample, amplified by PCR, and digested with a restriction enzyme. The resulting DNA samples are then loaded onto an agarose gel for segregation by electrophoresis (see Figure 5).

**Figure 5: Using PTC to Link the Phenotype and Genotype of Students**

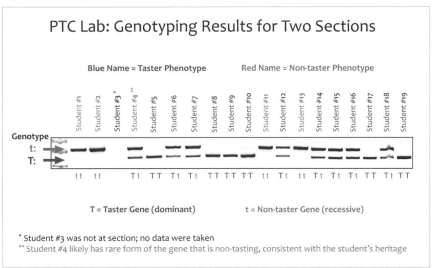

PTC Lab: Genotyping Results for Two Sections

Blue Name = Taster Phenotype        Red Name = Non-taster Phenotype

Student #1, Student #2, Student #3*, Student #4**, Student #5, Student #6, Student #7, Student #8, Student #9, Student #10, Student #11, Student #12, Student #13, Student #14, Student #15, Student #16, Student #17, Student #18, Student #19

Genotype
t:
T:

tt  tt    Tt  TT  Tt  Tt    TT  TT  TT    tt  Tt    tt  Tt    Tt  Tt    TT  Tt  TT

T = Taster Gene (dominant)        t = Non-taster Gene (recessive)

* Student #3 was not at section; no data were taken
** Student #4 likely has rare form of the gene that is non-tasting, consistent with the student's heritage

Phenotype was established in class by direct taste testing of PTC-infused paper strips. Genotype of the corresponding taste receptor (*TAS2R38*) was established with a PCR/digestion assay, using cheek cell samples taken from students. Student number 4 is believed to have a rare form of the *TAS2R38* gene that does not digest in this assay (thereby mimicking the common tasting form of the gene) but does not enable PTC taste sensitivity; this finding is consistent with his African heritage.

The results are shown to students the following week, enabling them to see their own DNA as amplified by modern biotechnology. From the gel read-out (which is easily explained), one can easily predict if a student is capable of tasting the bitterness of PTC: homozygous dominant tasters will see their amplified DNA band cut into two smaller fragments, and homozygous recessive non-tasters will see their DNA intact as a single band (see Figure 5; Merritt et al., 2008). Heterozygous tasters (individuals bearing one taster gene and one non-taster gene) will have all three bands present in their lane, corresponding to one intact band and two digested fragments. This visual evidence provides students with a direct connection between their genes and their own sensory experience, thereby intuitively demonstrating the central dogma.

The first unit of the course concludes with a pair of lectures that directly link steroids, sexual development, and sexual behavior. The first of the two lectures (L7) begins by recounting the discovery of testosterone, including the intriguing caponization experiments that identified its importance to sexual development. The process of sex determination in human beings is then traced through its biological stages: chromosomal, gonadal, hormonal, morphological, and behavioral. This sequence provides ample opportunity to discuss the biosynthesis of different steroids, the steroid modulation of receptor activity, and the transcriptional activation of genes by nuclear receptors. Specifically, students are introduced to the SRY gene and the TDF protein (a nuclear receptor/transcriptional activator), both of which are key participants in the sex determination pathway. This pathway is then related to pseudohermaphroditism, showcasing how signaling "miscommunications" can result in physiological abnormalities.

The ensuing lecture (L8) focuses on the development of modern birth control. The lecture first introduces how man-made ligands can be used to regulate receptor proteins. Students are taught the differences between agonism, antagonism, and enzyme inhibition. When these principles are applied to the estrus cycle (as governed by estrogen and progesterone), a basic understanding of "the pill" emerges: physiological regulation through well-timed doses of estrogen and progesterone agonists. These concepts are then applied to the development of breast cancer therapeutics in the form of estrogen receptor antagonists (tamoxifen) and aromatase inhibitors (exemestane). The lecture concludes with a discussion of hormones and sexual behavior. The proper steroids are shown to be necessary for both sexual behavior organization *and* activation (Balthazart et al., 2004). The lecture also touches on the public fiascos that can emerge from incomplete or misunderstood scientific research.

To provide a social context for the process of sex determination, the corresponding week's section meeting (Wk 4) focuses on the history of gender determination at the Olympics. This practice has its roots in the Cold War, when Western nations suspected Soviet-bloc nations of entering male athletes in female competitions (Simpson et al., 2000). As a consequence, female athletes were required to submit themselves for visual inspection. Eventually, this demeaning practice gave way to more advanced biochemical techniques, such as karyotyping and SRY gene detection. However, such tests have their pragmatic limitations. Many athletes do not fit cleanly into preconceived definitions of gender, thus clouding the issue. The controversy over gender identification in athletic competition continues to this day.

In this activity, students are charged with the task of determining the eligibility of a "female" athlete based on the results of a battery of tests. As the teaching fellow progressively reveals the results of each test (patient history, visual medical inspection, karyotype, SRY-gene test, and examination of the androgen receptor gene), students are asked to classify the patient as female or male. After they have been given all the available data and have made their final decision, their choices are compared to the official policy currently used by the International Olympic Committee. A discussion of such policies then follows.

*Part 2: Molecular Messengers in Humans*

The second unit of the course focuses on the body's use of small molecules as molecular messengers. Because students have already been introduced to the language of chemistry and the flow of genetic information, the emphasis shifts to teaching principles of biology and chemistry that are more specific. To provide a context for these lessons, the lectures utilize a series of well-known small molecules as focal points.

The first lecture of the series (L9) concentrates on thyroid hormones. Using these molecules as a theme, the lecture introduces the fundamental biochemical principles of acidity, hydrophobicity, hydrogen-bond complementarity, and cell-membrane permeability. The worldwide epidemic of iodine deficiency disorder raises an ethical question: given our scientific awareness of the cause, what is our obligation to assist the world's poor? Students are also taught the fundamentals of cell signaling, including nuclear-receptor binding, signal modulation by ligand concentration, and transcriptional activation. The lecture then introduces chirality. Samples of ($d$)-carvone and ($l$)-carvone, which respectively smell like spearmint and caraway, are passed around. This provides a direct sensory demonstration of the importance of chirality in biology.

The second lecture of the unit (L10) focuses on the hormones oxytocin and vasopressin. This lecture introduces key concepts relating to peptides, including their exponential structural potential and the resulting challenge of their primary structure elucidation. Conformational locking (through disulfide bond formation) is also covered. The lecture then addresses gene duplication and its significance to evolution.

A series of thought-provoking experiments are presented, connecting oxytocin and vasopressin to social interaction. One noteworthy experiment relates bloodstream oxytocin levels to trust between human peers (Kosfeld et al., 2005). In this study, "trust" was measured using a money game. The game requires a subject (the "investor") to invest a portion of money with a peer (the "trustee") in order to maximize profit: the greater the trust of the investor (as measured by the quantity of dollars invested), the greater the potential return payout. However, the game includes a counterincentive: the greater the sum invested with the trustee, the greater the risk of losing money because of betrayal by the trustee. The study showed that administration of oxytocin prior to playing the game resulted in higher levels of trust by the investor for the trustee.

The lecture also describes a classic experiment on induced monogamy: the transfer of monogamous behavior from prairie voles (a small, faithful rodent species) to a second, typically promiscuous vole species (Lim et al., 2004). This dramatic behavioral change manifests when the prairie voles' vasopressin receptor gene (*V1aR*) is introduced into the ventral forebrain cells of the montane voles through genetic therapy. These experiments present excellent discussion opportunities. In a practical sense, the experiments suggest the possibility of engineering behavior through designer drugs. In a philosophical sense, the experiments invite students to consider the nature of human behavior: are behavioral traits like promiscuity really determined by the presence of a single receptor?

To provide students with a more intimate understanding of the oxytocin trust experiment, the weekly section activity (Wk 5) recapitulates the trust game (Kosfeld et al., 2005) without the administration of oxytocin. Rather than competing for money, students instead compete for homework bonus points.

In the course of the section, each student plays the game twice: once in the role of the investor and once in the role of the trustee. All transactions occur via a worksheet that obscures each player's name, rendering each action anonymous.

Each student first serves as the investor (see Figure 6). The investor has the option of distributing zero, one, two, or three homework bonus points to his corresponding anonymous trustee. Points that are withheld from the trustee (that is, points that are *not* distributed) are guaranteed to the investor. The distributed points are multiplied by a factor of three, and one additional point is added. The new total is transferred to the trustee. The worksheets are collected, randomized, and redistributed by the teaching fellow.

Each student then acts in the role of trustee for another student. The number of points transferred by the corresponding investor is shown on the worksheet. The trustees choose how to divide the available points between themselves and their investor. (The investor has no recourse to punishment if the points are distributed inequitably.) The teaching fellow then re-collects the worksheets, adds each student's total from both games (the names are revealed only to the teaching fellow), and shows the results at the end of the section. Though the class results cannot be correlated to oxytocin levels (as was done in the real experiment; Kosfeld et al., 2005), the activity allows students to experience how research programs can measure abstract qualities such as trust. The exercise also provides some entertaining data about the class; for example, in the 2008–2009 class, economics majors were significantly less likely to trust their fellow classmates than were government majors.

The Molecular Messengers in Humans unit continues with a lecture on adrenaline and its analogs (L11). The lecture begins with a brief review of amino acid structure and hormone biosynthesis. Students are then introduced to signal transduction across cell membranes via GPCR activation. The diversity of the adrenergic receptors ($a_1$, $b_1$, etc.) demonstrates to students the necessity (and challenge) of finding selective agonists and antagonists (Liggett et al., 2006). Several adrenaline-based drugs, many of which bind to a different adrenergic receptor, are shown. Of particular note are the beta-blockers, which are frequently used to treat heart disease. The lecture also introduces the neurotransmitters dopamine and noradrenaline, enabling neurotransmitters and hormones to be contrasted. To engage the students' interest, the lecture also traces the history of dopamine-like recreational drugs from the discovery of ephedrine in ancient China to the invention of ecstasy by Alexander Shulgin. The differing effects of these analogs reemphasize the importance of three-dimensional shape to function. The lecture also stresses the complexity of neurological signaling, citing research revealing significant cross-communication between neural paths.

To provide a more thorough treatment of neurotransmission, the next lecture focuses on the small molecule serotonin (L12). The lesson begins by briefly tracing the historical divide between the neurological theories of elec-

**Figure 6: Schematic for the Trust Game**

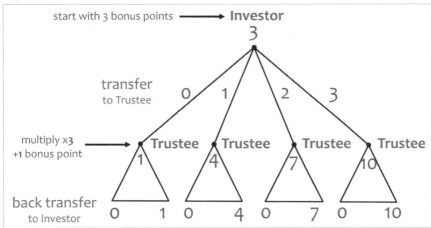

Students compete for bonus points, which are counted toward future homework assignments. Students participate in two games, in one as an investor and in one as a trustee. Starting with three bonus points, investors have a choice of investing zero, one, two, or three points with their given trustee. (Points not invested are retained by the investor.) The invested points are then multiplied by three, plus one additional point. The trustee then divides the remaining points between the investor and himself. The back-transfer can range anywhere from zero to all available points. All transactions are anonymous; only the teaching fellow knows the identities.

trical ("sparks") and chemical ("soups") signal transmission. The lecture then describes an intriguing experiment by Loewi (1957) that confirmed the dependence of nerve signaling on chemicals. As the two theories converged, neurotransmission was eventually shown to travel by both electrical (intracellular) and chemical (intercellular) means. To explain how small molecules can transmit nerve signals, students are introduced to the basic structure of the neuron. The focal point of the lesson is the synapse, including the biosynthesis, inactivation, and recycling of neurotransmitters.

The lecture concludes on a behavioral note. Research is shown indicating that variability in human behavior can be attributed largely to variability within synaptic proteins. Mutations in key macromolecules—such as tryptophan hydroxylase (Zhang et al., 2004), monoamine oxidase (Caspi et al., 2002), catechol o-methyl transferase (Montag et al., 2008), or the serotonin reuptake transporters (Caspi et al., 2003; Lesch et al., 1996)—are shown to correlate strongly with psychological disorders. Similarly, students are shown that human behavior can be modified using small molecules that inhibit or activate these proteins. The development of the antidepressant fluoxetine (Prozac), perhaps the most famous of the selective serotonin reuptake inhibitors, is used as a specific example.

Continuing the theme of neurotransmitters, the next lecture (L13) focuses on cannabinoids, endocannabinoids, and marijuana. After a brief survey of marijuana's history (tracing its path from a crop in ancient China to an inspiration for a modern television series), the lecture raises the curious point of marijuana's recreational potency: what is the biologically active small molecule?

Answering this question required the development of an animal-based assay. The lecture first traces the work of Roger Adams, whose search for the active ingredient resulted in the testing of marijuana extracts on dogs, prisoners, and the president of a well-known university (Adams, 1942). Though Adams's work was not finished in his lifetime, his ideas eventually led researchers to the discovery of $\Delta^9$-tetrahydrocannabinol (THC). Students are then asked to consider a second question: what is the receptor of this small molecule, and what is its normal function in the body? Students are introduced to the "radioactive bait" experiment, which enabled the discovery of the cannabinoid receptor (CB1), a type of G protein–coupled receptor (GPCR; Matsuda et al., 1990). The third question of the lecture is then raised: what is the endogenous ligand for the CB1 receptor? By modifying the radioactive bait experiment, scientists were able to identify the neurotransmitter anandamide (Devane et al., 1992). This finding, in turn, enabled the discovery of retrograde signaling. The search for cannabinoid-related drugs, including CB1 antagonists (rimonabant; Marsicano et al., 2002) and fatty acid amide hydrolase inhibitors, is discussed, thus linking the lecture to the modern pharmaceutical industry.

To forge a connection between the course's treatment of marijuana and the outside world, the weekly section activity (Wk 7) is organized as a debate on the legalization of marijuana. The discussion revolves around two short op-eds from a recent issue of *U.S. News and World Report*. The first article, "Too Dangerous Not to Regulate" (Moskos, 2008) argues for the legalization of marijuana, while the second, "End the Demand, End the Supply" (Brown, 2008), argues the contrary. Students are supplied with copies of both articles and are allowed to debate the merits and drawbacks of marijuana legalization. Emphasis is placed on a critical reading of the essays. The ensuing discussion is facilitated by the teaching fellow, who is provided with additional useful information: the official American Medical Association (AMA) position on medicinal marijuana, the list of Drug Enforcement Administration (DEA) drug schedules, and the latest FDA ruling on the medicinal benefits of marijuana. When the course was taught in 2008, this discussion topic was particularly relevant to current events in the state of Massachusetts: the November ballot included a referendum on the decriminalization of smaller quantities of marijuana. (The measure would go on to pass.)

The final lecture of the unit (L14) focuses on opioids and endorphins. The lecture begins by tracing opium addiction from the ancient Sumerians to modern times. It includes a selection from Thomas De Quincy's personal account of opium addiction, *Confessions of an English Opium-Eater*. Students are then introduced to the properties of freebases and hydrochloride salts. Because morphine is the most complicated chemical structure hitherto shown in class, molecular models are passed around to showcase morphine's unique three-dimensional shape. A thorough case study of morphine's features (see Figure 7) recapitulates the unit's key lessons: its basic molecular properties,

**Figure 7: An Examination of the Unique Structure of Morphine**

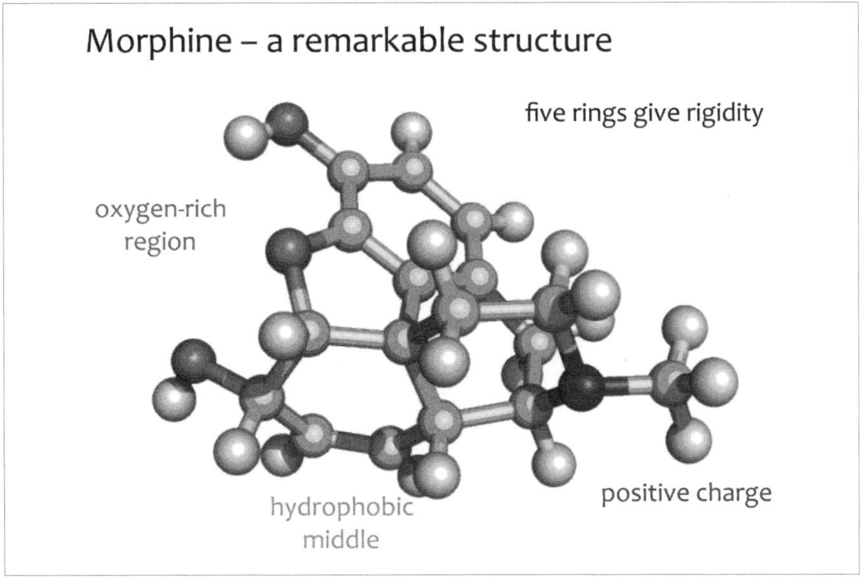

Studying morphine's structure provides an opportunity to review the key chemical concepts of the second unit.

its biosynthesis from amino acids, its chemical derivatization into morphine analogs (heroin, codeine, and so on), and its use as a biochemical probe. As with THC, morphine's use as a probe enabled the discovery of both endogenous receptors (μ-opioid receptors; Pert & Snyder, 1973) and endogenous ligands (the endorphins and enkephalins; Hughes et al., 1975). A discussion of analgesics and their relationship to the μ-opioid receptors follows.

The lecture concludes on a philosophical note. One of the key differences between human beings and their close primate relatives is that human beings exhibit higher expression levels of the prodynorphin gene. (Prodynorphin is a biochemical precursor to the endorphins; see Rockman et al., 2005.) These findings raise the questions: What makes us human? Is a primary factor simply our ability to activate a pleasure gene more easily and intensely than chimpanzees?

*Part 3: Molecular Medicines and Human Diseases*

The third unit of the course offers a molecular view of human disease and has two central goals: to demonstrate how chemistry enables us to understand the origins of disease and to demonstrate how that knowledge set can be used to develop new treatments and cures. The lectures focus on three human afflictions: diabetes, cancer, and infectious disease. Because of the widespread impact of these diseases, the importance of the lecture topics is easy for students to understand. Undoubtedly, many of them have been affected by these diseases, either directly or indirectly.

The first disease to be addressed in the unit is diabetes (L15). The lecture begins by describing its astonishing worldwide prevalence (an estimated 200 million cases worldwide). A brief historical account of the disease is given, noting descriptions of the disease as far back as 3,500 years ago. The lecture then details early diabetes research, which culminated in the identification of insulin as the critical hormone of blood glucose regulation.

The lecture then focuses on the modern perspective. Students are taught the difference between type I and type II diabetes at a basic physiological level. (Type I results from the inability to produce insulin, type II from decreased insulin sensitivity.) The lecture reviews the risk factors associated with type II diabetes: age, obesity, and genetics. A brief aside introduces the emerging technology of whole-genome analysis. A considerable amount of time is also spent discussing the startling rise of obesity in the American population.

The final segment of the lecture centers on existing molecular therapies for diabetes. The first treatment discussed is synthetic insulin, the standard treatment for type I diabetes. The engineered variants of insulin provide excellent examples of applied genetic engineering (Vajo & Duckworth, 2000). The focus of the lecture then shifts to small molecule treatments for type II diabetes (sulfonylureas and biguanides), highlighting their development and mechanism of action. Finally, to reemphasize the importance of lifestyle choices, the relative efficacies of drugs versus lifestyle adjustment for diabetic therapy are discussed (Ratner, 2006).

Though most students possess some level of familiarity with diabetes, relatively few have had the opportunity to use a modern blood glucose meter. In light of this fact, we give students the opportunity to monitor their own blood glucose levels as a section activity (Wk 8). This activity showcases the latest in portable biotechnology ("a laboratory that fits in your pocket!"), while connecting the students' knowledge of blood sugar regulation to their own bodies. As a safeguard of student privacy and safety, participation in this activity is voluntary.

Students are provided with commercially available blood glucose meters (Lifescan OneTouch UltraMini meters). Students are instructed how to measure their blood glucose level at the start of section. (To ensure safety, students use disposable lancets and meter strips; the strips require only about one microliter of blood for an accurate reading.) Following the first reading, flavored glucose tablets are distributed for consumption. After approximately thirty minutes (during which time the biochemistry behind the blood glucose meters is explained), students re-measure their blood glucose levels to observe how the levels have changed as a result of their glucose consumption (see Figure 8). Students may also opt to measure their blood glucose at additional time intervals, their schedule permitting. Alternatively, students may opt to eat prior to section and monitor the drop in their blood glucose level during the section.

The next two lectures focus on the class of diseases known collectively as cancer. The first lecture (L16) explains cancer as a molecular and cellular phe-

Figure 8: Monitoring Blood Glucose Levels at Various Time Intervals, Following the Consumption of Glucose Tablets

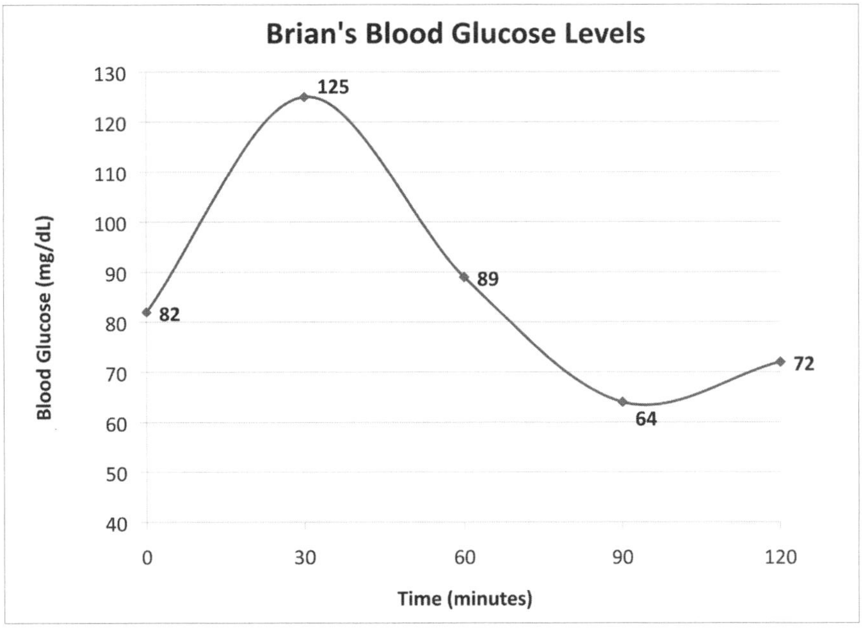

A commercial glucose meter (OneTouch UltraMini) was used for the measurements.

nomenon by framing it as a combination of cellular function abnormalities: self-sustained growth signaling, insensitivity to anti-growth signals, evasion of apoptosis, limitless replicative potential, sustained angiogenesis, and the ability to metastasize (Hanahan & Weinberg, 2000). A basic introduction to the cancer stem cell hypothesis is also given (Reya et al., 2001). The latter half of the lecture focuses on cancer as a genetic disease resulting from the accumulation of harmful mutations within a cell's genome. A brief mathematical primer on probability and mutation accumulation is provided. To emphasize the importance of lifestyle choices, the primary causes of cancer—viruses, radiation, chemicals, and inherited genes—are reviewed in the context of human behavior. Frequently used terms such as *oncogene* and *carcinogen* are formally defined.

The subsequent lecture (L17) approaches cancer treatment at the molecular level. The lecture begins by describing cancer therapies (such as radiation therapy and nonspecific chemotherapy) that rely on the general strategy of damaging all dividing cells in the body. A few chemotherapeutic agents (cisplatin, methotrexate, paclitaxel) are covered in greater detail, including basic descriptions of their biochemical mechanisms (DNA damage, DNA replication inhibition, and damage to cell division machinery, respectively). After discussing the drawbacks of such approaches, the lecture segues to newer therapies based on detailed knowledge of specific cancers. A few case studies are provided: imatinib (Gleevec) as a drug for chronic myelogenous leukemia; gefitinib (Iressa) for the treatment of epidermal growth factor receptor–dependent

**Figure 9: A Basic Introduction to Oncogenic Theories, including the Cancer Stem Cell Theory**

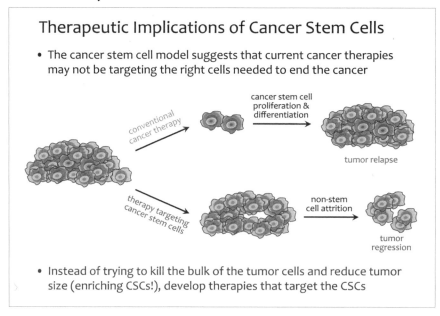

## Therapeutic Implications of Cancer Stem Cells

- The cancer stem cell model suggests that current cancer therapies may not be targeting the right cells needed to end the cancer

- Instead of trying to kill the bulk of the tumor cells and reduce tumor size (enriching CSCs!), develop therapies that target the CSCs

cancers; and bevacizumab (Avastin) for the treatment of vascular endothelial growth factor–dependent cancers. Finally, the lecture examines two newer theories related to cancer research and treatment: the oncogene addiction model and the cancer stem cell hypothesis (see Figure 9).

The lecture demonstrates that the improvements in our knowledge of cancer have enabled the development of more sophisticated cancer therapies. Many of these drugs offer hope to patients who would otherwise have no treatment options. The new therapies, however, come with a drawback: the high cost of their development typically results in a high price for treatment. This reality places the drugs beyond the reach of many patients, often forcing families to make difficult cost-to-benefit calculations. Furthermore, the value of these drugs frequently is unclear; for example, a drug can be shown to reduce tumor size without also showing a statistically significant increase in life expectancy.

The FDA approval of expensive cancer treatments has been a controversial topic. To provide a deeper understanding of the scientific and moral dilemmas faced by the FDA, the section activity (Wk 9) is organized as a simulation of the FDA approval process. Students serve as members of the FDA approval board and are asked to judge whether two fictional therapies should be approved for general use by cancer patients. Students are asked to make their decision based on the following six criteria: efficacy, survival rate, specificity, toxicity, economics, and statistical reliability. The data for the two drugs, while fictionalized, are simplified versions of the data on two real anti-cancer drugs chosen because of their controversial FDA review: bevacizumab (Avastin) and sipuleucel-T (Provenge). Once students complete their debates and submit their choices, the teaching fellow describes the real treatments on which the fictional drugs are based. The FDA's decision on each drug is revealed along with the published rationale. Students then discuss the merits and drawbacks of the FDA-approval process.

The final two lectures of the unit focus on infectious diseases. The first lecture (L18) begins with a discussion of the worldwide impact of infectious disease (which accounts for roughly one-third of all human deaths). The lecture then examines two massive epidemics that have significantly shaped history: the Black Death and the Spanish influenza. The story of the Black Death is traced from its emergence along the silk trade routes, including its unusual use as a biochemical weapon by the Mongols. After briefly discussing the questionable practices of medieval medicine (an era preceding germ theory), the cause is revealed: a type of bacteria (*Yersinia pestis*) that is transmitted by fleas. Students then discuss the importance of the Black Death as a catalyst for social and economic change.

The second infectious disease examined in L18 is the Spanish flu, which is believed to have killed between seventy-five and one-hundred million people worldwide. The lecture introduces students to viruses, emphasizing their morphological differences from human cells. The lecture raises two interrelated questions: First, what made the Spanish flu so uniquely deadly? Second, why is the age profile of those killed (ages twenty to forty) so different from that of the common flu? To answer these questions, three viral proteins are introduced: RNA polymerase, neuraminidase, and hemagglutinin. Only once they have learned how these proteins function within the common flu can students understand the unusual lethality of the Spanish flu. The lecture concludes with a look at modern viral research, including the laboratory resurrection of the Spanish flu (Taubenberger et al., 2005). The safety issues and ethical dimensions of this research are briefly discussed.

The final lecture of the unit (L19) focuses on the development of molecules that fight infectious disease. The lecture itself comprises three segments: vaccines, antibiotics and antiviral drugs, and the evolution of drug resistance. The segment on vaccines begins with an account of Jenner's early research on cowpox and smallpox. To aid in understanding vaccines, students are given a basic primer on the human immune system. The lecture then describes the success of modern vaccines in eradicating two major diseases: smallpox and polio. The ethics of producing the first polio vaccine stocks are discussed. Were the first vaccines worth the killing of more than one hundred thousand rhesus monkeys? A brief discussion on the benefits and shortcomings of vaccines concludes this portion of the lecture.

The lecture then switches to antibiotic and antiviral medications, starting with Paul Ehrlich's development of arsphenamine (Salvarsan), and details the discovery, development, and mechanistic basis for three antibiotic/antiviral drugs: penicillin, oseltamivir (Tamiflu), and saquinavir (Invirase). The molecular target of each drug is introduced (the bacterial cell wall, neuraminidase, and HIV protease, respectively) so that the specificity of each drug can be understood. The lecture concludes with a discussion of drug resistance, which emerges as an inevitable consequence of evolution (as outlined in L6). The three basic mechanisms of resistance are reviewed (avoiding the drug, removing the drug, and destroying the drug), using real examples from resistant bacterial and viral strains.

For the infectious disease section activity (Wk 10), students culture and visualize bacteria that are growing on their hands and test the effectiveness of both hand sanitizer and an antibiotic. For the visualization, each student is provided with ethanol-based hand sanitizer and a sterile blood agar plate. (The plates are regularly used by pathologists to culture and identify common bacterial strains and can be ordered in bulk.) Students are instructed to streak the surface of the agar plate by gently touching the plate with the fingers of their bare hands. One side of the plate is streaked *prior* to hand sanitizing, the other *after* hand sanitizing. Students are also given a strip of filter paper infused with ampicillin to place across the plate. At the end of section, the teaching fellow collects the plates and transfers them to a warm room, where they are left to grow overnight.

After sufficient growing time, the teaching fellow removes the plates and digitally scans them. The images can then be emailed to the students. If executed correctly, students should see a plethora of bacterial colonies growing on the "before" side, relatively few colonies growing on the "after" side, and almost no colonies growing in proximity to the antibiotic-soaked paper strip (see Figure 10). For added interest, some of the bacterial strains can be identified based on the hemolysis pattern the colonies leave in the blood agar. This exercise illustrates the omnipresence of bacteria, and demonstrates the effectiveness of both hand sanitizer and beta-lactam antibiotics, as well as the existence of microorganisms that resist a given antibiotic.

*Part 4: Molecules in Our Future*

The last unit focuses on four areas of emerging molecular technology: pheromones, drug discovery and personalized medicine, stem cells, and aging. The goal of the unit is to examine how advances in biotechnology and applied science are likely to affect our lifestyles in the near and distant future. Students are introduced to the fundamental concepts that underlie each topic, and recent advances in each field are surveyed. From here, the likely societal impacts of each technology—notably, the social, economic, and ethical conflicts that arise in each case—can be extrapolated (within reason).

The first lecture in the unit (L20) focuses on pheromones. Pheromones are small molecules produced by an organism for release into the environment in order to communicate with nearby members of the *same species*. The lecture comprises four sections. The first two describe well-understood examples from

**Figure 10: Visualizing Bacteria Using Blood-Agar Plates**

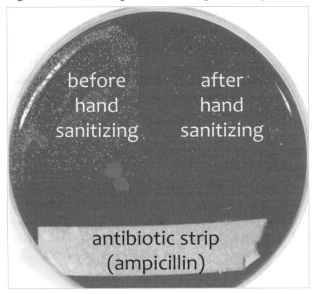

before hand sanitizing

after hand sanitizing

antibiotic strip (ampicillin)

Students streak their fingers both *before* and *after* the use of an ethanol-based hand sanitizer. The plate is then allowed to grow in a warm room overnight. A paper strip soaked with ampicillin is also provided to demonstrate the inhibitory power of beta-lactam antibiotics.

the insect world. The third section details how pheromones are used by mice. The last section discusses the latest research on human pheromones.

To prime students' interest in the link between smell and memory, the lecture begins with a quote from Marcel Proust's *Remembrance of Things Past*. An account is given of Jean-Henri Fabri's serendipitous discovery of moth pheromones, providing the perfect research-model organism. This story raises the question: what is the active molecule? The lecture details Adolf Butenandt's painstaking work (extraction from approximately five hundred thousand silkworm moths) toward identifying the molecule bombykol (Butenandt, Beckamnn & Hecker, 1961). The lecture then describes a more sophisticated insect pheromone system: the use of homovanillyl alcohol by queen bees to inhibit aversive learning by worker bees (Beggs et al., 2007). A brief allusion to Aldous Huxley's *Brave New World* provides some thoughtful perspective.

The lecture then transitions to more complex organisms: mice and human beings. Research on the importance of pheromone sensing in mouse mate selection is highlighted. An intriguing series of videos showing mice that have had their pheromone-sensing organ (the vomeronasal organ or VNO) genetically disabled illustrates how pheromones can dictate sexual behavior (Kimchi, Xu & Dulac, 2007). Suppressing the VNO results in male-like mating behavior in females. This surprising sexual behavior model is contrasted with the hormone-based model examined earlier in the course. Finally, a brief survey of the research on human pheromones is given, including examples such as mate selection by major histocompatibility complex compatibility, the phenomenon of menstrual synchrony (Stern & McClintock, 1998), and the search for human pheromones via PET scanning (Berglund, Lindstrom & Savic, 2006;

Savic & Lindstrom, 2008). Of particular interest is the finding that homosexual males have cerebral reception results similar to that of heterosexual females (Savic, Berglund & Lindstrom, 2005). Promising research toward identifying human receptor genes hints that exciting new discoveries will appear within the next decade.

To demonstrate vividly the phenomenon of pheromones, students observe an in-section demonstration of bombykol using live silkworm moths (Wk 11). Because adult moths have a lifespan of three to seven days (after emerging from their cocoons, their sole purpose is to mate; they cannot eat), the raising of the moths must be timed carefully. Large silkworm larvae are ordered from commercial sources several weeks in advance of the activity. After raising the silkworms through the final larval stage (using commercially available mulberry leaf chow as the food source), the larvae are left to cocoon in cardboard tubes. The completed silk cocoons are then segregated into plastic cups, where the moths begin to emerge some two to three weeks later. Females are identified through positive identification of a scent gland and are segregated from the males to prevent premature mating.

For the section demonstration, the live male moths are placed on one corner of a wide cardboard tray. In the absence of female moths, the males remain more or less motionless. A female is then introduced to the opposite corner of the tray, where it begins scenting. Upon sensing the pheromone, the males immediately become aroused and start violently stumbling toward the female's corner. (The moths are a domesticated species that cannot fly.) Students are then shown that dilute synthetic samples of bombykol elicit the same behavioral response from the males.[2] Afterward, students are given the opportunity to gently handle the animals. As a whole, the exercise provides students with the chance to witness the real-time use of pheromones by live animals. Repeating the excitation of the males with a synthetic bombykol sample clearly demonstrates the chemical nature of the signal.

As a supplementary activity, students test commercially available colognes that supposedly contain human pheromones. Samples from two different cologne companies (Pheromone Advantage and Alfa Maschio) were obtained for the course. Both companies claim to include active human pheromones in their colognes. At the request of the course instructors, each company sent one "active sample" (with the alleged pheromone) and one "control sample" (lacking the pheromone). Blind aliquots of the four samples were then prepared, with the identities of the samples known only by the preceptor. Volunteers from the class use the cologne over the span of a weekend. At the conclusion of the weekend, the volunteers fill out a short survey gauging whether they felt they had received an unusual amount of social attention that weekend. Though the sample size was small for Fall 2008, the results showed no significant difference between active and control samples. The activity allows students to

2. The synthetic bombykol used in Molecules of Life was obtained from Walter Leal and his research group in the Department of Entomology at the University of California, Davis.

participate in an entertaining experiment that extends beyond the classroom; it also provides an example of how scientific ideas can be co-opted by the business world, often in questionable ways.

The next lecture in the unit (L21) relates to drug development and personalized medicine. The lecture is broken into three segments: an overview of the drug development process; case studies in toxicity, clinical trials, and intellectual property; and a survey of personalized medicine. After a brief overview of the drug discovery process (a process that requires about $1 billion and ten to fifteen years per drug), students are introduced to the basic considerations of drug design: potency, specificity, bioavailability, biostability, and economics. The chemical features that contribute to potency (shape complementarity, hydrogen-bond alignment, and molecular rigidity) are examined in detail. The lecture then highlights three different modes of drug discovery: serendipity, rational design, and large-scale combinatorial approaches.

The lecture transitions to a series of case studies that highlight the importance of drug specificity and toxicity. The first example is the thalidomide tragedy, in which the sedative thalidomide (or more specifically, an enantiomer of thalidomide) was discovered to be teratogenic. The second example centers on a failed antihypertension drug that was found to induce an unusual but desirable side effect. The result was sildenafil, more popularly known as Viagra. These case studies provide excellent opportunities to discuss such key topics as clinical testing, the FDA approval process, and intellectual property law.

The final segment focuses on personalized medicine. Here, a series of examples illustrates how modern biochemical knowledge has resulted in new medicinal approaches. The first example, warfarin, illustrates how genetic testing enables doctors to set proper dosages for drugs with small therapeutic indices (Rieder et al., 2005). The second example, which focuses on the *BRCA1* and *BRCA2* genes, shows how genetic testing can help predict a patient's risk of disease (in this case, breast cancer; Struewing et al., 1997). The last example discusses how genetic testing can help doctors match a patient's disease to its best therapeutic treatment. For this example, the lecture describes trastuzumab (Herceptin) and its selective potency against human epidermal growth factor receptor 2–dependent cancers (Gown, 2008). A discussion of the outlook of such personalized treatments concludes the lecture.

The third lecture of the unit (L22) focuses on the controversial subject of stem cells. The lecture begins by defining what stem cells are (cells defined by their limitless replicative potential and their able to differentiate into specialized lines) and by reviewing important terminology (*totipotent*, *pluripotent*, *multipotent*, and *unipotent*). The lecture then focuses on the sources of stem cells: embryos, somatic cell nuclear transfer, and the reprogramming of differentiated adult cells (Yu et al., 2007). The ethical dilemmas associated with each source are discussed in turn.

Next, the lecture takes a pragmatic turn to discuss the use of stem cells in medicine. The first example presented is hematopoietic stem cell donation,

**Figure 11: A Demonstrated Use of Stem Cells in the Replacement of a Woman's Damaged Trachea**

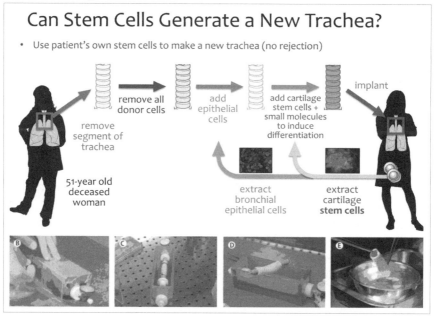

Cartilaginous stem cells enabled doctors to grow a new layer of patient-compatible cartilage on the transplanted organ. Source: Macchiarini, P., P. Jungebluth, T. Go, M. A. Asnaghi, L. E. Rees, T. A. Cogan, A. Dodson, et al. 2008. Clinical transplantation of a tissue-engineered airway. *Lancet* 372(9655):2023–2030.

which is used as a treatment for various blood-borne cancers. The second example focuses on a potential therapy, β-cell replacement for type I diabetics (Xu et al., 2008), an idea that was inconceivable only one year earlier. The third example is taken from a news report that appeared just weeks before the lecture was given during the 2008 iteration of the course: the use of stem cells to facilitate the replacement of a body part (see Figure 11; Macchiarini et al., 2008). In this case, cartilaginous stem cells were used to prevent the rejection of a transplanted trachea. The final example details how stem cells might be used to replace a controversial treatment for Parkinson's disease. The treatment in question requires the transplantation of dopamine-producing neurons from aborted embryos (Rossi & Cattaneo, 2002). With the advent of stem cells, such valuable neurons could be produced in vitro, obviating the need for embryos altogether. A look into the future examines how stem cells might eventually be used to cure "irreversible" neurological disorders such as paralysis (Deshpande et al., 2006). The final segment of the lecture examines the legal, ethical, and philosophical issues surrounding stem cells, including retrieval from embryos, animal reproductive cloning, and human reproductive cloning.

The final lecture of the unit (and of the course) centers on the science of aging (L23). The lecture begins with the Gompertz law of mortality (so named for mathematician Benjamin Gompertz). The concepts of life span and life expectancy are examined, including the historical improvement of life expectancy over time (largely as a consequence of applied scientific knowledge). A philosophical question is raised: if evolution can "perfect" organisms, why do our bodies age at all? In the context of evolution, aging is not a significant selective force, because extrinsic factors (starvation, the elements, predators, and so on) are more significant causes of death (Kirkwood & Austad, 2000). From this key observation, three theories emerge. First, the drop in population with increasing age results in poor selection of age-related genes (selection shadow). Second, beneficial traits are typically selected early, while deleterious traits are selected late (pleiotropic antagonism). Third, metabolic resources are often better used for reproduction than for repair (disposable soma).

The lecture then discusses the latest aging-related research. The first discussion focuses on the nematode *Caenorhabditis elegans* and how its metabolic pathways are modulated in response to environmental circumstances (Golden & Riddle, 1982; Butcher et al., 2007). A key conclusion from the nematode research is that *aging is largely a regulated process*, one that perhaps could be manipulated by small molecules. The lecture then documents the shift in approaches to regulating aging, from reversing its effects ("fountain of youth") to delaying its onset. A survey of age-related research follows: caloric restriction (CR; McCay, Crowell & Maynard, 1935), CR-activated genes, and small molecule mediators of those genes (Howitz et al., 2003). Resveratrol, a component of red wine, is shown to be one such small molecule (Baur et al., 2006). More potent analogs that are in consideration for use as diabetic treatments are discussed (Milne et al., 2007). The last section of the lecture focuses on mianserin and its analogs, small molecules that hold the potential to extend life through a specific serotonin-mediated pathway (Petrascheck, Ye & Buck, 2007). The lecture concludes with an interesting study on caloric restriction, perception, and reality (Libert et al., 2007). Value issues such as quality of life versus quantity of life factor heavily into the ensuing discussion.

## COURSE EVALUATIONS

As with all Harvard courses, Molecules of Life is evaluated using Harvard's Cumulative Undergraduate Education system (CUE guide). Overall, in 2008–2009 the course received a rating of 4.7 (based on a 1 to 5 scale), the second highest rating of any general education class offered over a three-year span (the top-rated course was a ten-student German culture class); this outcome is particularly noteworthy because the average score for a general education class is 3.8 (see Figure 12). Molecules of Life currently ranks as the highest-rated science general education course. When asked if they would recommend the course to their peers, students responded affirmatively; the question rated positively, at 4.8. Representative responses to the question "What would you like to tell future students about this class?" are shown in Figure 13.

## Figure 12: Cumulative Undergraduate Education Guide Evaluation for Molecules of Life

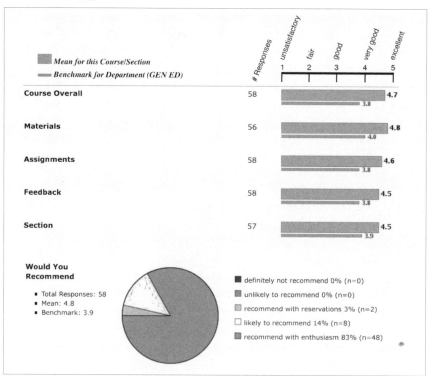

Responses based on the Fall 2008 offering of Molecules of Life.

The course materials received a rating of 4.8, while the assignments received a rating of 4.6. General education courses receive averages of 4.0 and 3.8 in the same respective categories. Course feedback by the faculty was rated at 4.5, versus a general-education average of 3.8. The course was praised for its well-structured lectures, its organization, its relevance to everyday life, and its balance of difficulty and accessibility. Students also approved of the course materials and website and liked the fact that no textbook was assigned for the course.

The course instructors received ratings of 4.8 and 4.7. The teaching fellows also received very high praise (an average rating of 4.7). The section component of the course received a rating of 4.5, versus a general-education average of 3.9. Students praised the activities as enjoyable and engaging, and many listed the section syllabus as a course strength. The silkworm moth pheromone demonstration was the most frequently cited favorite activity. The strawberry DNA extraction and the blood glucose monitoring session were also frequently listed as enjoyable.

**Figure 13: Representative Cumulative Undergraduate Education Guide Responses from Students in Molecules of Life**

| **What would you like to tell future students about this class?** |
| --- |
| • It is one of the best science cores you can take. Interesting, entertaining, great professors, and not hard! |
| • You will learn the scientific side of marijuana, understand what the hell people mean by stem cells, and learn abut the ongoing war on cancer. |
| • This was probably one of the most interesting options for a Science B or Science of Living Systems class -- it was easy without being a joke, and it looked at ethical, legal, and business issues surrounding the diseases we covered. |
| • I would recommend this course to everyone. The interesting material and engaging lectures generated excitement about current research in the field and provided practical knowledge that can be used in daily life. An excellent way to fulfill the core/gen ed. This is what general education should be. |
| • This course is an excellent way for non-science concentrators to be exposed to the intriguing world of medicine and diseases in an incredibly approachable way. |
| • By far the best core and possibly the best class I've taken at Harvard. Not an overwhelming amount of material and all material is presented in lecture. Lectures are fantastic, interesting, and even entertaining. Everyone should take this class. |
| • This is the perfect core: interesting, relevant, a subject area I would not learn about in my concentration, and not too time-consuming. |
| • It's like your interactive high school course, in a good way. |
| • I felt that it was a good core class because it wasn't too intense about science, it was actually relevant to my life, and the work load was reasonable. |
| • Great course and excellent way to fulfill a core (especially Science B, which is a tough one). No books to buy; no readings really. Great lecture notes. Very pertinent information to know for life. |
| • It was amazing. I learned so much and felt very engaged in the course. |
| • This course tells you everything you didn't know that you wanted to learn, from the basic scientific basis of hemaphrodites to why marijuana and opiates feel good. What more could you ask for from a science class? |
| • One of the best classes I've taken at Harvard. Everyone should know the material in this class! |
| • It's an amazing intro bio (if it can be called that) course about how molecules play crucial roles in our day-to-day lives. |
| • This is an amazing class that is relevant to life. |

Responses based on the Fall 2008 offering of Molecules of Life.

The most significant criticism was lack of depth in topical coverage. Some students desired more scientific detail. Others desired more structured reviews prior to the examinations. Several students felt that the course was not challenging enough.

Because the course is not a requirement for any student, the most concrete indication of its success is perhaps its changing enrollment. Since its 2008–2009 debut, Science of Living Systems 11 has grown from 80 students to 275, an enrollment increase of 244 percent.

COURSE UPDATES FOR FALL 2009

The Fall 2009 version of the course incorporated several improvements to the syllabus. The second unit of the course (*Molecular Messengers in Humans*) saw the reorganization of the "Cannabinoids and endocannabinoids" (L13) and "Opiods and endorphins" (L14) lectures into "Opiods and cannabinoids" and "Opiods, alcohol, and addiction." This change brings the noteworthy topic of alcohol abuse into the course, and provides a framework of addiction for the unit's recurring theme of illicit drug use.

The second unit also featured a new lecture, "Molecules of food and nutrition," which approaches food from a chemist's point of view. Using the ingredients label from a box of cereal as a road map, this lecture addresses such nutritional topics as calories, vitamins, carbohydrates, glycemic index, *trans*-fats, and the food pyramid from a molecular perspective, explaining the chemical role of vitamins and how the structure of different types of fat has profound consequences for their health impact. These topics better transition the course to the diabetes lecture (L15) through the subject of obesity.

To improve the syllabus organization, "Evolution as a molecular and human phenomenon" (L3) was moved to the end of the first unit, after small molecule–macromolecule interactions have been addressed. Additionally, "Drug discovery and personalized medicine" (L21) was moved to the start of the final unit as a better transition from the preceding unit on molecular medicines and human disease. Finally, all lectures were updated and revised based on feedback from the first offering of the course.

The second offering of the course also incorporated new section activities. As an introductory activity, students were provided with "miracle fruit" tablets that temporarily modify one's taste buds by virtue of a protein called miraculin (Theerasilp et al., 1989). After consuming one tablet, the students are provided with a series of sour foods (such as lemon juice and vinegar), which they will taste as intensely sweet. This activity introduces students to the interplay of small molecules (those we taste as sweet or sour) and proteins (miraculin and taste receptors) through a unique and memorable sensory experience.

The revised syllabus also introduced a field trip to the Harvard Museum of Natural History, providing students the opportunity to view the museum's exhibit on Darwinian evolution.


CONCLUSION

Molecules of Life is a novel general education science course that introduces students to the key ideas, facts, and theories underlying living systems by using the dynamic interplay of small molecules and proteins as a theme. The course was purposefully designed for non-science majors, with an emphasis placed on connections to everyday life. The syllabus includes such topics of widespread interest as heredity, evolution, human disease, sexual development, and aging. Considerable course time is spent evaluating the social, ethical, and philosophical dimensions of each topic.

The course also makes use of a novel section syllabus. This syllabus includes several interactive activities, including the extraction of DNA from strawberries, the genotyping and phenotyping of students' taste receptors, the debating of the legal merits of marijuana, the monitoring of students' blood sugar levels, and the live demonstration of pheromones using silkworm moths. These activities further engage students and provide them with concrete illustrations of the concepts taught in lecture.

Given the increasing importance of science and technology to modern life, general education science courses should have greater representation within liberal arts curricula. We believe that both the pedagogy and scientific content of Molecules of Life could serve as instructional models for these classes.

## REFERENCES

Adams, R. 1942. Marihuana: Harvey Lecture, February 19, 1942. *Bulletin of the New York Academy of Medicine* 18(11):705–730.

Balthazart, J., M. Baillien, C. A. Cornil, and G. F. Ball. 2004. Preoptic aromatase modulates male sexual behavior: Slow and fast mechanisms of action. *Physiology and Behavior* 83(2):247–270.

Baur, J. A., K. J. Pearson, N. L. Price, H. A. Jamieson, C. Lerin, A. Kalra, V. V. Prabhu, et al. 2006. Resveratrol improves health and survival of mice on a high-calorie diet. *Nature* 444:337–342.

Beggs, K. T., K. A. Glendining, N. M. Marechal, V. Vergoz, I. Nakamura, K. N. Slessor, and A. R. Mercer. 2007. Queen pheromone modulates brain dopamine function in worker honey bees. *Proceedings of the National Academy of Sciences of the United States of America* 104(7):2460–2464.

Berglund, H., P. Lindstrom, and I. Savic. 2006. Brain response to putative pheromones in lesbian women. *Proceedings of the National Academy of Sciences of the United States of America* 103(21):8269–8274.

Brown, L. P. 2008. Two takes: Drugs are a major social problem, we cannot legalize them. *U.S. News and World Report*, July 25.

Butcher, R. A., M. Fujita, F. C. Schroeder, and J. Clardy. 2007. Small-molecule pheromones that control dauer development in *Caenorhabditis elegans*. *Nature Chemical Biology* 3(7):420–422.

Butenandt, A., R. Beckamnn, and E. Hecker. 1961. Über den Sexuallockstoff des Seidenspinners. 1. Der biologische Test und die Isolierung des reinen Sexuallockstoffes Bombykol. *Hoppe-Seylers Zeitschriftfür Pysiologische Chemie* 324.

Carter, R., and K. N. Mendis. 2002. Evolutionary and historical aspects of the burden of malaria. *Clinical Microbiology Reviews* 15(4):564–594.

Caspi, A., J. McClay, T. E. Moffitt, J. Mill, J. Martin, I. W. Craig, A. Taylor, and R. Poulton. 2002. Role of genotype in the cycle of violence in maltreated children. *Science* 297:851–854.

———, K. Sugden, T. E. Moffitt, A. Taylor, I. W. Craig, H. Harrington, J. McClay, J. Mill, J. Martin, A. Braithwaite, and R. Poulton. 2003. Influence of life stress on depression: Moderation by a polymorphism in the 5-HTT gene. *Science* 301:386–389.

Deshpande, D. M., Y. S. Kim, T. Martinez, J. Carmen, S. Dike, I. Shats, L. L. Rubin, et al. 2006. Recovery from paralysis in adult rats using embryonic stem cells. *Annals of Neurology* 60(1):32–44.

Devane, W. A., L. Hanus, A. Breuer, R. G. Pertwee, L. A. Stevenson, G. Griffin, D. Gibson, A. Mandelbaum, A. Etinger, and R. Mechoulam. 1992. Isolation and structure of a brain constituent that binds to the cannabinoid receptor. *Science* 258:1946–1949.

Eugenides, J. 2002. *Middlesex*. New York: Picador.

Golden, J. W., and D. L. Riddle. 1982. A pheromone influences larval development in the nematode *Caenorhabditis elegans*. *Science* 218:578–580.

Gown, A. M. 2008. Current issues in ER and HER2 testing by IHC in breast cancer. *Modern Pathology* 21(Suppl. 2):8–15.

Hanahan, D., and R. A. Weinberg. 2000. The hallmarks of cancer. *Cell* 100(1): 57–70.

Howitz, K. T., K. J. Bitterman, H. Y. Cohen, D. W. Lamming, S. Lavu, J. G. Wood, R. E. Zipkin, et al. 2003. Small molecule activators of sirtuins extend *Saccharomyces cerevisiae* lifespan. *Nature* 425:191–196.

Hughes, J., T. W. Smith, H. W. Kosterlitz, L. A. Fothergill, B. A. Morgan, and H. R. Morris. 1975. Identification of two related pentapeptides from the brain with potent opiate agonist activity. *Nature* 258:577–580.

Imperato-McGinley, J., L. Guerrero, T. Gautier, and R. E. Peterson. 1974. Steroid 5-alpha-reductase deficiency in man: An inherited form of male pseudo-hermaphroditism. *Science* 186:1213–1215.

Kim, U., S. Wooding, D. Ricci, L. B. Jorde, and D. Drayna. 2005. Worldwide haplotype diversity and coding sequence variation at human bitter taste receptor loci. *Human Mutation* 26(3):199–204.

Kimchi, T., J. Xu, and C. Dulac. 2007. A functional circuit underlying male sexual behaviour in the female mouse brain. *Nature* 448:1009–1014.

Kirkwood, T. B., and S. N. Austad. 2000. Why do we age? *Nature* 408:233–238.

Kosfeld, M., M. Heinrichs, P. J. Zak, U. Fischbacher, and E. Fehr. 2005. Oxytocin increases trust in humans. *Nature* 435:673–667.

Lesch, K. P., D. Bengel, A. Heils, S. Z. Sabol, B. D. Greenberg, S. Petri, J. Benjamin, C. R. Muller, D. H. Hamer, and D. L. Murphy. 1996. Association of anxiety-related traits with a polymorphism in the serotonin transporter gene regulatory region. *Science* 274:1527–1531.

Libert, S., J. Zwiener, X. Chu, W. Vanvoorhies, G. Roman, and S. D. Pletcher. 2007. Regulation of *Drosophila* life span by olfaction and food-derived odors. *Science* 315:1133–1137.

Liggett, S. B., J. Mialet-Perez, S. Thaneemit-Chen, S. A. Weber, S. M. Greene, D. Hodne, B. Nelson, et al. 2006. A polymorphism within a conserved beta(1)-adrenergic receptor motif alters cardiac function and beta-blocker response in human heart failure. *Proceedings of the National Academy of Sciences of the United States of America* 103(30):11288–11293.

Lim, M. M., Z. Wang, D. E. Olazabal, X. Ren, E. F. Terwilliger, and L. J. Young. 2004. Enhanced partner preference in a promiscuous species by manipulating the expression of a single gene. *Nature* 429:754–757.

Loewi, O. 1957. On the background of the discovery of neurochemical transmission. *Journal of the Mount Sinai Hospital, New York* 24(6):1014–1016.

Macchiarini, P., P. Jungebluth, T. Go, M. A. Asnaghi, L. E. Rees, T. A. Cogan, A. Dodson, et al. 2008. Clinical transplantation of a tissue-engineered airway. *Lancet* 372(9655):2023–2030.

Marsicano, G., C. T. Wotjak, S. C. Azad, T. Bisogno, G. Rammes, M. G. Cascio, H. Hermann, et al. 2002. The endogenous cannabinoid system controls extinction of aversive memories. *Nature* 418:530–534.

Matsuda, L. A., S. J. Lolait, M. J. Brownstein, A. C. Young, and T. I. Bonner. 1990. Structure of a cannabinoid receptor and functional expression of the cloned cDNA. *Nature* 346:561–564.

McCay, C. M., M. F. Crowell, and L. A. Maynard. 1935. The effect of retarded growth upon the length of life span and upon the ulimate body size: One figure. *Journal of Nutrition* 10:17.

Merritt, R. B., L. A. Bierwert, B. Slatko, M. P. Weiner, J. Ingram, K. Sciarra, E. Weiner. 2008. Tasting phenylthiocarbamide (PTC): A new integrative genetics lab with an old flavor. *American Biology Teacher* online (May 2008):23–28.

Milne, J. C., P. D. Lambert, S. Schenk, D. P. Carney, J. J. Smith, D. Gagne, L. Jin, et al. 2007. Small molecule activators of SIRT1 as therapeutics for the treatment of type 2 diabetes. *Nature* 450:712–716.

Montag, C., J. W. Buckholtz, P. Hartmann, M. Merz, C. Burk, J. Hennig, and M. Reuter. 2008. COMT genetic variation affects fear processing: psychophysiological evidence. *Behavioral Neuroscience* 122(4):901–909.

Moskos, P. 2008. Two takes: Drugs are too dangerous not to regulate, we should legalize them. *U.S. News and World Report*, July 25.

Pert, C. B., and S. H. Snyder. 1973. Opiate receptor: Demonstration in nervous tissue. *Science* 179:1011–1014.

Peterson, R. E., J. Imperato-McGinley, L. Guerrero, T. Gautier, and E. Sturla. 1977. Male pseudohermaphroditism due to steroid 5-alpha-reductase deficiency. *The American Journal of Medicine* 62:170–191.

Petrascheck, M., X. Ye, and L. B. Buck. 2007. An antidepressant that extends lifespan in adult *Caenorhabditis elegans. Nature* 450:553–556.

Ratner, R. E. 2006. An update on the Diabetes Prevention Program. *Endocrine Practice* 12(Suppl. 1):20–24.

*Report of the Task Force on General Education.* 2007. Cambridge, Mass.: Harvard University.

Reya, T., S. J. Morrison, M. F. Clarke, and I. L. Weissman. 2001. Stem cells, cancer, and cancer stem cells. *Nature* 414:105–111.

Rieder, M. J., A. P. Reiner, B. F. Gage, D. A. Nickerson, C. S. Eby, H. L. McLeod, D. K. Blough, K. E. Thummel, D. L. Veenstra, and A. E. Rettie. 2005. Effect of VKORC1 haplotypes on transcriptional regulation and warfarin dose. *New England Journal of Medicine* 352(22):2285–2293.

Rockman, M. V., M. W. Hahn, N. Soranzo, F. Zimprich, D. B. Goldstein, and G. A. Wray. 2005. Ancient and recent positive selection transformed opioid *cis*-regulation in humans. *PLoS Biology* 3(12):e387.

Rossi, F., and E. Cattaneo. 2002. Opinion: Neural stem cell therapy for neurological diseases: Dreams and reality. *Nature Reviews: Neuroscience* 3(5):401–409.

Savic, I., H. Berglund, and P. Lindstrom. 2005. Brain response to putative pheromones in homosexual men. *Proceedings of the National Academy of Sciences of the United States of America* 102(20):7356–7361.

———, and P. Lindstrom. 2008. PET and MRI show differences in cerebral asymmetry and functional connectivity between homo- and heterosexual subjects. *Proceedings of the National Academy of Sciences of the United States of America* 105(27):9403–9408.

Simpson, J. L., A. Ljungqvist, M. A. Ferguson-Smith, A. de la Chapelle, L. J. Elsas II, A. A. Ehrhardt, M. Genel, E. A. Ferris, and A. Carlson. 2000. Gender verification in the Olympics. *JAMA* 284(12):1568–1569.

Stern, K., and M. K. McClintock. 1998. Regulation of ovulation by human pheromones. *Nature* 392:177–179.

Struewing, J. P., P. Hartge, S. Wacholder, S. M. Baker, M. Berlin, M. McAdams, M. M. Timmerman, L. C. Brody, and M. A. Tucker. 1997. The risk of cancer associated with specific mutations of *BRCA1* and *BRCA2* among Ashkenazi Jews. *New England Journal of Medicine* 336(20):1401–1408.

Taubenberger, J. K., A. H. Reid, R. M. Lourens, R. Wang, G. Jin, and T. G. Fanning. 2005. Characterization of the 1918 influenza virus polymerase genes. *Nature* 437:889–993.

Theerasilp, S., H. Hitotsuya, S. Nakajo, K. Nakaya, Y. Nakamura, and Y. Kurihara. 1989. Complete amino acid sequence and structure characterization of the taste-modifying protein, miraculin. *Journal of Biochemistry* 264(12):6655–6659.

Tishkoff, S. A., F. A. Reed, A. Ranciaro, B. F. Voight, C. C. Babbitt, J. S. Silverman, K. Powell, et al. 2007. Convergent adaptation of human lactase persistence in Africa and Europe. *Nature Genetics* 39(1):31–40.

Tsien, R. Y. 1998. The green fluorescent protein. *Annual Review of Biochemistry* 67:509–544.

Vajo, Z., and W. C. Duckworth. 2000. Genetically engineered insulin analogs: diabetes in the new millenium. *Pharmacological Reviews* 52(1):1–9.

Xu, X., J. D'Hoker, G. Stange, S. Bonne, N. De Leu, X. Xiao, M. Van de Casteele, et al. 2008. Beta cells can be generated from endogenous progenitors in injured adult mouse pancreas. *Cell* 132(2):197–207.

Yu, J., M. A. Vodyanik, K. Smuga-Otto, J. Antosiewicz-Bourget, J. L. Frane, S. Tian, J. Nie, et al. 2007. Induced pluripotent stem cell lines derived from human somatic cells. *Science* 318:1917–1920.

Zhang, X., J. M. Beaulieu, T. D. Sotnikova, R. R. Gainetdinov, and M. G. Caron. 2004. Tryptophan hydroxylase-2 controls brain serotonin synthesis. *Science* 305:217.

# CHAPTER 10

# Science for All in a Core Curriculum: Frontiers of Science at Columbia University

Darcy B. Kelley

## THE PROBLEM

Practicing scientists have strong views about what constitutes good preparation in a particular discipline. While these views shift as science evolves, every molecular biologist would agree that a student needs to understand the genetic code and the way in which proteins are assembled, and every neuroscientist would agree that a student needs to understand how an action potential is generated and how information is transmitted at the synapse. When it comes to preparing science majors outside their particular scientific discipline, we find few areas of agreement; even more contentious is what constitutes science education for non-science majors.

For the future parent, social worker, businessperson, senator, poet, or economist, what should completion of a science requirement confer? Is it important to know facts (the distance to the sun) or to be able to assess whether the facts averred (in the media, on the Internet) are plausible? Should all college graduates be expected to be able to read and understand a scientific article (Watson and Crick's *Nature* paper on the structure of DNA) as they are expected to read a piece of literature (Herman Melville's *Moby-Dick*)? That is, should they be able to explain the question the paper addresses, how the authors address the question, as well as explain what the findings mean?

I believe that the most important skill a science requirement can develop is the capacity for critical analysis. In episode twelve of the seventh season of *West Wing*, a runaway nuclear reactor in California is producing radioactive gas that has to be pumped into a building inadequate for containment. The gas is vented, and the reading just above the smokestack is at first 569 millirems; it then "stabilizes" (two readings) at 561 millirems. The "safe" level of exposure is 500 millirems, so the American people are informed of the exact levels recorded. Millions take to the highways. Is this a plausible scenario? Why is 500 millirems considered safe and anything greater not safe? What does exposure mean? How great is the risk that the building will explode (said to occur at 50 psi)? As I watch this episode, I think, "If I were there, should I stay home or set sail? Which way will the Santa Ana winds blow?"

Life has a way of turning hypotheticals into actuals. Your mother has a breast lump; it is biopsied and found to be estrogen-receptor negative. Her doctor prescribes a drug that antagonizes the effects of that hormone. Should you look for a new doctor? The effects of exercise and eating a diet rich in vegetables, fruit, and fish are independently beneficial for warding off Alzheimer's disease. Does this mean you should choose one strategy or adopt both? What is the probability of a meteor hitting Earth in your lifetime? If one were to hit, where should you be? The ability to analyze data and understand scientific knowledge is essential for an informed citizenry and thus for effective government. How can we achieve this goal within the context of a university education?

## AN APPROACH

In 2001, a group of Columbia University faculty members began to develop a one-semester course, Frontiers of Science, that is now taken by every entering Columbia College student. The immediate impetus for developing the course was a survey, undertaken by the University's Committee on Science Instruction, of the courses students were choosing to satisfy the University's three-course science requirement. The survey found, for example, that although more than five hundred entering students each year expressed some interest in preparing for a career in medicine, only seventy to eighty graduated having fulfilled the necessary requirements. For the rest, the typical science experience consisted of one introductory chemistry course and a year of calculus. Thus, the majority received a science education that did not even remotely expose them to the driving forces of modern science, such as exciting new discoveries about the way the physical universe and biological worlds work and interact.

The survey found that even for science majors the kind of training typically offered within a given department bore little resemblance to the multidisciplinary flavor of current research. The guild-like mentality of science training presumes that students need to reach the top of the disciplinary pyramid before they can grapple with anything "real." To ascend the pyramid, they must master a long series of preparatory courses. Because only a handful of majors ever reach the top, only a small percentage of students get to experience how science is really done in a given field and what problems the field is currently investigating. What if we could break the pyramid for students both with and without a professed interest in science? Introducing science across disciplines at the level at which it is actually practiced could set the nascent scientist on an interdisciplinary trajectory and bring the excitement of science to students whose major impression is that it involves simply memorizing a great many facts and equations.

An introductory, multidisciplinary science course for all students is usually considered impossible. That Frontiers of Science was launched in its current form is largely attributable to an existing curricular structure at Columbia College called the Core Curriculum, a series of seminars aimed at critical evaluation of important ideas in philosophy, literature, society, art, and music. All entering students take the Core: the poet takes Literature Humanities, the concert pianist Music Humanities, the accomplished historian Contemporary Civilization, the nascent cosmologist Frontiers of Science. The Core provides the required prescription for Frontiers: the early stages of a university education should include a common learning experience for a cohort of students with wildly different preparations, gifts, and interests.

## WHAT IS FRONTIERS OF SCIENCE?

Like other elements of the Core Curriculum, Frontiers of Science is taught in small seminars of twenty-two students. However, Frontiers of Science is multidisciplinary, with half the subject matter taken from the physical sciences and half from the life sciences. Thus, a number of faculty members are involved in teaching Frontiers over the course of the semester. Which sciences are taught —from among physics, chemistry, astronomy, earth science, molecular and evolutionary biology, biodiversity, and neuroscience—changes from semester to semester and from year to year depending on the faculty involved. In addition to teaching science and non-science majors together, Frontiers faces the challenge of faculty teaching across disciplines; a cosmologist might teach about molecular evolution.

Each unit of Frontiers of Science runs for three weeks; in addition to weekly seminars, a senior faculty member presents a lecture series on exciting discoveries in a particular field. No attempt is made to develop a single theme across the semester. The analytical skills that cut across disciplines are presented in the online text, *Scientific Habits of Mind* (http://www.fos-online.org/habitsofmind/index.html). Seminar sections are led by either a senior faculty member or a Columbia Science Fellow, a combined lecturer/postdoctoral position established specifically to meet the teaching needs of Frontiers of Science. The development of the curriculum is a joint faculty effort spearheaded by the Science Fellows.

## THE CHALLENGES OF FRONTIERS: TEACHING AND LEARNING

Frontiers of Science comprises twenty-eight seminar sections taught to 550 students each semester by (usually) sixteen members of the faculty. A course director and an assistant director of the Center for the Core Curriculum manage the logistics and organizational challenges. Teaching Frontiers of Science means mastering current research in at least three disciplines beyond a faculty member's area of expertise. For example, most astronomers have not had significant exposure to biology since high school, and many neuroscientists have never taken a geology course. In the tradition of the Core Curriculum, Columbia does not segregate science majors from non-science majors within Frontiers of Science. Teaching a small seminar with a diverse group of students (chemists-, poets-, and economists-to-be) is a significant challenge. The future chemist is chomping at the bit to get into preparative chemistry, and the future poet thinks she has escaped science by choosing Columbia. The Core Curriculum, however, mandates as an educational philosophy that entering students have a common experience in critical analysis.

The two cultures of C. P. Snow are forged in kindergarten. That they are so evident in college students is thus no surprise. Frontiers of Science is taught from the perspective of the ways in which scientists carry out their explorations, experiments, observations, and mathematical models; many students are stunned to discover that the memorization skills they so carefully mastered in high school—skills that were instrumental in their gaining admission to Columbia—do not serve them in the course. Frontiers of Science emphasizes analysis and problem-solving. Many units rely on mathematical skills (algebra and statistics), and most students are not used to viewing math as a tool to solve problems rather than as a self-contained subject matter. While university-level scientific research is increasingly multidisciplinary, few high school courses reflect this change. Students feel they have barely come to terms with one topic (for example, volcanoes) before they must switch to another (for example, the brain). Aspiring astronomers find three lectures too brief an introduction to the most important subject on the planet, and the assignments may not seem challenging enough—while their classmates may not even know where to begin. Students do not enter college with well-honed skills in group learning, and the day when their classmate from the Frontiers seminar is president of the United States and is responsible for deciding whether to vent that containment building described above seems impossibly distant.

## COLUMBIA FACULTY AND CORE COURSES IN SCIENCE

The Columbia science faculty began discussing a general science course in parallel with discussions about Contemporary Civilization, the first Core Curriculum course, which was launched in 1919. The motivation then for establishing a core science course was similar to the motivation that drove the development of Frontiers of Science beginning in 2001, but the courses that eventually were launched in 1934 bear little resemblance to Frontiers. Those courses, Science A (physics and chemistry) and Science B (geology and biology), were to be taken only by non-science students and could not serve as prerequisites for any "real" courses in any science department. They were terminated at the outbreak of war in 1941, and although we do not have course evaluations for those seven years, the experience must have been unsatisfactory. By 1945, with the Core Curriculum well under way, a general science course was again under discussion, but this time the goal was to create a course that would include all students. The idea was

> that a specially constructed and well-integrated two-year course in the natural sciences be a required course for all students who are candidates for a degree from Columbia College, quite irrespective of whether such students plan to enter one of the scientific professions or not . . . [and] that such a course be staffed by men who are prepared to give competent instruction in all of it, and not simply in some fragmentary portion of it.[1]

In her May 2006 address to the Columbia College graduating class, Dean Kathryn Yatrakis noted:

> The 1945 Committee was in fact quite emphatic about this general science course being required of all students saying that if it were to restrict the course to non-science students, it would amount to lowering the general standard of interest, enthusiasm, and inquisitiveness, and hence to exclude those who would supply the chief stimulus to both teachers and students.

The new attempt apparently had general support from the faculty as a whole but foundered on the antipathy of the science faculty. The resulting 1946 report amounted to a recommendation for the reinstatement of Science A and Science B when the financial climate permitted. Apparently the climate did not sufficiently improve between 1946 and 1983, the year in which a faculty committee again recommended a single course for all students. The seesaw continued, however: in 1990 another faculty committee recommended against a single science course but did recommend the creation of a standing Committee on Science Instruction (COSI). This committee, in the end, provided the impetus for Frontiers of Science.

The university administration (especially the provost and the dean of the college) was from the outset highly supportive of change. A working group adopted the 1983 recommendation, its form was shaped by the members of COSI, and the future directors went forth to sell the idea, first to the science faculties and then to the faculties as a whole. As in 1945, the science faculty was skeptical: one distinguished senior chemist even informed the vice presi-

---

1. Columbia College Committee on Plans, *A College Program in Action: A Review of Working Principles at Columbia College* (New York: Columbia University Press, 1946), 127.

dent for arts and sciences that the course would be created "over my dead body." While such a high level of opposition was unusual, the concerns voiced by members of the science faculty were thoughtful and well founded. But from their meetings with the science departments, the course directors usually emerged, like the Pied Piper of Hamlin, trailing at least one enthusiastic faculty member, typically a scientist of extreme distinction with a passion for conveying the beauty and power of science to the public. This initial group recruited another group of more junior faculty members (the Columbia Science Fellows), and after a pilot semester in Fall 2003, Frontiers of Science appeared as a five-year experiment in the Core Curriculum in 2004, an experiment renewed for an additional five years in Spring 2009. The chemistry department now feels that "Chemistry is too important not to be in Frontiers and Frontiers is too important not to include Chemistry," as James Valenti, director of undergraduate studies and former chair of the Department of Chemistry, put it.

Why the seesaw? What conditions in 1945, 1983, and 2001 made a single course seem important enough to be a possibility, and what in 1933, 1946, and 1990 engendered such grave reservations? The main factor was probably leadership, from both faculty committees and the university administration. However, world events may well have played a role in faculty opinions. In the 1940s, the atomic bomb and the nuclear arms race focused American attention on the power of science, how it should be harnessed, and how it must be constrained. At the millennium, a widespread appreciation of a new threat—global warming—emerged. Determining the causes and consequences of warming requires an extraordinary scientific effort to understand and political will to act; that will must be an informed one. Finally, there is money. In 1933 and 1941, funds for education (and all else) were in short supply because of, respectively, the Great Depression and World War II. Dreams of inclusive education, no matter how important, were a luxury. In the expansive economy of the early 2000s, the financial climate might have been relaxed enough for university leaders to consider seriously the ambitious goals of Frontiers of Science.

## FACULTY DEVELOPMENT AND FRONTIERS

A beginning science faculty member at a typical R1 university is expected to develop a research program and a series of graduate and undergraduate courses. Although the new faculty member has been training for the research program for more than ten years, he or she has no explicit preparation for developing a teaching program. "Sink or swim" is often an accurate summary of the new faculty experience. One useful feature of Frontiers of Science is that beginning faculty members are mentored in creating a curriculum and teaching small seminars both by more senior faculty and by other Science Fellows. The Fellows work in teams with other faculty members to create seminar materials for each unit, weekly assignments, and the midterm and final examinations. The teams include scientists both from within the discipline of the unit and from other disciplines. Seminar materials include computer simulations, experimental design, and data analysis—all tied to the unit and that week's lecture. The Fellows also lead a weekly seminar in how one might teach that week's seminar, going through the suggested class exercises and troubleshooting issues that were raised in the Monday lectures.

Columbia currently has eleven Science Fellows and twenty-three former Fellows. Of the latter, thirteen hold a tenure-track assistant professorship or its equivalent, five hold a non-tenure-track research position, one is a high school science teacher, two work in industry, one in policy, and one in educational consulting. Some former Fellows have launched Frontiers-like efforts at their new institutions. The network of former Fellows has great potential as a resource for the development of new faculty. We have also prepared a website (Frontiers of Science Online, or FOSO) with materials (lectures, seminar guides, *Scientific Habits of Mind*) from four representative units in the Frontiers of Science course. The site provides opportunities for faculty outside Columbia to engage in substantive discussions of science education and to share materials and approaches.

Frontiers of Science has also affected the educational approaches of the senior faculty at Columbia. Twenty-six faculty members, representing all the science departments at Columbia College, have taught the course, delivering lectures and leading seminars. An example of the impact of Frontiers of Science on their teaching is the weekly lecture that serves, together with *Scientific Habits of Mind*, as a text for the course. The idea behind the lecture is to present a cutting-edge topic in current research in a way that is comprehensible to any entering student. This goal means that the lecture has to have a clear road map and no jargon. The common themes of the course, embodied in *Scientific Habits of Mind*, are highlighted as they appear.

I give lectures in a unit on neuroscience. The third lecture in this unit explores "The Evolution of Language" (http://www.fos-online.org/?q=node/390). This one lecture required more than two hundred hours to prepare, including review of any relevant papers that appeared the week before. All Frontiers of Science lectures are extensively rehearsed and critiqued before and after delivery by the Frontiers faculty members. Through this process (and by observing and critiquing the lectures of other Frontiers faculty), I have learned an enormous amount about clearly and effectively presenting information, lessons that have informed all the other courses I teach. Before my involvement with Frontiers of Science, I was accustomed to lecturing but found the small seminar format challenging. The Frontiers of Science seminar materials, seminar practice, and tutorials on how to engage students in discussion (http://www.fos-online.org/?q=taxonomy/term/62,61) were a terrific help in learning how to engage with twenty-two students effectively and collaboratively.

At this point you may wonder why any senior faculty member would choose to teach Frontiers of Science. At Columbia, no department requires its faculty to participate. All who teach Frontiers of Science are volunteers. The faculty who volunteer do so for two major reasons, I believe. The first is that learning about the science you never got to explore while climbing the disciplinary pyramid is enormous fun. Using gravitational lensing to peer back in time to the origins of the universe: who knew? Those pyroclastic flows that consumed Pompeii: awesome! Aside from learning new things (and sharpening one's intellectual skills to be able to teach them), arguing about how to teach science with fifteen other extremely bright people from other disciplines is also enjoyable. It is worth pointing out that I had never discussed how to teach with fellow faculty members before Frontiers started, and I expect that I am not alone in this experience. After Frontiers was initiated, we started a periodic brown bag luncheon across the sciences to discuss new approaches; the lunches are attended by a very large swath of the faculty from many different disciplines as well as by postdocs preparing for teaching positions.

The second major reason Columbia faculty volunteer for Frontiers of Science is the strong feeling among many of the faculty that Frontiers represents a significant opportunity to influence how our graduates will view scientific information and its uses in the future. Before Frontiers of Science, concerns about Earth's climate had led the Department of Earth and Environmental Sciences to propose that all students be required to take a course on the planet. This concern has translated into sturdy departmental support for Frontiers of Science.

## EVALUATING THE IMPACT OF FRONTIERS

Frontiers is still evolving as a course, and the major effort in evaluation is to improve its effectiveness for all students. Students have difficulty determining how to approach their assignments, they have difficulty seeing the common threads of scientific analysis that run through different topics, and they find the relation between course readings and course topics opaque. These are the issues we are addressing using data from a thorough evaluation at the end of each semester and from meetings with students who have suggestions for course improvements. We are making progress, but much work remains.

The percentage of students majoring in science at Columbia has remained steady at approximately 20 percent for the past ten years. Within the sciences, we have seen some shift in the choice of courses taken by students to satisfy the science requirement, most notably a doubling of enrollments in earth and environmental sciences courses. We are currently gathering data on course choices and number of science courses taken before and after Frontiers by male and female Columbia College students not majoring in a science. Finally, a group of faculty led by David Krantz developed an instrument to survey changes in attitudes and aspirations toward science and scientific literacy. A Web-based questionnaire (http://www.columbia.edu/cu/psychology/

Krantzlabweb/Ques/Scienceideas04/scienceideas.html) was administered to coincide with the pilot version of Frontiers of Science taken by one-third of Columbia's entering class in Fall 2003. The questionnaire was completed in early Fall 2003 by some of the students enrolled in the course and by some who were not enrolled; it was completed again in Spring 2004 by a separate group of first-year students, again including some who had enrolled in the course and some who had not. The questionnaire included a scale for mathematics confidence, a scale for science confidence and positivity, an assessment of interest in several different careers (some of which were science-related), an assessment of important career goals (personal and social), and a test of "science literacy" adapted in part from a former National Science Foundation survey of scientific literacy.

Among students not enrolled in Frontiers of Science, mathematics confidence scores were lower in Spring 2004 than for the group tested in early Fall 2003. The decrease in math confidence was much smaller for students who were enrolled in Frontiers of Science. While this result suggests a positive effect of enrollment in the course, the sample was small, and the questionnaire return rate was substantially higher among those enrolled in the course. At Columbia College, approximately one-third of each entering class intends to major in science, but at graduation the actual number is approximately 20 percent. Questionnaire results suggest that substantial attrition takes place in the first year of college: openness to several science-related careers declined between early Fall 2003 and Spring 2004. Because openness to these science-related careers is related to math confidence, part of the attrition might be explained by the decline in math confidence. If Frontiers of Science does maintain math confidence in addition to stimulating interest in a variety of scientific fields, it will help Columbia College realize more of its potential in undergraduate science education.

## FRONTIERS FOR ALL?

How to provide a university-level education in the sciences is a persistent question for colleges as they periodically review their undergraduate curricula. The relevant issues have been discussed at a number of recent conferences (for example, http://www.aacu.org/meetings/engaging_science/index.cfm and http://www.reinventioncenter.miami.edu/conference2006/proceedings .htm) and are the subject of several studies, including the one sponsored by the American Academy of Arts and Sciences that led to this publication (see http://www.amacad.org/projects/sciLiberalArts.aspx). How an individual college or university tackles this issue will differ dramatically depending on its size, resources, students, faculty interests, and educational philosophy. What is generally true, however, is that we need a wealth of approaches and educational resources to meet this challenge. Providing a forum in which those approaches and resources can be shared among us all is one of the goals of Frontiers of Science Online. At Columbia, we hope to shape Frontiers of Science using discussions and resources from other programs and look forward to sharing what we develop.[2]

2. The 1983 committee that raised the possibility of a "great ideas in science" course was chaired by David Helfand, author of *Scientific Habits of Mind*. The committee on science instruction was chaired by Jacqueline van Gorkom during the period when Frontiers of Science was initiated and shaped. Darcy Kelley and David Helfand were the initial course directors, joined later by Don Hood and, in 2010, Nicholas Christie-Blick. Special thanks to them for their useful comments on this essay. Establishing Frontiers of Science would not have been possible without the strong support of Columbia's then-provost, Jonathan Cole, and Columbia College's then-dean, Austin Quigley, as well as the backing of David Cohen, vice president for arts and sciences. The Office for the Core Curriculum, especially Assistant Director Elina Yuffa, provides essential logistical, moral, and intellectual support. Special thanks are due to Dean Kathryn Yatrakis not only for her guidance during various reviews but also for her research into the history of science in the Core Curriculum. Frontiers of Science has a spectacular faculty who make teaching and learning a joy. Last but not least, the students of Columbia College are a special group who have freely shared their good ideas about how Frontiers of Science should evolve.

# CHAPTER 11

# Assessing Scientific Reasoning in a Liberal Learning Curriculum

Diane Ebert-May, Elena Bray Speth, and Jennifer L. Momsen

A well-rounded college education in the United States is synonymous with liberal education and includes science as one of the liberal arts (American Association for the Advancement of Science, 1990). The experience of learning science as a liberal art should contribute to students' preparation as informed and responsible citizens who think independently, reason analytically, and communicate effectively. Science education is not about learning a litany of facts; rather, it is about developing the thinking skills to engage in twenty-first-century science. To help students achieve this, scientists should teach science as it is practiced and, in particular, teach scientifically by fostering scientific reasoning and quantitative literacy skills in all students (Bybee, 1997; Handelsman et al., 2004; National Leadership Council for Liberal Education and America's Promise, 2007). All college graduates, regardless of their major, should know and be able to engage in the methods of scientific inquiry that lead to scientific knowledge. This capacity includes accessing and analyzing scientific information, using scientific evidence, and constructing reasoned arguments.

As the national interest in liberal learning in undergraduate education has accelerated, goals and outcomes, including the ability to use science as a way of knowing, have appeared on the institutional websites of nearly four in five institutions of higher education (Association of American Colleges and Universities, 2009). Although consensus about the need for scientific reasoning is widespread, few institutions have clearly outlined the curricular pathways and processes that should lead students to achieve scientific reasoning. Generally, we do not have evidence on whether faculty consider the liberal learning goals of their institution when designing their courses, or whether and how they translate these goals into instruction and assessment.

Designing specific course objectives and assessments that reflect a broad liberal learning goal (for example, scientific reasoning) and then implementing instruction that enables students to attain such a goal are challenging tasks for faculty. Faculty need to strive to guide students to reason scientifically through effective instructional design, teaching, and assessment strategies. Of course, faculty need to do so in the context of their course contents and objectives. Is this such a daunting task? We do not believe so. As we look into classrooms across campuses, however, we find that what faculty and students are actually doing to achieve scientific reasoning is not evident. Indeed, traditional lectures and classroom assessments—the metric with which we gauge student learning —fail to align with scientific reasoning goals. A passive, teacher-centered class-room does little to engage students in science as a way of knowing (Moore, 1993). An active, learner-centered classroom that models scientific teaching has a higher probability of helping students achieve scientific reasoning (Bransford & National Research Council Committee on Developments in the Science of Learning, 2000; Ebert-May & Hodder, 2008).

Currently, administrators and faculty committees at institutions of higher education are primarily occupied with articulating liberal learning outcomes for all students and pay less attention—except, perhaps, when preparing for accreditation by an external agency—to systematically assessing whether gradu-ates achieve these goals. Furthermore, few, if any, efforts are made to critically evaluate actual classroom instruction intended to help students achieve the liberal learning goals. In this essay, we focus on the gap we perceive between such goals and assessments and what actually occurs in the classroom. We want to draw attention to the necessary alignment between what universities expect students to know and be able to do and how teachers teach. For instance, do science faculty actively promote students' awareness, understanding, and achievement of scientific reasoning? If so, how? Passive lectures requiring minimal student engagement with the nature and process of science still reign in most large-enrollment introductory science courses. We cannot expect scientific reasoning to occur via diffusion.

We illustrate how a team of faculty incorporated scientific reasoning, a broad liberal learning goal of a large research university, into an introductory biology course and, within that course, a module on evolution (Figure 1). We used a process called backward instructional design to determine specific learning goals and objectives, develop assessments to measure students' achieve-ment, and implement instruction that aligns with the objectives and assessments (Wiggins & McTighe, 2005). Key to this process was the need for learner-centered instruction.

**Figure 1: Hierarchy of Learning Goals at Michigan State University**

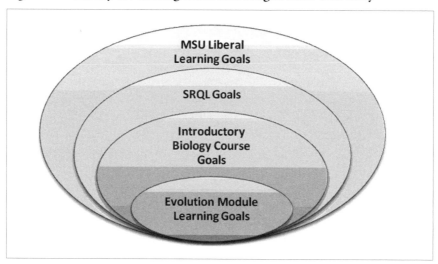

Science courses at MSU are influenced by a hierarchy of learning goals designed to actively engage students in learning both in and out of the classroom. Figure created and provided by the authors.

## TRANSLATING INSTITUTIONAL LIBERAL LEARNING GOALS INTO LEARNER-CENTERED SCIENCE COURSES

Recently, a campus-wide committee at Michigan State University (MSU) revised the liberal learning goals and outcomes that are intended to provide a framework for students' active engagement in learning both in and out of the classroom. The liberal learning goals are expressed in terms of knowledge, attitudes, and skills that all students who complete an undergraduate degree program at MSU should achieve. The outcomes include analytical thinking, cultural understanding, effective citizenship, effective communication, and integrated reasoning (Michigan State University, 2009). These liberal learning outcomes are intended to apply to any and potentially all subjects and courses.

Concurrently, another initiative led by a team of science, statistics, and mathematics faculty produced a set of scientific reasoning and quantitative literacy (SRQL) goals (see Table 1; Michigan State University Committee on Liberal Learning, 2007). Faculty from six colleges on campus ranked the SRQL goals based on what they thought were important learning outcomes for all students at MSU. This process included the development of a psychometrically valid and reliable multiple-choice instrument to assess students' SRQL skills at three points along their degree program: (a) during freshman orientation prior to the start of the academic year (baseline data); (b) midway through their degree; and (c) near the end of their degree program.

These two initiatives provide science faculty at MSU with two sets of liberal learning goals and outcomes—one set at the institutional level for all liberal arts and sciences and one set focusing on scientific reasoning and quantitative

**Table 1: Analytical Thinking and SRQL Goals at Michigan State University**

| Analytical Thinking (University Liberal Learning Goals and Outcomes) | Scientific Reasoning and Quantitative Literacy (SRQL) Goals |
|---|---|
| The MSU graduate uses ways of knowing from mathematics, natural sciences, social sciences, humanities, and arts to access information and critically analyzes complex material in order to evaluate evidence, construct reasoned arguments, and communicate inferences and conclusions:<br><br>• Acquires, analyzes, and evaluates information from multiple sources.<br><br>• Synthesizes and applies the information within and across disciplines.<br><br>• Identifies and applies, as appropriate, quantitative methods for defining and responding to problems.<br><br>• Identifies the credibility, use, and misuse of scientific, humanistic, and artistic methods. | 1. Describe the methods of inquiry that lead to scientific knowledge and be able to distinguish science from pseudoscience and non-science.<br><br>2. Make inferences and predictions and explain and justify conclusions based on data and other quantitative information. This includes discriminating between association and causation and identifying the types of evidence used to establish causation.<br><br>3. Evaluate the credibility, use, and misuse of scientific and mathematical information in scientific developments and public policy issues.<br><br>4. Use multiple representations to model real-world phenomena and, further, use models and theories as unifying principles that help us understand natural phenomena and make predictions.<br><br>5. Use graphical, symbolic, and numerical methods to organize, analyze, and interpret data and to effectively communicate findings. This includes:<br><br>  i. creating, reading, and interpreting representations of quantitative and scientific information such as tables, charts, and graphs; and<br><br>  ii. solving problems that require the application of geometric and algebraic properties, probability, statistics, computer software or techniques, or critical thinking skills.<br><br>6. Formulate hypotheses, identify relevant variables, and design and critique experiments, observational studies, and surveys to test hypotheses using appropriate research design relative to the research objectives.<br><br>7. Recognize the interdependence and value of basic research, applied research, and technology development and how they interact with society.<br><br>8. Illustrate the interdependence among social and ethical issues and scientific development. |

For a complete list of all MSU Liberal Learning Goals and Outcomes, see Michigan State University. 2009. Liberal learning goals and outcomes. http://undergrad.msu.edu/outcomes.html.

literacy. Both sets of goals are intended to make visible the dynamic relationships between the disciplinary goals defined by specific programs and courses and the knowledge, attitudes, and skills that characterize a liberal arts education.

The introductory biology course we developed targets students with a wide range of backgrounds and interests. Our course goals (Table 2) overlap almost entirely with the Analytical Thinking portion of the MSU Liberal Learning Outcomes. Within analytical thinking, the SRQL details explicit scientific reasoning and quantitative literacy goals. Specifically, students will make infer-

**Table 2: Introductory Biology Course Goals**

| What you should be able to do with your knowledge of biology | | |
|---|---|---|
| Organize it . . .<br>• by identifying the complex relationships among biological concepts;<br>• by creating conceptual frameworks that you can use, expand, and modify with new information. | Communicate it . . .<br>• by constructing models that show your understanding of concepts and relations among them;<br>• by articulating scientific explanations targeted to different audiences. | Use it . . .<br>• to interpret and evaluate scientific claims in the popular media;<br>• to appropriately justify your own scientific claims;<br>• to inform your decisions as citizens. |

ences and predictions and explain and justify conclusions based on data and other quantitative information. In addition, students will use graphical, symbolic, and numerical methods to organize, analyze, and interpret data and to effectively communicate the findings (Table 1). Our course goals specifically include SRQL Goals 2 through 6.

The biological concepts in our course are integrated by the theory of evolution. Students learn and apply the principles of evolution in the context of several different case studies. In class activities prior to the case studies, students work with the key concepts of evolution: (1) phenotypic variation in populations; (2) the molecular origin of variation; (3) how variation is inherited; (4) fitness of individuals within a population; and (5) populations evolve, not individuals. Following these activities, students apply their knowledge to a case study on antibiotic resistance. We developed several instructional modules, including the following on antibiotic resistance, to help students achieve several SRQL goals and discipline-based objectives for evolution. This module illustrates how backward design and learner-centered instruction were accomplished in a single class meeting within the course.

## CASE STUDY ON THE EVOLUTION OF ANTIBIOTIC RESISTANCE IN BACTERIA

The evolution of antibiotic resistance in bacteria is an engaging topic for many students. Bacteria are common model organisms for evolution, in part because of their rapid rate of mutation and short generation time. Evidence of bacterial evolution is abundant and approachable for first-year students.

The objectives for this class meeting were:

1. Use data (evidence) to make claims about variation, fitness, selection, and evolution in populations.

2. Apply the general definition of natural selection and the concept of trade-offs to the evolution of antibiotic resistance in bacteria.

These objectives, along with classroom instruction and the assessments used to measure students' achievement, align with three SRQL goals (Table 3):

> Goal 2: Make inferences and predictions and explain and justify conclusions based on data and other quantitative information.
>
> Goal 4: Use multiple representations to model real-world phenomena.
>
> Goal 5: Use graphical, symbolic, and numerical methods to organize, analyze, and interpret data, and to effectively communicate findings.

*Formative Assessment*

To prepare for the class, students read a short review paper on antibiotic resistance (Genereux & Bergstrom, 2005) and electronically submit responses to two questions prior to the start of class—an example of a Just-in-Time-Teaching (JiTT) strategy (Novak, 1999):

1. "Some mutations change the bacterial proteins that are often the targets of antibiotic treatment. . . . Consider a random mutation that changes a bacterial protein" (Genereux & Bergstrom, 2005): (a) How does a random mutation cause a change in a protein? (b) How can such a change affect fitness in bacteria populations?

2. Bacteria carrying a mutation that confers resistance to a given antibiotic have increased fitness, whether the antibiotic is present or not. Is this statement correct or incorrect? Explain (that is, provide adequate warrants for your claim).

*Alignment with SRQL Goal 2.* Although instruction has not yet occurred, the teacher (in question 2) is already asking students to *evaluate* a claim using evidence from either the paper or other sources. As class begins, the teacher engages students and solicits their prior knowledge of antibiotic resistance with a brainstorming activity: "Do you use antibacterial soap? Why or why not? Discuss in your groups." Students are given the opportunity to describe their experience with and opinions of antibacterial soap. As students report back, the teacher, using a tablet computer, categorizes student answers into "pro" and "con" and probes students to support their ideas with data and evidence. As in the JiTT homework, the teacher is focused on pushing students to use evidence as they evaluate their own claims regarding the use of antibacterial soap. The instructor is simultaneously probing: (a) students' ability to construct and evaluate reasoned scientific arguments (an MSU liberal learning goal); and (b) students' understanding of the bacterial evolution

**Table 3: Selected Learning Objectives for Teaching and Learning Evolution in Introductory Biology for Majors and Non-Majors**

| Selected Evolution Learning Objectives | Aligned with SRQL Goal(s) | Activities and Assessments |
|---|---|---|
| **Mechanisms of Evolution: 1. Natural Selection**<br>• Use the key principles of evolution by natural selection (phenotypic variation in a population, genetic origin of variation, heredity, and differential fitness) to explain how populations change over time.<br>• Apply the general principles of natural selection to multiple specific cases of evolution.<br>• Use conceptual models to explain how selection leads to changes in populations. | 2, 4, 5 | Antibiotic resistance in bacteria as a case study.<br>• Pre-class JiTT (Novak, 1999); in-class activities; assessment on exam |

**Figure 2a: Visual Evidence of Evolution**

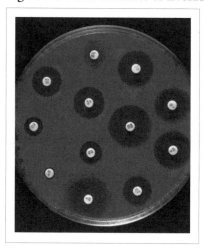

The heterogeneous bacterial lawn represents differing responses to various antibiotics administered by the white discs. At a basic level, students recognize the halo or ring surrounding the disc as evidence of phenotypic variation in bacteria: large rings indicate sensitivity to the drug, and small rings or halos indicate resistance. More advanced students quantify the evidence in this petri plate by measuring the rings or zones of inhibition that surround each antibiotic disc. Figure courtesy of Centers for Disease Control and Prevention.

process (a course- and discipline-specific objective). Immediate feedback to the students during the classroom discussion represents the transition from "probing" to "teaching" (formative assessment).

Now the teacher turns to an experiment on antibiotic resistance (Figure 2a). Because students are unfamiliar with this experiment and inexperienced with interpreting this type of representation, the teacher scaffolds the inquiry. First, students consider whether there is variation among the bacteria in the image. Students report back and quickly agree that, yes, there is variation. The teacher probes further: on what *evidence* do you base your answer? Eventually, students identify the halo surrounding the antibiotic disc as a mix of dead and living bacteria that correspond to antibiotic-susceptible and antibiotic-resistant bacteria, respectively.

**Figure 2b: Graphical Evidence of Evolution**

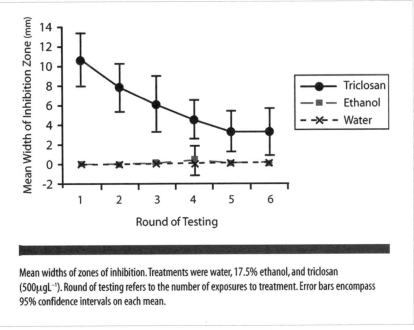

Mean widths of zones of inhibition. Treatments were water, 17.5% ethanol, and triclosan (500μgL⁻¹). Round of testing refers to the number of exposures to treatment. Error bars encompass 95% confidence intervals on each mean.

This graph represents an experiment in which bacteria were repeatedly exposed to triclosan, a common biocide used in consumer products. Students must carefully interpret the graph. Although the y-axis begins at -2, a negatively sized zone of inhibition is not possible. Source: Welden, C., and R. Hossler. 2003. Evolution in the lab: Biocide resistance in *E. coli*. *The American Biology Teacher* 65:56–61. Figure used with permission from the National Association of Biology Teachers.

The teacher then asks students to link this example to what they already know about evolution. She asks two simple questions: (a) What is the origin of this variation? and (b) Is the variation heritable? Students work quickly in groups and report their answers. Although many students recognize that mutation *causes* variation, the teacher asks students to link their knowledge of what mutations are and how they occur to this specific case. Students use their abstract, conceptual knowledge and apply it to this concrete example in order to explain why and how certain bacteria are resistant to antibiotics and how this resistance spreads in populations over time.

*Alignment with SRQL Goals 4 and 5*. In a second exercise, the teacher switches to a graphical representation of the problem (Figure 2b). This activity aligns with SRQL Goals 4 and 5 because students will work with another representation of the problem and will interpret data. Returning to what students already know, the teacher begins by asking them to describe the variation implicit in the graph. Students readily offer that some bacteria must be resistant and others susceptible to the antibiotic. The teacher asks students to identify and explain the error bars, which are quantitative *evidence* of variation in the graph. The teacher then challenges students to interpret the graph in terms of bacterial fitness and selection.

**Figure 2c: Modeling Evidence of Evolution**

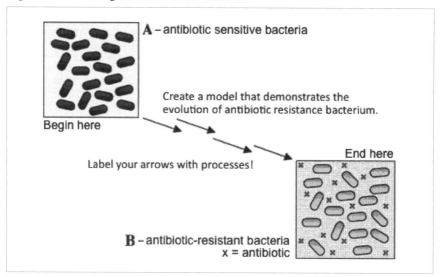

Students build a box-and-arrow model to show the evolution of antibiotic resistance in bacteria. Source: Adapted from Genereux, D., and C. Bergstrom. 2005. Evolution in action: Understanding antibiotic resistance. In *Evolutionary Science and Society: Educating a New Generation.* Ed. J. Cracraft and R. W. Bybee. Colorado Springs: BSCS; Washington, D.C.: American Institute of Biological Sciences. http://bscs.org/curriculumdevelopment/highschool/evolution/pdf.html.

*Alignment with SRQL Goal 4.* A final activity of this class meeting asks students to *create* a model of how antibiotic-resistant bacteria might evolve (Figure 2c). Students must organize their ideas into a concept model with clearly labeled structures and processes. This activity is another example of SRQL Goal 4.

*Summative Assessment*

Throughout the unit on evolution, the teacher incorporates SRQL goals into a variety of case studies that drive instruction. As she creates the exam, she revisits the goals of each class meeting and the broader course goals. Because the students have worked with multiple representations of evolution—including bacteria and antibiotic resistance—the instructor decides that the exam must help students unify the principle of evolution across exemplars (SRQL Goal 4). On the exam, students are asked to complete a table (Figure 3) by explaining how each of the key concepts listed in the left-hand column applies in the context of two specific examples, one of which is the evolution of antibiotic resistance by bacteria. An ideal student answer may seem repetitive between the two examples, differing only in specific details, but demonstrates a solid understanding of the principles of evolution.

**Figure 3: Summative Assessment Item from the Course Midterm**

| Concepts: | Evolution of Antibiotic Resistance in Bacteria 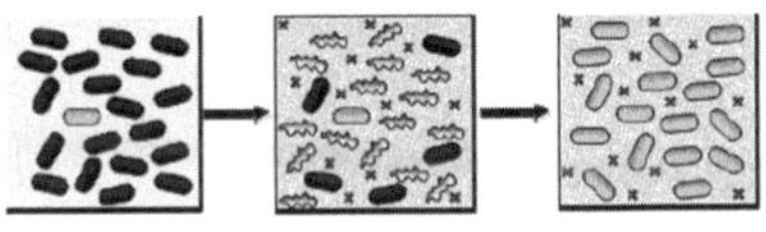 Antibiotic-sensitive bacterium; Antibiotic-resistant bacterium; Dead bacterium; Antibiotic molecule. | Evolution of Wild Tobacco Populations 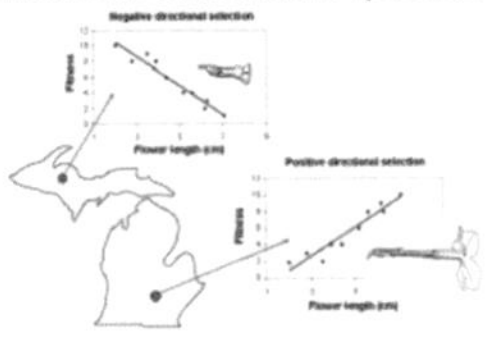 |
|---|---|---|
| PHENOTYPIC VARIATION | | |
| ORIGIN OF VARIATION | | |
| INHERITANCE | | |
| FITNESS | | |
| CHANGE IN POPULATION | | |

Students analyzed both evolution cases in class. Source: Antibiotic resistance figure adapted from Genereux, D., and C. Bergstrom. 2005. Evolution in action: Understanding antibiotic resistance. In *Evolutionary Science and Society: Educating a New Generation*. Ed. J. Cracraft and R.W. Bybee. Colorado Springs: BSCS; Washington, D.C.: American Institute of Biological Sciences. http://bscs.org/curriculumdevelopment/highschool/evolution/pdf.html; Wild Tobacco Populations figure developed by Amy Angert, Frances Kapczyk, Angela Roles, and Heather Sahli, students of PLB 802 at MSU.

## LOOKING AHEAD

The national imperative for teaching science in the liberal arts curriculum is hardly new. In 1983, *A Nation at Risk* (National Commission on Excellence in Education, 1983) called for educational reform that included lifelong learning in science, focusing on concepts, methods of inquiry and reasoning, application, and the social and environmental implications of science. More than forty years prior to that report, John Dewey (1940) described the need for all students to achieve a proficient level of science education to meet the needs of the twentieth century. Now we want our students to achieve the scientific and quantitative reasoning goals so they have the tools to keep pace with science in the twenty-first century.

Much of the teaching we observe in university science classrooms is still primarily based on teacher-centered lectures and on the assessment of factual recall. Courses aimed exclusively at delivering knowledge of discipline-specific science facts provide students with only a limited, finite view of the world. The liberal learning goals for science are intended to prepare students to deal with the complexities of science as a way of knowing and with the intricate relationships of science and society.

To teach science as a liberal art, faculty must think more broadly about their courses and their teaching practices. Indeed, they may perceive that their students have accomplished some of these goals already, but their classroom assessments fail to demonstrate adequately the corresponding student outcomes.

As faculty begin to explicitly align their course objectives and assessments with department, college, and university learning goals, they may see this as a daunting task. The unit of instruction we described is an example of how to embed broader institutional outcomes into discipline-specific instruction and illustrates how learner-centered instructional designs help students achieve higher-level thinking, including analysis and synthesis.

In recent years, new program accreditation standards for engineering and pharmacy education stirred a great deal of discussion about how to equip students with the knowledge, skills, and attitudes represented by the new program outcomes (Abate et al., 2003; Felder & Brent, 2003). The practical issue of translating broad program outcomes into curricula has brought attention to the central role of the faculty and the need for guiding and supporting faculty throughout a process of change. Change at the program level can happen only if all faculty adopt a systematic, scientific approach to instruction by (a) identifying outcome-related course learning objectives; (b) teaching to address the outcomes; and (c) assessing learning appropriately. Key to this process is the implementation of backward instructional design and learner-centered pedagogies (Felder & Brent, 2003).

The liberal learning outcomes designed by universities for all their students could and should drive a similar effort in rethinking science education. Institutions need to invest in faculty, support their professional development, and ensure that they reflect the institution's goals in their courses. Faculty need to invest in teaching strategies that allow *all* students in the liberal arts curriculum to achieve the scientific literacy and reasoning skills needed for effective citizenship. Nurturing the talents and abilities of all students in science is a necessary and long-overdue investment in our future.[1]

1. Thanks to Donna Sundre, of James Madison University, for inviting a team from MSU to participate in her NSF-funded project (DUE-0618599) on assessing scientific and quantitative reasoning. We appreciate the input of our team members, Megan Donahue, Jennifer Kaplan, and Gabe Ording, in this endeavor. In addition, thanks to our students and to the instructors and graduate and undergraduate assistants with whom we teach.

# REFERENCES

Abate, M., M. Stamatakis, and R. Haggett. 2003. Excellence in curriculum development and assessment. *American Journal of Pharmaceutical Education* 67:89.

American Association for the Advancement of Science. 1990. *Science for All Americans*. New York: Oxford University Press.

Association of American Colleges and Universities. 2009. *Learning and Assessment: Trends in Undergraduate Education*. Washington, D.C.: Hart Research Associates. http://aacu.org/membership/documents/2009MemberSurvey_Part1.pdf.

Bransford, J., and National Research Council Committee on Developments in the Science of Learning. 2000. *How People Learn: Brain, Mind, Experience, and School*. Expanded ed. Washington, D.C.: National Academy Press.

Bybee, R. W. 1997. *Achieving Scientific Literacy: From Purposes to Practices*. Portsmouth, N.H.: Heinemann Publishing.

Dewey, J. 1940. *Education Today*. New York: Putnam.

Ebert-May, D., and J. Hodder. 2008. *Pathways to Scientific Teaching*. Sunderland, Mass.: Sinauer Associates.

Felder, R., and R. Brent. 2003. Designing and teaching courses to satisfy the ABET engineering criteria. *Journal of Engineering Education* 92:7–25.

Genereux, D., and C. Bergstrom. 2005. Evolution in action: Understanding antibiotic resistance. In *Evolutionary Science and Society: Educating a New Generation*. Ed. J. Cracraft and R. W. Bybee. Colorado Springs: BSCS; Washington, D.C.: American Institute of Biological Sciences. http://bscs.org/curriculumdevelopment/highschool/evolution/pdf.html.

Handelsman, J., D. Ebert-May, R. Beichner, P. Bruns, A. Chang, R. DeHaan, J. Gentile, S. Lauffer, J. Stewart, S. M. Tilghman, and W. B. Wood. 2004. Scientific teaching. *Science* 304:521–522.

Michigan State University. 2009. Liberal learning goals and outcomes. http://undergrad.msu.edu/outcomes.html.

Michigan State University Committee on Liberal Learning. 2007. Quantitative and scientific reasoning. http://ucll.msu.edu/node/66.

Moore, J. A. 1993. *Science as a Way of Knowing: The Foundations of Modern Biology*. Cambridge, Mass.: Harvard University Press.

National Commission on Excellence in Education. 1983. *A Nation at Risk: The Imperative for Education Reform*. Washington, D.C.: The National Commission on Excellence in Education.

National Leadership Council for Liberal Education and America's Promise. 2007. *College Learning for the New Global Century*. Washington, D.C.: Association of American Colleges and Universities.

Novak, G. M. 1999. *Just-in-Time Teaching: Blending Active Learning with Web Technology*. Upper Saddle River, N.J.: Prentice Hall.

Welden, C., and R. Hossler. 2003. Evolution in the lab: Biocide resistance in *E. coli*. *The American Biology Teacher* 65:56–61.

Wiggins, G. P., and J. McTighe. 2005. *Understanding by Design*. 2nd ed. Danvers, Mass.: Association for Supervision and Curriculum Development.

# CHAPTER 12

# The Conceptualization and Measurement of Civic Scientific Literacy for the Twenty-First Century

Jon D. Miller

The health of American democracy in the twenty-first century will depend on the development of a larger number of scientifically literate citizens. Today's political agenda includes a debate over the consequences of and solutions for global climate change, a continuing debate over the use of embryonic stem cells in biomedical research, a spirited set of disagreements over future energy sources, and a lingering concern over the possibility of a viral pandemic. In Europe, the political landscape is still divided over nuclear power and genetically modified foods. No serious student of public policy or science policy thinks that the public-policy agenda will become less populated by scientific issues in the twenty-first century. Yet only 28 percent of American adults have sufficient understanding of basic scientific ideas to be able to read the Science section in the Tuesday *New York Times* (Miller, 1998, 2000, 2001, 2004), and some research suggests that the proportion may be substantially lower when citizens are faced with strong advocates on both sides.

At the same time, most adults will learn most of their science information after they leave formal schooling. How many current adults can claim that they studied stem cells or nanotechnology when they were students? In the decades ahead, the number and nature of new scientific issues reaching the public-policy agenda will not be limited to subjects that might have been studied in school but will reflect the dynamic of modern science and technology.

Does this mean that formal schooling is irrelevant? No. To the contrary, framing science education and scientific literacy in terms that recognize that formal education, when done well, can provide a necessary conceptual foundation for a lifetime of scientific learning is essential. The evidence from the last thirty years of international testing indicates that American secondary schools do a poor job in providing this foundation of basic understanding (Schmidt, McKnight & Raizen, 1997), and the recent Programme for International Student Assessment report from the Organisation for Economic Co-operation and Development reconfirms our national mediocrity in this area (Baldi et al., 2007). Unbeknownst to most Americans, the United States is the only major country in which almost all its college and university students are required to complete a year of general education, including a full year of science. Recent international comparisons have shown that approximately one in four American adults qualifies as scientifically literate and that exposure to college-level science courses is the primary factor in the performance of American adults (Miller, 2001, 2004).

The need for adults to learn new science after formal schooling is obvious. The overwhelming majority of American adults age thirty-five or older could not have learned about stem cells, nanotechnology, or climate change in school twenty years ago because these were new topics for scientists at that time and were not included in any textbook or curriculum. Similarly, few adults could have learned about the Human Genome Project in school; but the results of that work are often mentioned in public-policy debates, and surveys show that approximately 44 percent of American adults understand the role of DNA in heredity (Miller, 2001, 2004). Few scientists would assert that they could predict the science issues in the news twenty-five years from now, but the majority of today's adults will have to make sense of those issues at some time in their life if we hope to preserve more than the rituals of democracy.

## A CONCEPTUALIZATION OF SCIENTIFIC LITERACY AS A FOUNDATION FOR FUTURE LEARNING

Most of the definitions of scientific literacy that have been advanced in recent decades focus on the mastery of a set of terms, ideas, and concepts, reflecting a traditional view of student or adult learning. This ideal is rooted in a conceptual model of learning as a warehouse: an individual acquires pieces of information and places them on a mental shelf or in a cognitive warehouse and then turns to those facts when he or she needs them. This model is the foundation of most of our current school curricula and many of our informal learning institutions, such as museums and science learning centers. The adoption of this metaphor is the understandable legacy of a long period of industrialization, but it may be a poor conceptualization of learning in the twenty-first century.

In constructing a conceptualization of scientific literacy for the twenty-first century, we may be better served by returning to the idea of literacy itself. The basic idea of literacy has been to define a minimum level of reading and writing skills that an individual must have to participate and communicate in society. Historically, an individual was thought of as literate if he or she could read and write his or her own name. In recent years, many adult educators have translated this requirement into more functional terms: for example, the ability to read a bus schedule, a loan agreement, or the instructions on a bottle of medicine. Adult educators often use the term "functional literacy" to refer to this new definition of the minimal skills needed to function in a contemporary industrial society (Cook, 1977; Harman, 1970; Kaestle, 1985; Resnick & Resnick, 1977).

Building on this basic conceptualization of literacy as the acquisition of tools needed to function in one's society, we might define scientific literacy as the level of understanding of scientific and technological constructs needed to function as citizens in a modern industrial society (Miller, 1983a, 1983b, 1987, 1995, 1998, 2000, 2001, 2004; Miller & Pardo, 2000; Miller, Pardo & Niwa, 1997; Shen, 1975). In an earlier essay on the conceptualization of scientific literacy, Shen (1975) suggested that we differentiate among consumer scientific literacy, civic scientific literacy, and cultural scientific literacy. Consumer scientific literacy would be the ability to understand and choose among contemporary consumer choices involving foods, medicines, chemicals, computers, and similar products. Cultural scientific literacy would focus on understanding the role of science in society and its relationship to other ways of knowing. And civic scientific literacy would encompass the level of understanding necessary to follow and make sense of public-policy issues involving science or technology. As a political scientist who believes that democratic systems are the best way to make collective decisions and perhaps the only way to sustain civil society over long periods of time, I have focused most of my work on the definition and measurement of *civic scientific literacy*. And, as I will argue in my concluding discussion, I think that schools and universities have a special responsibility to foster civic scientific literacy in our society.

The conceptualization of civic scientific literacy (CSL) as the acquisition of a set of foundation constructs is not a pedantic issue. Properly understood, CSL should provide valuable curricular guidance for high school science courses for all students and college science courses for non-science majors. I argue, for example, that it is more important for non-science majors to understand $E = mc^2$ at a conceptual level (the relationship of mass and energy) than at a mathematical level and that it is more important for non-science majors to understand the processes and dynamics of plate tectonics than to be able to differentiate between a sedimentary rock and a piece of basalt. Reflecting this orientation, the University of California, Berkeley, has changed the name of its introductory physics course from Physics for Poets to Physics for Future Presidents.

The task, then, is to develop a set of measures of CSL that reflects the acquisition of basic scientific constructs that are likely to be useful to students and adults over the course of a lifetime in acquiring and making sense of emerging scientific ideas and developments. The good news is that much progress has been made in this area over the last twenty years. The bad news is that the task is never-ending.

## THE MEASUREMENT OF CIVIC SCIENTIFIC LITERACY

If we conceptualize scientific literacy as the acquisition of basic constructs for future use, then we must take care to design an instrument that will be useful over a period of years and will be sufficiently sensitive to capture changes in the structure and composition of public understanding. If a time-series indicator is revised too often or without consciously designed linkages, it may be impossible to separate the variation attributable to measurement changes from real change over time. The periodic debates over the composition of consumer price indices in the United States and other major industrial nations are a reminder of the importance of stable indicators over periods of time.

The durability problem can be seen in the early efforts to develop measures of the public understanding of science in the United States. In 1957, the National Association of Science Writers (NASW) commissioned a national survey of public understanding of and attitudes toward science and technology (Davis, 1958). The interviews for the 1957 study were completed only a few months prior to the launch of *Sputnik I*, making this the only measure of public understanding and attitudes to precede the space race. Unfortunately, the four major items of substantive knowledge the survey examined were (1) radioactive fallout, (2) fluoridation of drinking water, (3) the polio vaccine, and (4) space satellites. Fifty years later, at least three of these items are no longer central to the measurement of public understanding.

Recognizing this problem, my colleagues and I attempted to identify a set of basic constructs, such as atomic structure or DNA, that form the intellectual foundation for reading and understanding contemporary scientific issues but that will have a longer durability than specific terms, such as "the fallout of strontium 90 from atmospheric testing." In the late 1970s and early 1980s, when the National Science Foundation began to support comprehensive national surveys of public understanding and attitudes in the United States, investigators had little experience beyond the 1957 NASW study in the measurement of adult understanding of scientific concepts. In a 1988 collaboration between Thomas and Durant in the United Kingdom and me in the United States, an expanded set of knowledge items was developed that asked respondents direct questions about scientific concepts. The 1988 studies included a combination of open-ended and closed-ended items that provided significantly better estimates of public understanding than had been collected in any prior national study. From this collaboration, a core set of knowledge items emerged that has been used in studies in Canada, China, Japan, Korea, India, New Zealand, and all twenty-seven members of the European Union.

To a large extent, these core items have provided a durable set of measures of a vocabulary of scientific constructs, but continually enriching the mix to reflect the growth of science and technology is important. For example, my recent studies of the American public have included new open-ended measures of stem cell, neuron, and carbon footprint construct understanding and new closed-ended measures of the public's understanding of the genetic modification of plants and animals, nanotechnology, ecology, and infectious diseases. Using item response theory (IRT), we can link survey results across years to obtain comparable measures on a common metric even as the set of items changes over time (Zimowski et al., 1996).

It is useful to look briefly at the primary items used recently in the measurement of civic scientific literacy in the United States and at the percentage of American adults able to answer each item correctly. A core set of items focuses on the meaning of studying something scientifically and the nature of an experiment (Table 1). Data collected over the last twenty years reveal that the proportion of American adults who are able to define the meaning of a scientific study has increased from 22 percent to 34 percent. By 2008, 61 percent of American adults were able to describe an experiment correctly. Although these percentages are low in terms of our expectations, each percentage point represents 2.3 million adults; thus, we can estimate that 78 million adults understand the meaning of a scientific study and 140 million adults understand the structure and purpose of an experiment.

Similarly, the proportion of American adults able to understand simple probability statements has increased from 56 percent to 72 percent since 1988. Nearly one in four can describe a molecule as a combination of two or more atoms. Many adults know that atoms, molecules, and electrons are very small objects but are confused about their relationship to each other. Four out of five adults know that light travels faster than sound, but only half know that a laser is not composed of focused sound waves (see Table 1). All these basic physical-science constructs are a part of middle school and high school science instruction and should have been acquired during formal schooling. If these basic ideas were understood during the school years, many Americans appear not to have retained them as adults and are unable to use them in reading a newspaper story or seeking to understand a television show.

Adult understanding of the universe and our solar system is uneven. Four out of five adults know that the center of Earth is very hot, and 72 percent understand the basic idea of plate tectonics (expressed as continents moving their positions; see Table 1). Two out of three adults know that Earth goes around the sun once each year, but only 30 percent understand or accept the idea of the Big Bang. The slight decline since 1988 in the acceptance of the Big Bang is undoubtedly the result of increased pressure from religious fundamentalists who reject both it and biological evolution. Three in five adults recognize that astrology is "not at all scientific."

The level of public confusion is greatest in the life sciences, reflecting both fundamentalist pressures and a general unfamiliarity with genetic concepts. Only 37 percent of American adults accepted the concept of biological evolution in 2008, and the level of acceptance has declined over the last twenty years (see Table 1). Approximately 44 percent of American adults can define DNA correctly, but only 20 percent can define the meaning of a stem cell. Although

## Table 1: Percentage Correct on Selected Knowledge Items, 1988, 1999, 2008

| | Percent Correct | | |
| --- | --- | --- | --- |
| | 1988 | 1999 | 2008 |
| Indicate that light travels faster than sound. | 78% | 75% | 86% |
| Agree: "All plants and animals have DNA." | – | – | 85 |
| Agree: "The center of Earth is very hot." | 82 | 81 | 80 |
| Agree: "The continents on which we live have been moving their location for millions of years and will continue to move in the future." | 81 | 80 | 72 |
| Understanding of the meaning of the probability of one in four. | 56 | 55 | 72 |
| Indicate that Earth goes around the Sun once each year. | 50 | 49 | 67 |
| Provide a correct open-ended definition of an "experiment." | – | 35 | 61 |
| Agree that astrology is not at all scientific. | 62 | 59 | 59 |
| Disagree: "Antibiotics kill viruses as well as bacteria." | 31 | 45 | 55 |
| Agree: "Electrons are smaller than atoms." | 46 | 46 | 54 |
| Disagree: "Ordinary tomatoes . . . do not have genes but genetically modified tomatoes do." | – | – | 51 |
| Disagree: "Lasers work by focusing sound waves." | 40 | 43 | 48 |
| Disagree: "The earliest humans lived at the same time as the dinosaurs." | 40 | 51 | 47 |
| Provide a correct open-ended definition of "DNA." | 27 | 29 | 44 |
| Agree: "Human beings, as we know them today, developed from earlier species of animals." | 47 | 45 | 37 |
| Provide a correct open-ended definition of "what it means to study something scientifically." | 22 | 22 | 34 |
| Agree: "The universe began with a huge explosion." | 34 | 33 | 30 |
| Agree: "More than half of human genes are identical to those of mice." | – | – | 27 |
| Provide a correct open-ended definition of a "molecule." | – | 13 | 25 |
| Provide a correct open-ended definition of a "stem cell." | – | – | 20 |
| Number of cases | 1,600 | 1,883 | 1,147 |

Given the size of the samples, differences from year to year of less than three points may reflect sampling error rather than real differences.

85 percent of adults recognize that all plants and animals have DNA, only 27 percent of Americans think that "more than half of human genes are identical to those of mice." The level of misunderstanding is not limited to human genetics: only half of adults reject the statement that "ordinary tomatoes do not have genes but genetically modified tomatoes do." The proportion of adults who understand that antibiotics do not kill viruses has increased from 31 percent in 1988 to 55 percent in 2008 (see Table 1).

## A MODEL OF THE FACTORS RELATED TO CIVIC SCIENTIFIC LITERACY

Although these descriptive results are interesting, a good summary measure of the level of adult understanding of these basic constructs is more useful. With IRT, we can construct a summary index of CSL, with scores ranging from roughly zero to one hundred. IRT is a standard testing technology and is widely used in many national tests, including the Graduate Record Examination (GRE) and other tests produced by commercial test publishers (Zimowski et al., 1996). IRT technology also allows the construction of time-series measures over a period of years, even when the mix of questions asked has varied slightly over time.

Using IRT estimates, the percentage of American adults who scored seventy or higher on the index of CSL increased from 10 percent in 1988 to 28 percent in 2008 (Figure 1). Although any cut point is inherently arbitrary, a careful examination of the mix of items that would be required to score seventy or higher suggests that individuals with this level of understanding would be able to read most of the stories in the Tuesday Science section of *The New York Times* or understand an episode of the *Nova* television program.

Using data from a 2007–2008 panel study conducted in the United States using Knowledge Networks' online probability sample (Miller, Augenbraun, Schulhof & Kimmel, 2006), we can explore the relative influence of several major sources of scientific literacy among adults. It is useful to outline the major propositions to be examined.

First, we must assess the relative contribution of college science courses to adult CSL. Holding constant age, gender, and other background factors makes the identification of this effect possible.

Second, we expect that college science courses will provide a core vocabulary of scientific constructs that will facilitate and enhance the use of informal science learning resources. A simple structural equation model[1] will allow us to

---

1. In general terms, a structural equation model is a set of regression equations that provides the best estimate for a set of relationships among several independent variables and one or more dependent variables. For the structural analysis presented in this paper, the program LISREL was used; it allows the simultaneous examination of structural relationships and the modeling of measurement errors. For a more comprehensive discussion of structural equation models, see Hayduk (1987) and Jöreskog and Sörbom (1993). For a more detailed example of the use of this technique in the analysis of CSL, see Miller, Pardo, and Niwa (1997).

**Figure 1: Civic Scientific Literacy in the United States, 1988–2008**

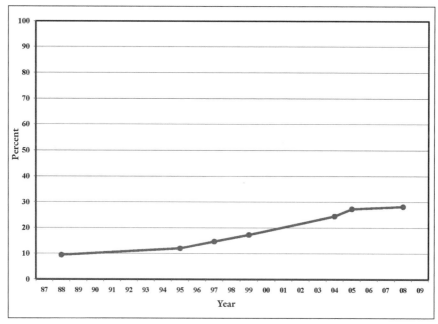

Source: Data for 1988 through 1999 from NSF *Science and Engineering Indicators* surveys. (See Miller, 2004, 2010.) Data for 2004, 2005, and 2008 from *Science News Studies*. (See Miller, Augenbraun, et al., 2006; Miller, 2010.)

test this proposition and to isolate the indirect effect of college science courses on the use of informal learning resources without diminishing our ability to assess the direct or residual impact of those courses.

Third, we will be able to examine the impact of fundamentalist religious beliefs on adult use of informal science learning resources and on retained information in the form of CSL, while holding constant other factors in the general model.

To explore the relative influence of selected factors on the development of CSL, a structural equation analysis of the 2007 U.S. data set was conducted. The analytic model included each individual's age; gender; highest level of education; number of college science courses completed; presence or absence of minor children in the household; interest in science, technology, medical, or environmental issues; personal religious beliefs; and level of use of television, print resources, and the Internet (Figure 2).

A path model is useful for examining the relative influence of variables that have a known chronological or logical order. Each individual has a gender at birth and an age based on his or her birth date. An individual's gender may influence his or her education, although this influence appears to be diminishing in the United States and several European countries. For most adults, educational attainment and the number of college science courses have been determined by the time they reach their mid-thirties, although more adults

**Figure 2: A Path Model to Predict Civic Scientific Literacy in Adults, 2007**

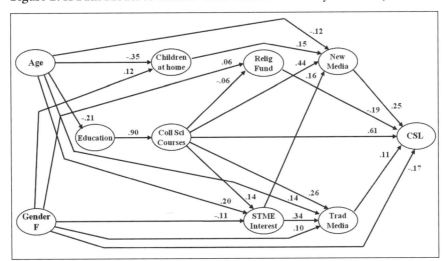

are returning to formal education than ever before. An individual's level of CSL at any specific time may be thought of as the result of the combination of these and other factors (see Figure 2). In a path model, chronological or logical causation flows from left to right. The product of the path coefficients is an estimation of the total effect of each variable on the outcome variable—CSL in this case. It is useful to look first at the total effect of each of the variables in this model, and then return to examine some of the specific path coefficients.

The number of college science courses taken is the strongest predictor of CSL, with a total effect of 0.74 (Table 2). It is important to understand this variable and its impact. The variable is a measure of the number of college science courses, including courses in both community colleges and four-year colleges and universities. The number of courses was divided into three levels: (1) no college-level science courses; (2) one to three courses; and (3) four or more courses. Individuals with one to three courses typically took college science courses as a part of a general education requirement rather than as part of a major or a supplement to a major. The use of an integer measure would have given undue weight to majors and minimized the impact of general education science courses in the analysis.

Formal educational attainment[2] is the second best predictor of adult CSL (0.69). This result indicates that students gain some additional value from the full range of university courses, including other general education courses in

---

2. Educational attainment was measured with a five-category ordinal variable. The lowest level included all individuals who did not complete secondary school or obtain a general equivalency diploma (GED). The second category included high school graduates and GED holders. The third category included respondents with an associate's degree. The fourth category included individuals who earned a baccalaureate but not a graduate or professional degree. The highest category included all individuals who completed a graduate or professional degree.

## Table 2: Total Effect of Selected Variables on Civic Scientific Literacy, 2007

|  | Total Effect |
|---|---|
| Respondent age | -.22 |
| Gender (F) | -.18 |
| Educational attainment | .69 |
| College science courses | .74 |
| Children at home | .03 |
| Religious fundamentalism | -.20 |
| Interest in science, technology, medical, or environmental issues | .05 |
| Television use | -.10 |
| Print use | .15 |
| Internet and electronic media use | .22 |
| $R^2 =$ | .75 |
| Chi-squares | 192.1 |
| Degrees of freedom | 25 |
| Root mean square error of approximation (RMSEA) | .025 |
| Upper confidence limit (90%) of RMSEA | .038 |
| N | 1,116 |

the humanities and the social sciences. The influence of formal educational attainment may also reflect a greater respect for and acceptance of academic authority as a source of knowing about the world.

After the effects of educational attainment and college science courses, five additional indicators had a total positive or negative effect between 0.15 and 0.22. It is not useful to try to differentiate among these indicators by the magnitude of their total effect, but it is useful to discuss briefly the meaning of each of these relationships.

The model finds a negative relationship between fundamentalist religious views[3] and civic scientific literacy (-0.20), meaning that adults with fundamentalist religious beliefs are significantly less likely to be scientifically literate than adults with more moderate or liberal religious beliefs, holding constant differences in age, gender, education, children at home, and issue interest. Religious beliefs are placed to the right of college science courses in this path model because the religious variable reflects current religious beliefs and exposure to college science courses may have occurred several years prior to the interviews in the 2007–2008 panel study. In a longitudinal study that followed the same individuals over a period of time, we would likely find that parental and pre-

3. The index of religious beliefs is a count of the number of times a respondent indicated agreement with (1) "The Bible is the actual word of God and is to be taken literally"; and (2) "There is a personal God who hears the prayers of individual men and women"; and indicated disagreement with (3) "Human beings developed from earlier forms of life." Individuals who scored three on this index were classified as fundamentalist (22 percent); individuals who scored two were classified as conservative (15 percent); individuals who scored one were classified as moderate (25 percent); and individuals who scored zero on the scale were classified as liberal-none (38 percent).

college religious views influence the number of college science courses taken, but in a cross-sectional or short adult panel study, accurately assessing earlier influences of that kind is impossible. We are comfortable, however, in asserting that current religious beliefs may be influenced by prior educational experiences and that a negative path (-0.10) exists between educational attainment and religious attitudes in this model, which indicates a small but statistically significant effect between the two variables.

The model also indicates that adults who are relatively more frequent users of print and Internet information sources are more likely to be scientifically literate (0.15 for print and 0.22 for the Internet), holding constant the other variables in the model (see Figure 2 and Table 2). This relationship suggests that adults with better information acquisition skills are more likely to obtain and retain core scientific information and constructs than adults without those skills. Again, it is useful to recall that these effects are additive to the effects noted previously that were related to educational attainment and college science course experiences.

Finally, the model indicates that females and older adults are less likely to be scientifically literate than other adults (-0.18 for females and -0.22 for older adults), holding constant the other variables in the model. Although younger respondents are more likely to be scientifically literate than older adults because they would have had more education and more science education than older adults, it is important to recognize that the total effect reported in Table 2 is net of differences in education, gender, and other factors. Similarly, the differential in favor of males is net of differences in education and other factors (Hayduk, 1987; Jöreskog & Sörbom, 1993).

The level of personal interest in scientific, technical, environmental, or medical issues had only a small positive effect on CSL (0.05), as did the presence of preschool or school-age children in the home (0.03).

This model explains 75 percent of the total variance in civic scientific literacy among U.S. adults in 2007–2008. This is a very good fit for the model, and other indicators confirm the fit of the model. The model appears to have no measurement problems.


DISCUSSION

What do these results tell us about the conceptualization and measurement of civic scientific literacy in the twenty-first century?

First, at the conceptual level, one can make a strong case for thinking about scientific literacy as acquiring the tools to make sense of science and technology in the future as opposed to learning the details of current science. Science is a dynamic activity that will continue to produce new results requiring new terms and constructs, and the citizens of the twenty-first century will have to be able to use their understanding of basic ideas—atoms, molecules, the structure of matter—to make sense of new concepts such as nanotechnology. F. James Rutherford's original conceptualization of Project 2061, an effort by the American Association for the Advancement of Science (AAAS) to improve science education in the United States, was designed to capture this sense of the science we will need to know to understand the future (AAAS, 1989).

Second, Shen's distinctions among CSL, consumer scientific literacy, and cultural scientific literacy are useful. Good arguments can be advanced for each of these three aspects of scientific literacy, but my colleagues and I have focused on CSL because it is the key link between science and technology policy and democratic government. As modern science has become more expensive and more controversial, it has inevitably moved into the public arena. Science and technology are essential to a wide array of public policy objectives in environmental and biomedical areas but are also essential tools for sustaining American competitiveness in the emerging global economy (National Academies, 2007).

Third, the thirty-year time-series measurements that I and others have created provide a useful indicator of national progress in CSL, but these are indices that must continue to grow and change to reflect the nature of science and technology in the twenty-first century and beyond. Just as the contents of the household market basket used for computation of the U.S. Consumer Price Index periodically change to reflect national habits and tastes, so must our measures of CSL and related constructs.

Fourth, this analysis found that the nearly unique American requirement for general education at the university level has been a major factor in fostering CSL. The origins of this requirement are murky, but a consensus in favor of "general education" first emerged in the early decades of the twentieth century and was soon adopted by both land-grant and leading private colleges and universities. Dewey, Hutchins, and their colleagues were influential in promoting this conceptualization of higher education. As we approach the centennial of this American experiment in higher education, the results reported in this analysis suggest that the experiment has been beneficial.

Fifth, the accelerating pace of scientific development means that most Americans outside the scientific community will learn most of their science after they leave formal schooling. Few adults could have learned about stem cells, global climate change, or nanotechnology as students because the relevant science had not been done. The challenge today is to prepare students to understand science that will not occur for another twenty, thirty, or forty years. This is not easy, but it is possible. Although we cannot know the precise dimensions of future science, we can be sure that existing constructs such as atom, molecule, DNA, and energy will still be applicable.

In this context, the model of factors related to CSL demonstrates that acquiring a core vocabulary of basic scientific constructs can confer a distinct advantage on adults who use emerging information technologies to become and remain informed about scientific and other matters. Nearly four decades ago, Tichenor and colleagues observed that better-educated adults gain more from any information campaign than less-well-educated adults; they referred to this differential as the *knowledge gap* (Tichenor, Donohue & Olien, 1970). With the emergence of new electronic technologies, more Americans have access to a wider array of information at lower cost than at any time in human history. Those adults with the ability to understand the information landscape and to make sense of new scientific and technical information will have important advantages in the decades ahead. Scientific literacy has become an essential component of the skills that every adult needs to thrive in the twenty-first century.

Finally, science policy has become a part of the political agenda, and it is unlikely to disappear in the foreseeable future. In broad terms, the twentieth century was the century of physics, and the twenty-first century will be the century of biology. The twentieth century was characterized by enormous advances in transportation, communication, and nuclear science—from the radio to the airplane to the transistor. Although these new developments and technologies eventually changed the very character of American society, most of them successfully avoided direct confrontation with traditional beliefs and values, especially religious values. As science continues to expand our understanding of the nature and structure of life and develops the technologies to intervene in those processes, the resulting political disputes will become more personal and more directly confrontational with traditional religious values.

Looking to the future, we must increase the proportion of scientifically literate adults in our society. As the survey results presented here demonstrate, formal education and informal science learning are partners in the process of advancing scientific literacy. Without a solid foundation of basic scientific constructs, even the best science journalism and communication will fall on deaf ears. Scientific literacy is not a cure or antidote in and of itself. It is, however, a prerequisite for preserving a society that values science and is able to sustain its democratic values and traditions.[4]

4. The U.S. national data sets for the years 1985 through 2007 were collected with support from the National Science Foundation (awards SRS8105662, SRS8517581, SRS8807409, SRS9002467, SRS9217876, SRS9732170, SRS9906416, ESI0131424, ESI0201155, ESI0515449). The 2008 wave of the Science News Study was funded by Dean Charles Salmon of Michigan State University. The 2008 participation in the American National Election Study was funded by Vice President Ian Gray of Michigan State University. The author gratefully acknowledges this support, but any errors or omissions are the responsibility of the author and not of the sponsors or any of their staff or officers.

# REFERENCES

American Association for the Advancement of Science. 1989. *Science for All Americans*. Washington, D.C.: AAAS.

Baldi, S., Y. Jin, M. Skemer, P. J. Green, and D. Herget. 2007. *Highlights from PISA 2006: Performance of U.S. 15-Year-Old Students in Science and Mathematics Literacy in an International Context*. Washington, D.C.: National Center for Education Statistics. NCES 2008-017. http://nces.ed.gov/pubsearch/pubsinfo.asp?pubid=2008016.

Cook, W. D. 1977. *Adult Literacy Education in the United States*. Newark, Del.: International Reading Association.

Davis, R. C. 1958. *The Public Impact of Science in the Mass Media*. Monograph no. 25. Ann Arbor: University of Michigan Survey Research Center.

Harman, D. 1970. Illiteracy: An overview. *Harvard Educational Review* 40:226–230.

Hayduk, L. A. 1987. *Structural Equation Modeling with LISREL*. Baltimore: Johns Hopkins University Press.

Jöreskog, K., and D. Sörbom. 1993. *LISREL 8*. Chicago: Scientific Software International.

Kaestle, C. F. 1985. The history of literacy and the history of readers. *Review of Research in Education* 12:11–54.

Miller, J. D. 1983a. *The American People and Science Policy*. New York: Pergamon Press.

———. 1983b. Scientific literacy: A conceptual and empirical review. *Daedalus* 112(2):29–48.

———. 1987. Scientific literacy in the United States. In *Communicating Science to the Public*, ed. D. Evered and M. O'Connor. London: Wiley.

———. 1995. Scientific literacy for effective citizenship. In *Science/Technology/Society as Reform in Science Education*, ed. R. E. Yager. New York: State University Press of New York.

———. 1998. The measurement of civic scientific literacy. *Public Understanding of Science* 7:1–21.

———. 2000. The development of civic scientific literacy in the United States. In *Science, Technology, and Society: A Sourcebook on Research and Practice*, ed. D. D. Kumar and D. Chubin, 21–47. New York: Plenum Press.

———. 2001. The acquisition and retention of scientific information by American adults. In *Free-Choice Science Education*, ed. J. H. Falk, 93–114. New York: Teachers College Press.

———. 2004. Public understanding of, and attitudes toward scientific research: What we know and what we need to know. *Public Understanding of Science* 13:273–294.

———, E. Augenbraun, J. Schulhof, and L. G. Kimmel. 2006. Adult science learning from local television newscasts. *Science Communication* 28(2):216–242.

———, and R. Pardo. 2000. Civic scientific literacy and attitude to science and technology: A comparative analysis of the European Union, the United States, Japan, and Canada. In *Between Understanding and Trust: The Public, Science, and Technology*, ed. M. Dierkes and C. von Grote, 81–129. Amsterdam: Harwood Academic Publishers.

———, R. Pardo, and F. Niwa. 1997. *Public Perceptions of Science and Technology: A Comparative Study of the European Union, the United States, Japan, and Canada*. Madrid: BBV Foundation Press.

National Academies. 2007. *Rising above the Gathering Storm: Energizing and Employing America for a Brighter Economic Future*. Washington, D.C.: The National Academies Press. http://www.nap.edu/catalog.php?record_id=11463.

Resnick, D. P., and L. B. Resnick. 1977. The nature of literacy: An historical exploration. *Harvard Educational Review* 47:370–385.

Schmidt, W. H., C. C. McKnight, and S. A. Raizen. 1997. *A Splintered Vision: An Investigation of U.S. Science and Mathematics Education*. Boston: Kluwer Academic Press.

Shen, B. J. 1975. Scientific literacy and the public understanding of science. In *Communication of Scientific Information*, ed. S. Day. Basel: Karger.

Tichenor, P. J., G. A. Donohue, and C. N. Olien. 1970. Mass media and differential growth in knowledge. *Public Opinion Quarterly* 34:159–170.

Zimowski, M. F., E. Muraki, R. J. Mislevy, and R. D. Bock. 1996. *BILOG-MG: Multiple-Group IRT Analysis and Test Maintenance for Binary Items*. Chicago: Scientific Software International.

# Contributors

**Jon Clardy**, a Fellow of the American Academy since 1995, joined Harvard Medical School in 2003 as a Professor in the Department of Biological Chemistry and Molecular Pharmacology. His research involves many aspects of biologically active small molecules, especially those known as natural products. Clardy is closely affiliated with the Initiative in Chemical Genetics, an effort to broaden the range of small molecule therapeutic agents, and more generally, moderators of all biological processes, through the screening of libraries of structurally diverse compounds in both ad hoc and systematic screens. In the area of malaria, Clardy's laboratory defined the structure of a crucial enzymatic target, P. falciparum's dihydroorotate dehydrogenase (DHODH), for antimalarial agents. Current research includes finding new molecular templates for DHODH inhibitors and understanding the structural basis of its mechanism. He is also engaged in forward chemical genetic screens to find new targets for antimalarial and antitrypanosomal therapy. Awards for his research include fellowships from the Alfred P. Sloan Foundation, the Camille and Henry Dreyfus Foundation, and the John Simon Guggenheim Foundation. He has also received the Ernest Guenther Award and an Arthur C. Cope Scholar Award from the American Chemical Society, and the Research Achievement Award from the American Society of Pharmacognosy. He is a Fellow of the American Association for the Advancement of Science.

**Diane Ebert-May** is a Professor in the Department of Plant Biology at Michigan State University. She provides national leadership for promoting professional development, evaluation, and improvement of faculty, postdoctoral scholars, and graduate students who actively participate in creative research about teaching and learning in biology. Her research group has developed and tested a model for faculty, postdoctoral, and graduate student training in teaching, and is investigating the impact of students' design and use of models to build conceptual connections in biology. Ebert-May is the Principal Investigator of FIRST IV, a professional development program funded by the National Science Foundation to help postdoctoral scholars learn to teach scientifically in preparation for their academic careers. Her recent book, *Pathways to Scientific Teaching*, is based on active learning, inquiry-based instructional strategies, assessment, and research. She teaches plant biology and introductory biology to majors, environmental science to non-majors in large enrollment courses, and a graduate seminar on scientific teaching. As a plant ecologist, she continues to conduct research on alpine tundra plant communities on Niwot Ridge, Colorado.

**Martha P. Haynes**, a Fellow of the American Academy since 1999, is the Goldwin Smith Professor of Astronomy at Cornell University. She graduated with special honors from Wellesley College and received her M.A. and Ph.D. degrees from Indiana University. From 1978 to 1981, she served on the staff of the Arecibo Observatory of the National Astronomy and Ionosphere Center in Puerto Rico; from 1981 to 1983, she was the Assistant Director of Operations of the National Radio Astronomy Observatory in Green Bank, West Virginia. She joined the Cornell faculty in 1983. She has served on numerous institutional, observatory, and federal agency boards and advisory committees and is currently Vice President of the International Astronomical Union. Her scientific research concentrates on observational cosmology, galaxy evolution, and the application of radio astronomy techniques. She is a member of the National Academy of Sciences and is a recipient of the 1989 Henry Draper Medal for her scientific work on mapping the three-dimensional filamentary large-scale structures in the local universe.

**Robert M. Hazen** is a research scientist at the Geophysical Laboratory of the Carnegie Institution for Science and the Clarence Robinson Professor of Earth Science at George Mason University. His recent research focuses on the role of minerals in the origin of life, including such processes as mineral-catalyzed organic synthesis and the selective adsorption of organic molecules on mineral surfaces. He has also developed a new approach to mineralogy, called "mineral evolution," which explores the coevolution of the geo- and biospheres. In addition to his mineralogical research, he is Principal Investigator of the Deep Carbon Observatory. A Fellow of the American Association for the Advancement of Science (AAAS), he has received numerous awards, including the Mineralogical Society of America Award, the American Chemical Society Ipatieff Prize, and the Educational Press Association Award. Hazen served on the Committee on Public Understanding of Science of the AAAS, and on advisory boards for *NOVA* (WGBH Boston), *Earth & Sky*, Encyclopedia Americana, and the Carnegie Council.

**John G. Hildebrand**, a Fellow of the American Academy since 2001, is Regents Professor of Neurobiology and holds joint appointments in Chemistry and Biochemistry, Entomology, and Molecular and Cellular Biology at the University of Arizona in Tucson. He served on the faculties of Harvard Medical School (1970–1980) and Columbia University (1980–1985) before moving to the University of Arizona, where he is currently founding Head of the Department of Neuroscience and a founder of the University's new School of Mind, Brain and Behavior. Hildebrand's research focuses on insect neurobiology and behavior and emphasizes studies of olfaction, neuroethology, chemical ecology of insect-host interactions, neural development, neurochemistry and neurosecretion, and the biology of disease-vector insects. Among his honors are the Einstein Professorship of the Chinese Academy of Sciences, the Silver

Medal of the International Society of Chemical Ecology, and a Humboldt Research Award. He is a member of the National Academy of Sciences, the German Academy of Sciences (Leopoldina), and the Norwegian Academy of Science and Letters. He is past President of the International Society of Chemical Ecology, the International Society for Neuroethology, and the Association for Chemoreception Sciences. He is Cochair of the Academy's study on Science in the Liberal Arts Curriculum.

**Sally G. Hoskins** is a Professor of Biology at the City College of the City University of New York (CCNY). A developmental biologist and science educator, she (with collaborator Dr. Leslie M. Stevens, University of Texas at Austin) developed the C.R.E.A.T.E. process—using intensive analysis of journal articles as a means of demystifying and humanizing research science—for undergraduate biology majors at CCNY. With continued NSF support, C.R.E.A.T.E. approaches have since been extended successfully to diverse cohorts of students at additional colleges and universities and also adapted for use in general education science courses. A three-time CCAPP Teacher of the Year at City College, Hoskins feels that primary literature and newspaper/Internet versions of science, used effectively in the classroom, can both clarify "who does science, and why" and reveal the creativity of scientific thinking, thus making research science appealing to science majors and non-majors alike.

**Chris Impey** is University Distinguished Professor at the University of Arizona. He is also Deputy Head of the Department of Astronomy, overseeing all the department's academic programs. His research focuses on observational cosmology, gravitational lensing, and the evolution and structure of galaxies. He has 160 refereed publications and 60 published conference proceedings; his work has been supported by $18 million in grants from NASA and the National Science Foundation (NSF). As a professor, he has won eleven teaching awards and has been heavily involved in curriculum and instructional technology development. Impey is a past Vice President of the American Astronomical Society. He has also been an NSF Distinguished Teaching Scholar, a Phi Beta Kappa Visiting Scholar, and the Carnegie Council's Arizona Professor of the Year. He was Cochair of the study group that summarized Astronomy Education and Public Outreach for the 2010 Astronomy Decadal Survey of the National Academy of Sciences.

**Darcy B. Kelley** is the Harold Weintraub Professor of Biological Sciences at Columbia University. She codirected the "Neural Systems and Behavior" course at the Marine Biological Laboratory in Woods Hole, Massachusetts, and founded Columbia's doctoral program in neurobiology and behavior. She is Editor of the journal *Developmental Neurobiology*. Kelley's research uses the South African clawed frog, *Xenopus laevis*, to study the neurobiology of social communication, in an effort to determine how one brain communicates with another. Her Howard Hughes Medical Institute project is a Web-based resource (http://www.fos-online.org/) that makes educational materials generated in Frontiers of Science, Columbia's new interdisciplinary core course in science, freely available to educators and the general public.

**Eugene H. Levy** is the Andrew Hays Buchanan Professor of Astrophysics at Rice University, where he also served as Provost from 2000 to 2010. At the University of Arizona for twenty-five years before coming to Rice, he frequently taught science general education. Levy's research focused on planetary physics and astrophysics, magnetohydrodynamics, and solar and space physics. He has served as member or chair of numerous national and international science advisory committees, including the Space Science Board of the National Academy of Sciences/NRC, from 1978 to 1982, and as Chair of the SSB Committee on Planetary and Lunar Exploration. He currently chairs the Board of Trustees of Associated Universities, Inc., serves on the NASA Advisory Council's Science Committee, and chairs the NASA Planetary Protection Subcommittee.

**David R. Liu** is a Professor of Chemistry and Chemical Biology at Harvard University, a Harvard College Professor, a Howard Hughes Medical Institute Investigator, and an Associate Member of the Broad Institute of Harvard and MIT. His major research interests include the development and application of new approaches to the evolution of biological macromolecules, and the application of evolutionary principles to the discovery of synthetic small molecules, synthetic polymers, and new chemical reactions. Liu has earned three university-wide distinctions for undergraduate and graduate student teaching at Harvard, including the Joseph R. Levenson Memorial Teaching Prize in 2007, the Roslyn Abramson Award in 2003, and a Harvard College Professorship in 2007. He was appointed a Howard Hughes Medical Institute Investigator in 2005 and joined JASON (a group of academic advisors to the U.S. government on matters of science and technology) in 2009. His many research accomplishments have earned distinctions including the American Chemical Society Pure Chemistry Award in 2006, the American Chemical Society Arthur C. Cope Young Scholar Award in 2004, the Sloan Foundation Fellowship in 2002, the Beckman Foundation Young Investigator Award in 2002, and the Office of Naval Research Young Investigator Award in 2000.

**Jerrold Meinwald**, a Fellow of the American Academy since 1970, is the Goldwin Smith Professor of Chemistry Emeritus at Cornell University, where his research has spanned a wide range of topics in organic chemistry and chemical ecology. Meinwald's recent research has been concerned with the isolation and identification of biologically active compounds from insect and other arthropod sources (particularly spiders). In addition to arthropod-related work, Meinwald has also been concerned with plant allelochemicals, as well as the pheromone and defensive systems of vertebrate species. He assisted in the establishment of chemical ecology/biodiversity-oriented research centers in Kenya, Costa Rica, Germany, and Brazil. He has shared the Tyler Award for Environmental Achievement with his biological collaborator, Thomas Eisner, and has won the Roger Adams Award, the Cope Scholar Award, and the Guenther Award in Natural Products Chemistry from the American Chemical Society. Meinwald is Secretary of the American Academy of Arts and Sciences and Cochair of its Committee on Studies. He also is Cochair of the Academy's study on Science in the Liberal Arts Curriculum. He was elected a member of the National Academy of Sciences in 1969 and a member of the American Philosophical Society in 1987.

**Jon D. Miller** is the Director of the International Center for the Advancement of Scientific Literacy at the Institute for Social Research at the University of Michigan. Miller has measured the public understanding of science and technology in the United States for the last three decades, and has examined the factors associated with the development of attitudes toward science and science policy. He directed biennial national surveys for the National Science Board for twenty years, the results of which were reported in *Science and Engineering Indicators*. He has pioneered the definition and measurement of scientific literacy; his approach to the public understanding of science has been replicated in more than forty countries. He continues to conduct studies of the public perception of science in the United States and other nations. Miller is also the Director of the Longitudinal Study of American Youth (LSAY) and a Fellow of the American Association for the Advancement of Science.

**Jennifer L. Momsen** is an Assistant Professor of Biology at North Dakota State University, where she teaches introductory biology for science majors. Trained as a historical ecologist, she earned her Ph.D. at Rutgers University, where she studied long-term vegetation community dynamics. Momsen recently completed her postdoctoral work at Michigan State University in biology education. Her research focused on the undergraduate biology classroom; in particular, she investigated the cognitive level routinely assessed in introductory biology and how students develop systems thinking in biology. She will continue her research on undergraduate biology education, concentrating on student understanding of ecology, student development of quantitative skills, and professional development of postdoctoral associates.

**Richard A. Muller**, a Fellow of the American Academy since 2010, is a Professor of Physics at the University of California, Berkeley. He discovered the "cosine anisotropy" of the cosmic microwave radiation, and he invented "Accelerator Mass Spectrometry," work which earned him the Alan T. Waterman Award of the National Science Foundation and a MacArthur Prize. Muller has also made seminal contributions to the study of supernovas, to the science of climate change, to patterns of extinction and biodiversity, and to the "Nemesis" theory.

He has been a longtime consultant to the U.S. government on national security. He has received the Distinguished Teaching Award from UC Berkeley, and is a Fellow of the American Physical Society, the American Association for the Advancement of Science, and the California Academy of Sciences.

**Don M. Randel**, a Fellow of the American Academy since 2001, is President of the Andrew W. Mellon Foundation and a prominent musicologist. He previously served as President of the University of Chicago, where he worked to strengthen the academic work of the University in many areas, from humanities and arts to physical and biological sciences. In his academic work, Randel specializes in the music of the Middle Ages and the Renaissance. Among musicologists, he is particularly known for his publications on Mozarabic chant, Arabic music theory, and Panamanian folk music. In 1968, Randel joined the Cornell University faculty in the Department of Music. He served for thirty-two years as a member of Cornell's faculty, where he was also Department Chair, Vice Provost, and Associate Dean and then Dean of the College of Arts and Sciences. He became Provost of Cornell University in 1995.

**Frank H.T. Rhodes**, a Fellow of the American Academy since 1989, is President Emeritus and Professor of Geological Sciences at Cornell University. He has served as Chairman of the National Science Board, as a member of the President's Educational Policy Advisory Committee, and as Chairman of the governing boards of the American Council on Education, the American Association of Universities, and the Carnegie Foundation for the Advancement of Teaching. He is the recipient of numerous awards, including the Bigsby Medal of the Geological Society, the Justin Morrill Award, the Ian Campbell Medal, the Higher Education Leadership Award, and thirty-seven honorary degrees. He is a former Fulbright Scholar and Fulbright Distinguished Fellow, a National Science Foundation Senior Visiting Research Fellow, a former Distinguished Fellow of University College, Oxford, a Life Fellow of Clare Hall, Cambridge, and a Distinguished Fellow of Robinson College, Cambridge, among others.

**Elena Bray Speth** is an Assistant Professor of Biology at Saint Louis University in St. Louis. She earned her Ph.D. in biochemistry and molecular biology at Michigan State University, where she studied the cellular and molecular bases of the interaction between plants and pathogenic bacteria. For her postdoctoral research, sponsored by the Michigan State University Center for Research on College Science Teaching and Learning, she joined Diane Ebert-May's research group. Under Dr. Ebert-May's mentoring, she developed her interest and expertise in conducting research on biology education at the college level. At Saint Louis University since 2009, she teaches introductory biology for science majors and a graduate-level course in scientific communication; she conducts research on teaching and learning about complex biological systems.

**James Trefil** is the Clarence J. Robinson Professor of Physics at George Mason University. A physicist and author, Trefil is known for his interest in teaching science to non-scientists. He has served as Contributing Editor for Science for *USA Today Weekend* and as a regular contributor for the *Smithsonian* and *Astronomy* magazines. In addition, Trefil was a science commentator and member of the Science Advisory Board for NPR and for numerous PBS productions. He also served as the Chief Science Consultant to the McDougal-Littell Middle School Science Project. He held postdoctoral, visiting, and junior faculty appointments at the Stanford Linear Accelerator Center, European Center for Nuclear Research (CERN), Laboratory for Nuclear Sciences at MIT, German Electron Synchrotron Laboratory in Hamburg, University of Illinois, Fermi National Accelerator Laboratory, and Argonne National Laboratory before joining the faculty at the University of Virginia. He is a Fellow of the American Physical Society and a former Guggenheim Fellow.

**Brian N. Tse** is currently serving as an AAAS Science & Technology Policy Fellow with the Department of Health & Human Services. Previously he served as a Christine Mirzayan Science & Technology Policy Fellow at the National Academies, working at the Koshland Science Museum on educational programming related to climate change. Tse's graduate research focused on an evolution-inspired approach to drug discovery called DNA-templated synthesis. As a graduate student, he helped assemble a new interdisciplinary science course, Life Sciences 1A, with four members of the Harvard faculty. Upon graduation, he joined the Harvard faculty for the 2008–2009 academic year as Preceptor for the SLS 11: Molecules of Life course.

# Participants

## Science in the Liberal Arts Curriculum

A Conference at the American Academy of Arts and Sciences, August 16, 2007

**Katherine Bergeron**
Brown University

**Gene Bickers**
University of Southern California

**Andrew Binns**
University of Pennsylvania

**Selma Botman**
City University of New York
(now at University of Southern Maine)

**Susan Bourque**
Smith College

**Ronald Braeutigam**
Northwestern University

**John Bravman**
Stanford University
(now at Bucknell University)

**Alvin Crumbliss**
Duke University

**Margaret Curtis**
Bennett College

**Ron Daniel**
Virginia Polytechnic Institute
and State University

**Mike Doyle**
University of Maryland

**John Frederick**
University of Chicago

**Terri Givens**
University of Texas at Austin

**Ariel Gomez**
University of Virginia

**Donna Hamilton**
University of Maryland

**J. K. Haynes**
Morehouse College

**Martha P. Haynes**
Cornell University

**Robert M. Hazen**
George Mason University

**John G. Hildebrand**
University of Arizona

**Morton Hoffman**
Boston University

**Sally G. Hoskins**
City College, City University
of New York

**Eric Jacobsen**
Harvard University

**Adam Jaffe**
Brandeis University

**Darcy B. Kelley**
Columbia University

**Donald Lehman**
George Washington University

**Peter Lepage**
Cornell University

**Eugene H. Levy**
Rice University

**Daniel Linzer**
Northwestern University

Jed Marsh
Princeton University

Terrence McDonald
University of Michigan

Jerrold Meinwald
Cornell University

Jon D. Miller
Michigan State University
(now at University of Michigan)

Mark Morris
University of California, Los Angeles

Richard A. Muller
University of California, Berkeley

Robert Pangborn
Pennsylvania State University

Caty Pilachowski
Indiana University

Barry Qualls
Rutgers, The State University
of New Jersey

Peter Quimby
Princeton University

Sharon Salinger
University of California, Irvine

Matthew S. Santirocco
New York University

Barbara Sawrey
University of California, San Diego

William Segraves
Yale University

John H. Shaw
Harvard University

Robert Silbey
Massachusetts Institute of Technology

Craig Swan
University of Minnesota

Patricia Turner
University of California, Davis

Ruth Watkins
University of Illinois at
Urbana-Champaign

Nancy Westphal-Johnson
University of Wisconsin-Madison

Paul Woodruff
University of Texas at Austin

Martin Wybourne
Dartmouth College

## Schools Represented in Survey Responses:

Bennett College
Boston University
Brandeis University
Brown University
City University of New York
Columbia University
Cornell University
Dartmouth College
Duke University
George Mason University
George Washington University
Harvard University
Indiana University
Massachusetts Institute of Technology
Michigan State University
Morehouse College
New York University
Northwestern University
Pennsylvania State University
Princeton University
Rice University
Rutgers, The State University of New Jersey
Smith College
Stanford University
University of California, Berkeley
University of California, Davis
University of California, Irvine
University of California, Los Angeles
University of California, San Diego
University of Chicago
University of Illinois at Urbana-Champaign
University of Maryland
University of Michigan
University of Minnesota
University of Pennsylvania
University of Southern California
University of Texas at Austin
University of Virginia
University of Wisconsin-Madison
Virginia Polytechnic Institute and State University
Yale University

# AMERICAN ACADEMY
## OF ARTS & SCIENCES

The Academy was founded during the American Revolution by John Adams, James Bowdoin, John Hancock, and other leaders who contributed prominently to the establishment of the new nation, its government, and its Constitution. Its purpose was to provide a forum for a select group of scholars, members of the learned professions, and government and business leaders to work together on behalf of the democratic interests of the republic. In the words of the Academy's Charter, enacted in 1780, the "end and design of the institution is...to cultivate every art and science which may tend to advance the interest, honour, dignity, and happiness of a free, independent, and virtuous people." Today the Academy is both an honorary learned society and an independent policy research center that conducts multidisciplinary studies of complex and emerging problems. Current Academy research focuses on science and technology policy; global security; social policy and American institutions; the humanities and culture; and education. The Academy supports early-career scholars through its Visiting Scholars Program and Hellman Fellowships in Science and Technology Policy, providing year-long residencies at its Cambridge, Massachusetts, headquarters. The Academy's work is advanced by its 4,600 elected members, who are leaders in the academic disciplines, the arts, business, and public affairs from around the world.